POWER OF THE
GREAT
LINERS

Patrick Stephens Limited, a member of the Haynes Publishing Group, has published authoritative quality books for enthusiasts for more than twenty years. During that time the company has established a reputation as one of the world's leading publishers of books on aviation, maritime, military, model-making, motor cycling, motoring, motor racing, railway and railway modelling subjects. Readers or authors with suggestions for books they would like to see published are invited to write to: The Editorial Director, Patrick Stephens Limited, Sparkford, Nr Yeovil, Somerset, BA22 7JJ.

POWER OF THE GREAT LINERS

DENIS GRIFFITHS

A HISTORY OF ATLANTIC MARINE ENGINEERING

Foreword by Dr J.Cowley
Past President of the Institute of Marine Engineers

Patrick Stephens Limited

Dedication

For
PATRICIA
my wife
with love and thanks

First published in 1990

British Library Cataloguing in Publication Data
Griffiths, Denis, *1943-*
    Power of the Great Liners: a history of
    Atlantic marine engineering.
    1. Marine engineering, history
    I. Title
    623.8'7'09

    ISBN 1-85260-016-0

Endpaper illustrations A century of Atlantic marine engineering: Cunard's first screw-driven steamship *Calabria* of 1869 (front), and *Queen Elizabeth 2* of 1969 (rear, photo G. Johnson), originally powered by steam turbines but since converted to diesel.

Patrick Stephens Limited is a member of the Haynes Publishing Group, P.L.C., Sparkford, Nr Yeovil, Somerset, BA22 7JJ.

Printed in Great Britain by The Bath Press, Bath, Avon

1   3   5   7   9   10   8   6   4   2

Contents

Foreword

by Dr J. Cowley CBE BSc PhD C Eng FIMarE FIMechE
Past President of the Institute of Marine Engineers, former Surveyor General of
Shipping and Chief Examiner of Engineers

Denis Griffiths' fascinating history of Atlantic marine engineering is as readable as a novel yet it provides a comprehensive record of the development of marine engines and boilers with a perspective and accuracy which even the most critical marine engineer will admire.

Evidently, it is the product of long and painstaking research and selection coupled with an ability to lucidly explain engineering problems within the contemporary commercial and technological constraints. These factors and Mr Griffiths' attention to the influence of personalities and pride on technical achievement will make compulsive reading for all who are interested in ships and Britain's heritage. For whilst the book covers Atlantic liners without partiality, it shows that British-built and British-owned vessels played a dominant role over most of the era.

In examining the 'power' of the great liners, he demonstrates the part that the early pioneers played in ensuring the reliability of machinery and the safety of seafarers in general. The recurring theme of 'bigger, better and faster' meant that the experience gained in the operation of the passenger liners and the corresponding advances in technology became available to the operators and designers of cargo ships.

Having been deeply involved in maritime safety matters, I was particularly interested to learn that, as early as 1888, a Clydeside shipbuilder was building vessels with 15 watertight compartments designed to withstand the flooding of any three compartments and with a watertight longitudinal bulkhead between the two engine rooms. However, this is but one of the dozens of advances ranging from measurement of vibration (1890), integrity of boilers, introduction of electric lighting, refrigeration systems, evaporators, efficient bilge pumping arrangements, power steering gears and stabilizers to lifesaving arrangements. Seafarers the world over (albeit often as a result of legislation) have benefited from these developments which were originally introduced quite voluntarily by the shipowners. On the other hand, I also noted with some feeling Mr Griffiths' reference to 'the Board of Trade surveyor insisting on a prolonged sea trial before he would issue a passenger certificate' following failures of the boiler tubes.

These are but some of the highlights within my special interest. For others it will be the introduction of surface condensers, steam turbines, or water tube boilers; or learning of complements of 195 men in the engine department, or that 46 water tube boilers were installed in a single ship!

Much has been written on the romanticism of the great ocean liners, but 'few passengers ever knew or cared about those who laboured beneath their feet'. Yet the massive reduction in lives lost at sea resulted from advances in technology following the change from sail to steam. Denis Griffiths' book redresses the balance and fills a significant gap in the literature. He is a highly qualified professional engineer with the gift of narrative, and the clear sketches and well-written text of the book will provide hours of pleasure for the interested reader. It is not only a compendium of engineering knowledge, it is also an authoritative history of marine engineering well worthy of the profession.

Prelude

A copy of this poem graces the control room bulkhead of the last Atlantic liner, *Queen Elizabeth 2*. Its author is unknown to the writer of this book, but copies have appeared in engine rooms of a number of ships over the years and that is, perhaps, praise in itself. If the author is still alive and reads this then the present writer would very much like to hear from him, for he really understands the purpose of this book.

Tribute to the Forgotten Man

The siren shrieks its farewell note, and proudly on her way
The brand-new giant liner moves in grandeur down the Bay.
A marvellous creation, her builders' joy and pride,
The great hope of her owners as she floats upon the tide.
The passengers in festive mood, 'mid laughter, jest and quip,
With keen delight enjoy the great ship's maiden trip.
She's sure to break the record, she'll do thirty knots or more,
Is the hope of all on board as she leaves her native shore.

Upon the bridge the Captain, a skipper proud and bold,
Bedecked in glorious raiments, navy blue and gold.
All eyes are fixed upon him, and it's going to his head,
He stops to drop the pilot, then rings 'full speed ahead'.
And 'down below' the battle starts for the trophy of the seas,
By engineers — not clad in gold — but greasy dungarees.

On deck the scene is bly and gay — fair ladies, song and wine,
But hell is popping down below, beneath the Plimsol Line.
The Chief raps out his orders to the men on watch below.
His men obey his mandates, about their tasks they go.
Steam pressure must not fluctuate, the bearings not run hot,
Revs must not be allowed to drop to make the thirty knots.
At dinner on the first night out the Captain proudly boasts:
'We'll surely break the record', as the gallant ship he toasts.
But breaking records puts no grey hair upon his head,
His contribution ended when he ordered 'full speed ahead'.

Through weary days and sleepless nights to consummate his dream
The engineers slave ceaselessly till Ambrose Light's abeam.
The record has been broken with thirty-one point four,
The Captain wears another stripe, he's now a 'Commodore'.
And thus he gets the credit for what other men have done
He boasts to press and radio the victory he has won.
Neglecting e'en to mention as he swings his ballyhoo
The men of brain and brawn and guts, who shoved the great ship through.

The moral of this poem then is quite conclusively,
The glory seldom goes to those who win the victory.
To keep this simple thought in mind about a record trip,
The man behind the throttle is the man who drives the ship.

Acknowledgements

As a former seagoing engineer the author has always had a high regard for the marine engineering profession, considering the works of those who designed and operated such plant to be undervalued. This work, hopefully, goes some way to redress the neglect and the author wishes to thank all who have helped in some way to make this book possible.

The award to the author of the first ESAB Fellowship in Maritime Technology at the National Maritime Museum, Greenwich, provided valuable stimulus and special thanks must be directed to John Wilkinson of ESAB Ltd for having the courage to sponsor that fellowship, the first in Maritime Technology. Without the award inspiration for the book might have been much longer in coming. Fred Walker, Naval Architect at the NMM, must also be thanked for his enthusiasm during my tenure of the ESAB Fellowship and for his kindness, friendship and guidance since.

The author is indebted to many individuals on the staffs of various establishments and libraries whose names are unknown. Staff at the National Maritime Museum, Science Museum Library, Liverpool City Library, Liverpool Maritime Museum Records Office, Liverpool University Archives, The Mitchell Library Glasgow, The University of Glasgow Archives and Bristol Central Library.

In years past a number of shipping companies provided a youthful and enthusiastic author with pictures of their ships and machinery. To these companies, Cunard, French Line and Canadian Pacific, grateful thanks are expressed. The Archives unit at CP Rail is also thanked for recent help.

Individuals to be thanked include Dave Williams of Liverpool Maritime Museum, Mr M. Cook of Liverpool University Archives Unit, Paul Neilsen of MAN–B&W Diesel and the late Harry Weston who donated books and photographs to the author, then only a youth with an interest in marine engineering. Martin Harrison has provided valuable information and photographs relating to QE2 and her machinery. John Banks and Mark Falcus of Liverpool Polytechnic and the author's colleagues in the School of Engineering and Technology Management at that establishment have been most useful. Finally, but by no means least, my grateful thanks go to Patricia, Sarah and Patrick, my family.

Introduction

When one considers famous ships such as *United States*, *Queen Mary*, *Normandie*, and *Titanic* it is difficult to imagine that the era of the Atlantic liner lasted for less than 140 years. Just as steam ousted sail, so jet engined aircraft despatched the 'Atlantic Ferry' to its place in history. Although passenger liners operated in all waters of the world, it was the North Atlantic which held special significance. One reason was the obvious bond which existed between the peoples of Europe and America due to the massive migration from old to new worlds. The only way to cross the Atlantic was by ship, and as trade grew so did the number and size of vessels to cater for such expansion. Competition resulted in better service for those able to afford the best and even the less well-off found themselves being wooed by improved facilities, in most cases much superior to those from which they were fleeing.

Speed of passage became an important factor as it meant that suffering from seasickness was reduced to days rather than weeks. It also resulted in more crossings each year and so more fare paying passengers. Larger ships were able to accommodate more people, but that in itself induced problems as they not only had to be fed but sanitary, heating and lighting facilities had to be provided. In terms of comfort and care the Atlantic passenger liner became something of a multi-class hotel, but no hotel of that size had to provide all its own services and dash across uncertain water at high speed.

Atlantic liners were at the forefront of passenger ship development, the market being large enough to encourage competition which promoted change and search for improvement. Governments were not slow to see an advantage in faster ships. Not only could they be employed for more rapid delivery of mails, but also provided a military advantage in their ability to be converted to fast troopships or armed cruisers in times of conflict. Subsidies financed shipowners in their scramble for higher speeds.

That essentially mythical award, the 'Blue Riband', has done much to promote the image of fast luxurious vessels and many books have been written about them. Millions of words have described hotel facilities such as cabins, public rooms and catering whilst countless more have praised the speed of the ships across that 3,000 mile stretch of usually inhospitable water. No book has yet devoted itself to the machinery which produced that speed and the requirements of lighting, ventilation, food preservation and a fairly steady deck upon which to walk. Without these the liner was nothing — it could go nowhere, nor provide facilities for its passengers.

Why the neglect of such an essential topic? Was it too dull to be of interest? Nothing of the sort, the whole subject of marine engineering was, and still is, of immense variation and even beauty. A steam reciprocating engine is sheer poetry in motion. Rudyard Kipling knew what he liked and the marine engine came at the top of his list: 'A locomotive is, next to the marine engine, the most sensitive thing man has ever made' (*The Day's Work*, 1898). Is then engineering too difficult to understand? Possibly in some respects, but nobody needs to know all technical details to be able to understand the workings of a machine or appreciate its significance. By not having some basic knowledge of power plant and equipment the shipping enthusiast is missing the most important part in the development of Atlantic liners and his education is incomplete.

This book aims to rectify matters and provide some information relating to the development of machinery placed aboard the Atlantic liner. Propulsion plant is a major part of the subject matter, but it is by no means the only topic. Introduction of electric lighting to ships not only removed the gloom from public rooms but made them easier to clean and resulted in a safer ship, as the risk of fire from oil lamps and candles was removed. Development of electrical installations proceeded more rapidly at sea than ashore. Carriage of sufficient fresh provisions for increasing numbers of passengers presented problems, so when refrigeration came to the rescue the marine industry led the way. The marine environment posed many difficulties, with provision of adequate fresh air being a particular problem. Windows could not simply be opened as they are ashore and a number of very elaborate forced ventilation systems, with air heating and cooling, were developed.

The sea is an inhospitable place and the North Atlantic in winter is one of the foulest stretches of water imaginable, as the writer knows only too well. Naturally passengers prefer calm conditions and good sea ships were popular; the greater its ability to remain fairly upright during all weather the more popular a liner became. Excessive rolling was not only uncomfortable for passengers, but resulted in broken crockery and furniture. Anything which could be done to minimize the magnitude of rolling was seized upon. Anti-rolling tanks and other stabilizing systems were tried over the years with varying degrees of success. The machinery generally went unnoticed, but the effect did not.

From the first Atlantic liners in 1838 until the end of the era in the 1970s there has been constant improvement in propulsive plant. Paddle steamers gave way to screw propulsion and then reciprocating engines were overtaken by steam turbine drives. Oil firing of boilers replaced coal at the end of the First World War and that had a marked effect on both crew numbers and also on ship design as oil, unlike coal, could be carried in double bottom tanks, thus freeing space for more cabins. The diesel engine was slow to make inroads, but eventually its better fuel economy proved to be the telling factor and the final Atlantic liner has now become a motorship.

Machinery always presents a certain amount of danger to its operators, but its misuse posed dangers to the passengers. Boiler explosions on early steamships killed many engineers and firemen, but very few ships were lost as a result. By the time steamers ventured across the Atlantic boilers and machinery in general had become much more reliable. Unfortunately those responsible for the 'driving' of the ship had not. Many liners were lost through groundings and collision, with other ships and with icebergs, because the navigators did not fully understand the basic power that engines gave to the ship. Speed was underestimated, resulting in the ship going aground whilst power was employed to charge on recklessly through ice or fog. Speed was of great help to large liners on trooping duties during the war, but became a menace in the wrong hands.

Few passengers ever knew or cared about those who laboured in engine rooms beneath their feet. Coal burning ships required armies of stokers and trimmers to keep large boilers fed. The labour was both hard and dangerous but was carried out with skill and care; even the 'black gang' were concerned about soot or ash irritating the human cargo. A coal fired liner of 1910 required an engine room staff of many hundred, although few passengers enjoying the fruits of their labours ever became aware of their existence. Oil firing eased the burden and put many out of work, but its introduction was a great move forward for marine engineering. By the 1960s new Atlantic liners only required a few dozen highly skilled engineers and engine room hands to tend much more complex and powerful machinery, but that is progress and now the liners have all but gone from the Atlantic.

This book aims to tell the story of the Atlantic liner's development in terms of its machinery. It is not complete, the history is too extensive for that, but it should enable the reader to understand the problems and technical qualities of the solutions. It should also, hopefully, go some way to completing the education of the liner enthusiast. References to published source material are included in order that any reader might investigate his chosen vessel, or vessels, in more detail. For original material the reader is advised to consult contemporary engine room and engine drawings, most of which have been pre-served at surviving shipyards or are stored at local libraries. The shipyard draughtsman was a true artist, in the real sense of the word.

Conversion of Dimensions

Dimensions for ships and their components are expressed in the units in which they were built. In most cases this is imperial, but in the case of some continental vessels the specifications were in metric. For the benefit of those who wish to draw comparisons, imperial/metric conversion factors are given below.

Mass
1 lb = 0.4545 kg; 1 kg = 2.2 lb
1 ton = 2,240 lb = 1,016 kg
1,000 kg = 1 tonne (ie one metric ton)

Length
1 in = 25.4 mm = 0.0254 m
1 ft = 304.8 mm = 0.3048 m

Area
1 sq in = 645 sq mm = 0.645×10^{-3} sq m
1 sq ft = 0.0929 sq m

Volume
1 cu ft = 0.0283 cu m

(Note: 1 gross ton = 100 cu ft or 2.83 cu m of enclosed space)

Pressure
Unless stated, values quoted in the text are gauge pressure, ie they are as registered on a pressure gauge which gives values above atmospheric pressure. Atmospheric pressure is taken as 14.7 psi or 101.325 kN/sq m (N is the unit Newton)
1 psi = 6.9 kN/sq m = 0.069 bar

Power
1 horsepower (1 hp) = 746 Watts = 0.746 kW

Consumption
1 lb/hp = 0.339 kg/kW

Speed
1 knot is one nautical mile per hour
1 nautical mile = 6,080 ft = 1,852 m

CHAPTER 1

Paddle Steamers

A single feature characterized all major British paddle driven Atlantic liners and that was the side lever engine. It was fitted aboard Brunel's pioneering *Great Western* and propelled the final paddle driven Atlantic mail liner, Cunard's magnificent *Scotia*. There was nothing special about the arrangement of side lever engines, they just fitted the bill as far as paddles were concerned. Other forms of machinery were proposed, and even fitted, to turn the paddles of ocean going vessels, but none came near the side lever type in terms of effectiveness or simplicity. Over the years from *Great Western* to the somewhat archaic *Scotia* of 1862 side lever engines remained very much the same apart from one modification of great significance, the surface condenser.

Layout of Great Western *as in 1846.*

When she entered service in April 1838 *Great Western* was the most powerful ship afloat but, although of substantial construction in order to resist the effects of an Atlantic winter, her power plant was similar to that of contemporary smaller coastal craft. That is not intended to denigrate the undoubted quality of the work involved and the craftsmanship of the workers employed by Maudslay, Sons & Field, but it serves to illustrate that nothing else could have provided the necessary power. Based upon the Watt beam engines, the marine side lever engine basically had the beams placed alongside the cylinders rather than above in order to reduce overall height. By means of a connecting rod the beams rotated a cranked paddle rod. Two such engines were employed in order to provide the necessary power and allow for propulsion should one ever fail.

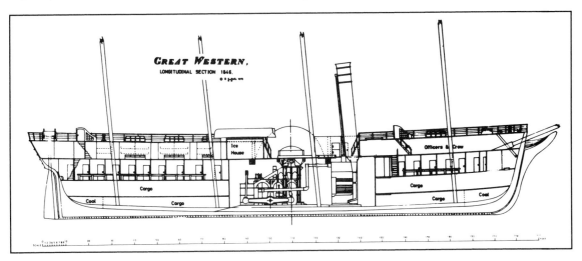

Engines were self contained in that they incorporated a condenser, air pump and hot-well. Water circulating, bilge and other pumps would also be operated from the side levers. The system was simple and effective, which accounts for its longevity as far as major paddle steamers were concerned. The early engines operated at relatively low boiler pressure, that of *Great Western* being only 5 psi maximum, and most of the cylinder power was developed because a partial vacuum existed on the exhaust side of the piston. The greater the vacuum the higher the power developed. Spray condensers were developed for the purpose, sea water being sprayed into the condenser chamber in order to convert the exhaust steam back into water and so produce the very low pressure. With such a system it was essential that the boilers operated on salt water feed as hot water from the condenser was pumped into the boiler. Regular blowing down of boilers reduced the feed salinity and restricted salt scale formation. For low pressure boilers there were no major problems with salt feed, but it did restrict heat transfer and impaired efficiency.

Surface condensers avoided the problem, fresh water only being pumped into the boiler as steam and cooling water were kept apart. That at least was the theory and the units as applied to *Sirius* (1838) and *British Queen* (1839) were effective in performing that duty. Fresh water could be employed in the boilers, but a reserve supply had to be carried in order to provide make-up for losses. At the time little was known about corrosion and although fresh water feed reduced scale formation it did allow galvanic action to take place within the boiler; a layer of salt scale prevented that action when sea water feed was employed. An additional disadvantage manifested itself in that the tallow and grease used to lubricate piston and valve rods would eventually coat the tubes reducing the effectiveness of condensation. These defects prevented widespread adoption of surface condensation and spray condensers remained the order of the day for Atlantic paddle steamers as far as most British owners were concerned. American owners made greater use of tubular surface condensers.

Great Western, the first steamship actually constructed for service on the Atlantic, was a product of the fertile mind of Isambard Kingdom Brunel, but his rather wild ideas concerning maritime affairs were tempered by the prudent advice of his friend Captain Christopher Claxton. Construction of the ship marked a change in the fortunes of Britain as a mercantile force on the Atlantic and her success spawned many rival ventures. By later standards her engines were of low rating, developing some 750 indicated horsepower (ihp) to drive the ship at about 10 knots, but they were the most powerful put in a ship to that date. At the time engine power was usually classified by nominal horse power which related to cylinder dimensions and boiler pressure, rather than anything actually produced by the cylinders. Engines fitted aboard *Great Western* were of 450 nominal horsepower (nhp).

Of typical side lever form with two cylinders 73.5 in diameter and 84 in stroke, the engines turned 28 ft 9 in diameter paddle wheels fitted with cycloidal paddle floats. This arrangement, originally devised by Joshua Field, employed four staggered floats on each paddle arm arranged so that they entered the water with the minimum of shock. Theoretically more efficient

Steamship Sirius.

THE BRITISH STEAM-SHIP "SIRIUS,"
LIEUT. R. ROBERTS, R. N.

than single floats, the cycloidal wheels became a continual source of trouble and were replaced by single float wheels in 1843.[1]

Sirius was not constructed for Atlantic service but the British and American Steam Navigation Company chartered her for two voyages in order to claim the honour of being first on the Atlantic, their own steamer *British Queen* having been delayed due to financial problems affecting her builders. The tiny 700 ton *Sirius* had engines of some 320 nhp, but her coal capacity was totally inadequate for Atlantic voyaging. At 1,850 tons *British Queen* was larger than her 1,350 ton Bristol rival and her side lever engines were rated at 500 nhp. Despite that *Great Western* was always the faster and more popular ship.

Both *Sirius* and *British Queen* were fitted with Hall's surface condensers, the latter probably being so equipped due to experience gained from the smaller vessel. However, *Sirius* was originally constructed for the coastal trade where fresh water for the boilers could be readily obtained. That was not the case for prolonged Atlantic passages and difficulty must have been experienced in providing fresh water feed for the boilers.

When Cunard commenced operations in 1840 he dictated that his original four ships *Britannia, Acadia, Caledonia* and *Columbia* should be basic and without frills. Surface condensers were frills and caused more problems than they solved at the time. Side lever engines for these 1,150 ton craft were claimed to be as powerful as those of *Great Western*, but cylinder diameters were 1.5 in smaller and piston stroke some 2 in shorter.

For the larger *Hibernia* of 1843 and the 1,850 ton 'America' class ships of 1848 the same type of propulsion plant was specified, though of increased power. *America*'s engines could develop about twice the power of the original Cunarders but cylinder dimensions were not that much greater, 88.75 in diameter by 90 in stroke.[2] Increased power also resulted from slightly higher boiler pressure, 13 psi compared with *Britannia*'s 5 psi, but most cylinder power still came from the vacuum effect.

Boilers at that time were of the return flue type in which gases passed from furnace to funnel through fairly large section flues. They were inefficient and subject to fouling by deposits of

Cunard's Britannia.

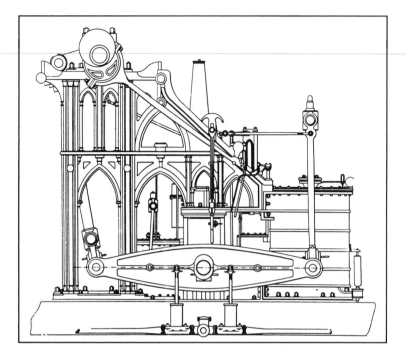

Left *'Britannia' class side lever engines.*

Below *Cunard 'America' class paddle steamer* Europa *at Boston.* (Cunard Archives, University of Liverpool.)

Right *Sectional view of America's side lever engines.*

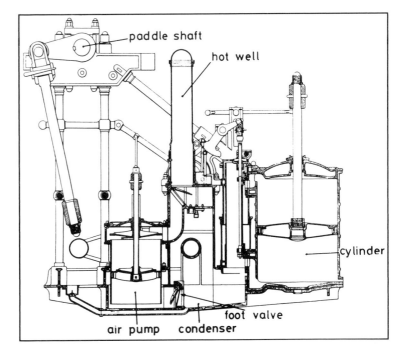

Below *The original flue boilers of* Great Western.

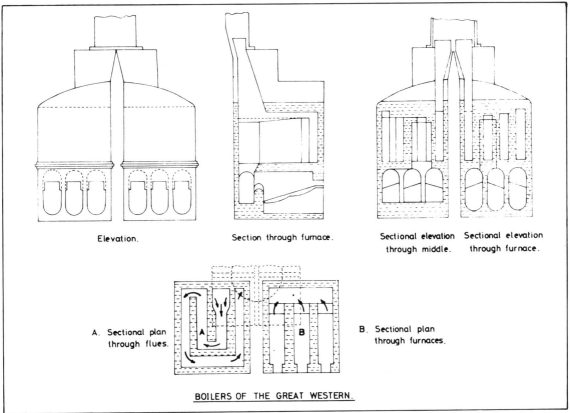

Elevation.

Section through furnace.

Sectional elevation through middle.

Sectional elevation through furnace.

A. Sectional plan through flues.

B. Sectional plan through furnaces.

BOILERS OF THE GREAT WESTERN.

soot on the fire side as well as the salt scale on the water side. Low pressures involved allowed the use of unsupported flat sided flues, but that arrangement limited the development of higher pressures as the high forces on unstayed flat surfaces could cause collapse. Flue boilers were, however, relatively inexpensive to manufacture and, as they required replacement due to corrosion at about five year intervals, they remained popular.

The Great Western Steam Ship Company, owners of *Great Western*, on advice from its engineer, Thomas Guppy, decided to fit a higher pressure tubular boiler to its paddle steamer at the end of the 1843 season. A single five furnace tubular unit operating at 12 psi replaced the four original flue boilers which had a maximum pressure of 5 psi. With these new boilers specific coal consumption per horsepower fell from 6.25 lb to 5.6 lb, but steam output was less and the ship could not produce the same performance as originally.[3] Without a mail subsidy coal consumption was of more critical concern than speed to *Great Western*'s owners. With the security of a mail contract and its guaranteed income Cunard was more interested in performance

reliability and that company remained faithful to the trusted flue type boiler after other concerns had progressed.

A number of American companies introduced steamer services during the late 1840s and early 1850s but they all failed to make any mark. Outstanding though American sailing packets had been, their steamers failed to compete. To the fore amongst American challengers was the New York and Havre Steam Navigation Company with its 2,410 ton *Franklin* (1850) and 2,856 ton *Humbolt* (1851). Engines and boilers for these ships were constructed by Stillman, Allen & Co of the Novelty Iron Works, New York.

In both cases side lever engines of conventional form were fitted, those of *Humbolt* being slightly larger and more powerful; 95 in diameter cylinders by 108 in stroke. Boilers for both ships differed considerably and it would appear that the builders were experimenting with different arrangements. The four iron cylindrical boilers fitted in *Franklin* were of return flow tubular form whilst *Humbolt* was provided with

Engine room of Humbolt.

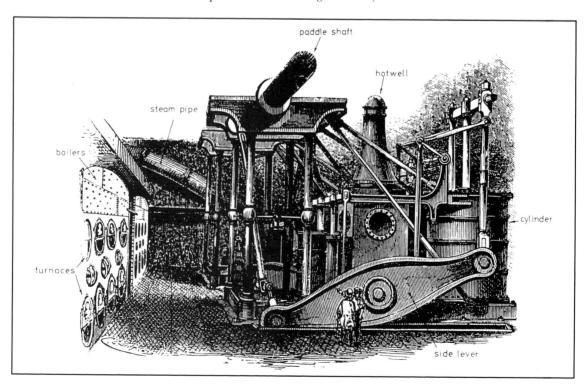

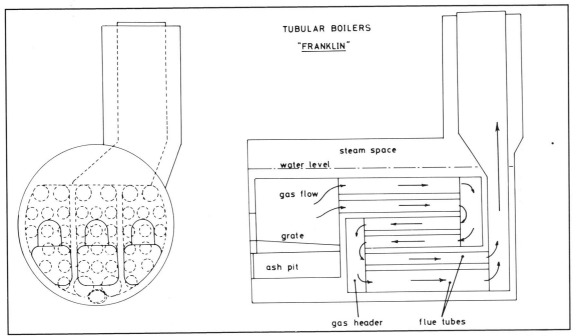

Tubular boiler of Franklin.

four return flue type boilers each having eight furnaces placed in two rows, one above the other. These operated at a pressure of 15 psi compared with 13 psi for the tubular boilers.[4] How efficient these boilers were is unknown, both ships being lost within four years of entering service.

The firing of *Humbolt's* boilers must have presented considerable difficulties as feeding coal into a low level furnace was no easy task during foul Atlantic weather. To distribute coal evenly over an eye level grate would have been almost impossible under such circumstances. An upper level firing platform could have reduced the problems, but a contemporary illustration of the engine room published in *Harper's New Monthly Magazine* vol. II, December 1850 to May 1851, does not indicate any arrangement of that type. The picture does provide a rather idealized view of the engine room with some degree of artistic licence being allowed. No coal or ash clutters the stokehold, nor is there an indication of an inspection platform around the upper part of the engine. More strikingly it would appear that American engineers and firemen of the period were all dwarfs some 4 ft high! These defects apart, the illustration provides a reason-able contemporary impression of a side lever engine.

Stillman, Allen & Co also constructed the side lever engines for the Collins Line ships *Atlantic*, *Pacific*, *Arctic* and *Baltic* of 1850. The boilers of these 2,850 ton paddle steamers were to the design of John Faron, Chief Engineer to the company. Each of the four boilers was 22 ft long and 14 ft 3 in high, two of them being 14 ft wide and the other two 15 ft. The design was novel in that 2 in diameter vertical water tubes were used, these passing through combustion chambers fed with gases from pairs of furnaces, one above the other. Each boiler, which operated at 17 psi, had four furnaces and all four boilers connected to a single funnel placed forward of the engines. The basically conventional side lever engines, with 95 in diameter cylinders having a 108 in stroke, differed from normal British practice in that poppet valves rather than slide valves controlled steam supply and exhaust. Paddle wheels of 35 ft diameter gave *Atlantic* and her sisters a speed of about 12 knots on some 85 tons of coal per day.[5]

Third amongst the American Atlantic steamship companies of the period was the Vanderbilt Line. Although two ships *North Star* and *Ariel* operated services from New York since 1855 it was the 3,350 ton *Vanderbilt* of 1857 which attracted attention. This ship made use of the walking beam engine, a variation of the side lever type in which a single beam was positioned above the engine rather than two beams low down. The piston rod connected with one end of the beam whilst the other end of the beam turned the paddle shaft by means of a crank and connecting rod. That arrangement necessitated the beam being placed high up above the deck. Actually two such engines were fitted and the individual sections of paddle shaft could be disconnected, allowing one engine to turn its paddle wheel ahead whilst the other rotated its wheel in the opposite direction. This would have allowed the ship to turn about its own mid point.

The 90 in diameter pistons had a stroke of 144 in and turned paddle wheels 41 ft in diameter. Whilst operating at 16 rpm the engines developed some 2,800 ihp which could drive the ship at 12.5 knots. *Vanderbilt's* return tube boilers were positioned two forward and two aft of the engines, each pair having its own funnel.[6] The ship must have presented a rather remarkable sight with two rocking levers observable above a massive paddle wheel thrashing water and the whole animated clutter enclosed between two funnels belching smoke.

Almost as a last gasp to capture Atlantic trade

of the period for American interests, the Collins Line introduced *Adriatic* in 1857. This wooden construction 3,650 ton ship was built at the New York yard of George Steers, but her machinery was built by the Novelty Iron Works. A two cylinder oscillating engine powered her 40 ft diameter paddle wheels, the plant developing some 2,500 ihp at 17 rpm from boilers working at a maximum pressure of 25 psi. The two 101 in diameter cylinders had a stroke of 144 in and were positioned one forward and one aft of the paddle shaft, being inclined towards the shaft with piston connecting rods attaching to cranks set at 90°.

Steam inlet and exhaust valves differed from the more usual form in that they were conical, like the plugs of gas cocks. In operation the valves would be withdrawn slightly from their seating, rotated and then returned to the seat. They never proved to be satisfactory and replacement with poppet valves followed before the ship entered service. A surface condenser to the design of the Novelty Iron Works proved troublesome just like the valves and Collins put the machinery in the care of other parties for the fitting of new valves and a more effective surface condenser system. The $50,000 to $70,000 expended in rectifying machinery defects certainly contributed to the collapse of the Collins

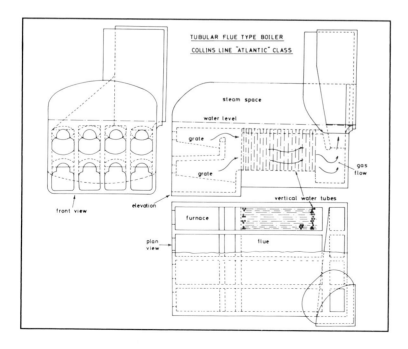

Tubular boiler of Collins Line's 'Atlantic' class.

Line and *Adriatic* only made two trips for her original owners. Following purchase by the Galway Line, *Adriatic* operated across the Atlantic between 1861 and 1864 but was never a success.

Vertical tubular boilers originally fitted in the ship remained with her until she was converted to sail in 1869. Of a design similar to that installed in *Atlantic* and her sisters, these eight boilers were each 20 ft long, 11 ft 3 in wide and 14 ft tall and contained a total of 13,064 tubes of 2 in diameter. Boilers were arranged in two groups of four with one set placed forward and one set aft of the paddles. It has been claimed that coal consumption amounted to between 85 and 90 tons per day at 13 knots, her 1,200 ton capacity bunkers stowing sufficient for about 15 days' steaming.[7]

Like other ships of the period, *Adriatic* offered fairly rudimentary facilities for her 316 first and 60 second class passengers. Her main saloon was 75 ft long by 28 ft wide and could seat 200 people at one sitting. The 130 cabins were ventilated after a fashion and all had heating by means of pipes through which steam circulated.[8] That system, by no means new, was not fitted to all steamers then operating on the Atlantic and passengers aboard many ships still had to contend with the minimal heat provided by simple coal fired stoves.

Lighting remained firmly the province of oil lamps or candles. Such forms of illumination were a positive hazard against which the only safeguard was diligence. Regarding the provision of lifeboats, *Adriatic* and most of her contemporaries were better equipped than their later sisters and this Collins Line vessel had been provided with 16 iron boats each capable of carrying 60 persons.[9] Her crew totalled about 175 and with a full complement of 376 passengers there would have been lifeboat space to spare. Iron lifeboats had been fitted to *Great Western* as early as 1844, these being to a patent of Thomas Guppy for boats containing iron buoyancy tanks. The screw propelled *Great Britain* also had such 'unsinkable' lifeboats.[10]

Growth of American interest in Atlantic trade was helped by British involvement in the Crimean War, many Cunard steamers being taken for transport duties in accordance with terms of the mail contract. Prior to that conflict, however, Cunard had introduced the 2,400 ton *Arabia* as competition for the Collins 'Atlantics'. The 3,000 ihp side lever engines of that ship were of conventional form, but her box type tubular boilers marked a dramatic change allowing for higher steam pressure and increased efficiency. Comparisons with *America* of 1848 show considerable differences, despite the simi-

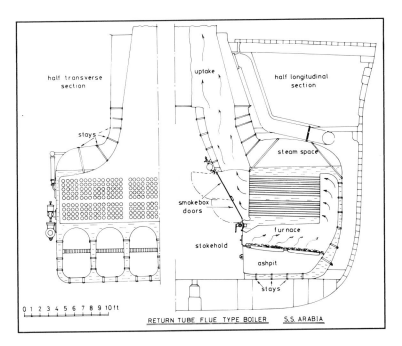

Return tube flue boilers of Arabia.

larity of engine type. The earlier ship was smaller, slower and of less power, some 1,400 ihp, and she consumed only 60 tons of coal per day whilst *Arabia* burnt twice that amount. The significant point was, however, that the smaller vessel consumed 4 lb of coal per ihp per hour whilst the figure for the larger ship was 3.75 lb. Speed had to be paid for, but it was becoming obvious that economic advantages could be derived from higher boiler pressures and better designed boilers.

For a number of years the advantage of screw propulsion over paddles had been evident to all but those at the Admiralty. Mail contracts stipulated paddle steamers and so Cunard had to operate such ships. A similar condition regarding wooden construction had been relaxed and in 1856 the Cunard Line introduced the magnificent *Persia*. This iron ship of 3,300 tons could carry 250 passengers and required side lever engines of 3,600 ihp to propel her at 13 knots. Again box type tubular boilers provided the steam, but the specific coal consumption had been reduced. From an engineering viewpoint *Persia* was only an enlarged version of *Arabia* using an iron hull, but her impact on the maritime scene was considerable for she recaptured the Atlantic record from the Collins Line ships.

Whilst Atlantic companies, including Cunard, invested heavily in screw propelled vessels there was still one throw of the dice left to the paddle steamer before it became part of Atlantic history. Naturally Cunard made that throw with the most powerful and fastest ocean paddle steamer ever built. At 3,850 tons *Scotia* (1862) was an enlarged version of *Persia* and followed the traditional arrangement of side lever engines and box type tubular boilers. In that respect there was little of note about the ship's machinery, it was just larger and more powerful than

any before.

Cylinders of 100 in diameter and 144 in stroke could develop an output of 4,570 ihp from boilers working at 25 psi. Such power allowed *Scotia* to capture the Atlantic record during December 1863 with a crossing from New York in just over eight days. The following June she made a run in the opposite direction from Queenstown to New York at an average speed of 14.54 knots. Records like that were achieved at considerable cost in terms of fuel, *Scotia* consuming some 350 tons per day. Her 300 passenger and 1,400 ton cargo capacity could not cover operating costs without help from the mail subsidy and even Cunard needed to remain competitive.[11]

When the Admiralty finally abandoned its obstinate 'paddles only' policy for mail ships and the mail contracts were opened to wider competition, the Cunard company had no alternative but to seek more economical forms of propulsion. Paddle wheels and side lever engines had had their day and the era of screw propulsion blossomed. In fact the 1862 built *Scotia* was but little advance on *Great Western* of 1838. The pioneering Atlantic liner had employed grades of steam expansion in her machinery and no subsequent side lever engine took the matter further. As far as the engines were concerned only size changed. Boilers improved and pressures increased, but that was an advantage to screw as well as paddle steamers.

The success of Brunel's *Great Western* spawned further Atlantic steamships, but the form of propulsion she employed was effectively a dead end, only screw propulsion offered a real way to future advance.

Cunard Line's Persia. (Harry Weston Collection.)

CHAPTER 2

Turn of the Screw

As might be expected, Brunel started it. Screw propulsion as an idea had been around since the early years of the nineteenth century and Sir Marc Isambard Brunel, father of the renowned Isambard Kingdom Brunel, had conducted trials with screw propellers in 1820. During the ensuing years a number of small craft were constructed employing variations on the Pettit Smith and Ericsson patented screws, but the Americans were first off the mark for deep sea propulsion. The navy frigate *Princeton* was fitted with a 14 ft diameter Ericsson screw in the early 1840s. A 'race' between *Princeton* and I. K. Brunel's paddle steamer *Great Western* in New York harbour seemed to demonstrate the superiority of the screw, as the warship outpaced the merchant vessel over the short course.[1] Brunel had been convinced long before that and at Bristol his mammoth iron steamer *Great Britain* had already been modified for screw propulsion.

Francis Pettit Smith was able to interest sufficient people of capital to finance the Screw Propulsion Company which constructed the 125 ft, 90 horsepower vessel *Archimedes*. Trials in 1839 proved the ship to be a success and she was sent on a sales tour of British ports. One of these was Bristol, and one of the observers I. K. Brunel. He wanted to know more and borrowed *Archimedes* for further trials. These convinced him as to the advantages of screw propulsion over that of the paddle and his enthusiastic report to the Great Western Steam Ship Company directors resulted in work on the paddle steamer *Great Britain* being stopped and construction on the screw steamer *Great Britain* being commenced.

That move cost the company a considerable amount of money as work on the paddle engines and hull had already begun, but it did herald a new era in ocean steamers. Even though the screw form was not so well refined as it was to become later, it was still considered

Great Britain *under restoration at Bristol.*

to be a more efficient form of drive. Conversion from paddle propulsion also had many other advantages, including a saving in top weight and a reduction in overall breadth. *Great Britain* was not only propelled by screw but she was then the largest ship in the world and was constructed of iron. In 1845 any one of these factors would have been a major talking point as far as Atlantic passenger vessels were concerned but Brunel had the lot, in a single ship.

Steam engines of the period were relatively slow running and some form of 'gearing-up' was necessary in order to produce the higher rotational speed required for efficient operation of the screw. Brunel chose a triangular form of engine based upon a patent of his father, Sir Marc, with four cylinders inclined upwards and connected to a crankshaft above. Each cylinder had a bore of 88 in and stroke of 72 in, but the steam pressure was only 5 psi thus limiting the potential power. Four sets of chains with a width of 38 in provided the means of driving the screw shaft from the engine crankshaft. The main driving wheel had a diameter of 18 ft 3 in whilst the lower driven drum was of 6 ft diameter, giving a gear ratio of 2.95 to 1. With the engines designed for a normal speed of 18 rpm, the propeller could then rotate at 53 rpm.

The screw itself was a built-up affair having six arms to which were riveted flat tapered palms constituting the main driving portion of the propeller. Made from wrought iron, this 15 ft 6 in diameter screw weighed some 3.85 tons and it performed well, considering that so little data then existed on large ship screw propulsion. At the designed operating speed of 12 knots a thrust of about 10 tons was exerted by the 18 in diameter propeller shaft and a suitable thrust bearing was required to transmit this force to the hull in order to achieve a drive. Again Brunel and his fellow engineer Thomas Guppy were working at the limits of knowledge but their solution was effective, if a little crude by later standards. A 2 ft diameter gunmetal plate, connected to the forward end of the screw shaft, pressed against a steel plate of similar diameter attached to the hull by means of a large block. In order to keep the plates apart, and so minimize friction, water was forced into a space at the centre of the plates and escaped radially between them. A sufficiently powerful pump would have been required to supply water at pressures in excess of 60 psi for normal running. Boilers operated on sea water feed at comparatively low pressure and were no advance on common practice of the time.[2] Use of higher pressure tubular boilers as fitted to *Great Western* at about the same time would have improved the plant's efficiency considerably.[3]

Although *Great Britain* was the maritime wonder of her day, that engineering development was not continued due to the economic disaster which befell her owners when she was wrecked in 1846. Even Brunel did not pursue screw propulsion with complete enthusiasm, preferring to 'hedge his bets' by adopting screw and paddle propulsion for his mammoth *Great Eastern*.

It was in 1850 that the next real development regarding screw propulsion took place, and it proved to be a significant one not only for Atlantic steam navigation but for steam powered shipping in general. Some shipbuilders of the time were in the habit of constructing vessels on their own account when orders were not forthcoming from other sources, the hope being that a buyer could be found before construction was too far advanced, although that could not be guaranteed. Clydeside shipbuilders Tod & MacGregor took such a step in 1849 by laying down a 1,600 ton propeller driven iron steamer. *City of Glasgow*, as the vessel was named, did not find a buyer and in 1850 commenced a Greenock–New York service on Tod & MacGregor's own account. Four voyages that year confirmed the expectations of her builders and attracted the attention of William Inman.

City of Glasgow had been fitted with two overhead beam steeple engines, which were similar to side lever engines of the period except that a single beam was placed above the engine rather than two beams either side of the cylinder. (At that time each cylinder was still classed as an engine.) Other features such as jet condenser and eccentric operated valve gear remained much the same. Connecting rods attached to each beam rotated a gear wheel positioned between the two cylinders. That gear wheel rotated the screw shaft with a multiplying ratio of 2 to 1. Cylinders of 66 in diameter and 60 in stroke were arranged on the starboard side of the ship with the gearing on the port side giving an unbalanced effect, but the system was in perfect balance. That was not all which was in balance, for the economics of operation also showed up to advantage. Using steam from three tubular boilers rated at 10 psi, the 350 horsepower engines allowed the iron hulled *City of Glasgow* to maintain 8.5 knots on only 20 tons of coal per day. She could carry almost as many passengers as Cunard's newest vessel *Asia* and had space for 1,200 tons of cargo against *Asia*'s 500 tons. Although the Cunarder had a speed of 12 knots she also consumed 76 tons of coal each day. Economics like that were inescapable and at a stroke *City of Glasgow* hammered home the advantage of screw propulsion.[4]

Inman bought the ship towards the end of 1850 for a Liverpool to Philadelphia service under the banner of his Liverpool & Philadelphia Steam Ship Company, more commonly known

as the Inman Line. An almost identical vessel with a higher powered engine, *City of Manchester*, was ordered from Tod & MacGregor at the same time, with the similar *City of Philadelphia* being delivered in 1854. That unfortunate vessel was wrecked on her maiden voyage, whilst *City of Glasgow* was lost without trace in the Atlantic during the same year. Although such events were a setback, Inman Line's Atlantic services resumed in 1856 at the end of Crimean War hostilities and thrived on the basis of screw propelled vessels.

The Cunard company was not slow to experiment with screw propulsion, but restrictions were placed upon the type of propulsion which could be employed by the mail steamers. Until the 1860s screw propulsion was still looked upon suspiciously by the 'old guard' at the

Overhead beam engine of Inman's City of Glasgow.

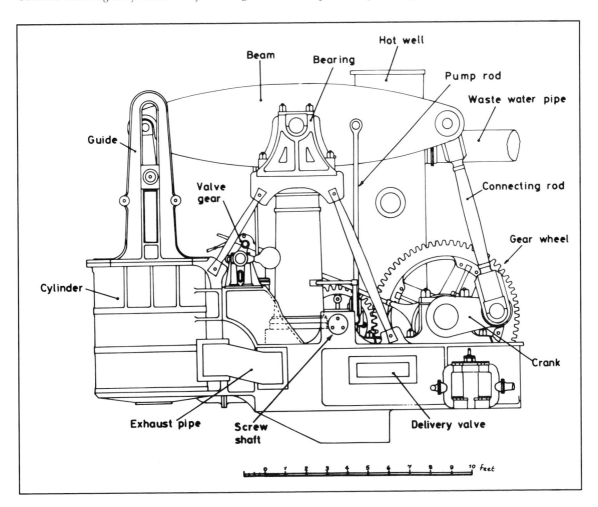

Admiralty. Early in the 1850s two 1,450 ton iron hulled screw steamers *Andes* and *Alps* were constructed for a trans-Atlantic service which would also take in a passage down to Panama. Two larger vessels, *Jura* and *Etna*, entered service in 1856 but none of these ships ever ventured south of New York during their brief Cunard careers. These vessels must have proved to those responsible for Cunard Line operations that screw propulsion was more economical than that provided by paddles and the company almost certainly made representations to the Admiralty for removal of the embargo placed on the use of screws for mail ships. *Jura* and *Etna* were fitted with steeple engines similar to those employed in the original Inman Line steamers, which is appropriate since *Etna* was purchased by than concern in 1861. Following reconstruction ten years later she was renamed *City of Bristol*.[5]

The first screw driven mail ship in the Cunard fleet was purchased from the bankrupt European & Australian Royal Mail Company in 1860. *Australian* was a product of the Clyde shipbuilders J. & G. Thompson and only lasted two years in her original owner's service. Not designed for Atlantic conditions, this 338 ft long 2,760 ton ship did not perform too well, suffering from vibration and heavy rolling. Her vertical direct acting engines were replaced in 1869 with similar engines of greater power. At the same time reconstruction increased her size by some 200 tons and she was given the name *Calabria* to comply with the Cunard system of naming.

Calabria's machinery provided further variety for the Cunard engineers, but the first screw propelled mail steamer actually ordered by the company had a different type of engine again. *China* was an iron built vessel constructed at the same time as the paddle mail ship *Scotia* and by the same builder, Robert Napier. The engine cylinders were of the oscillating type, with piston rods connecting to an overhead crankshaft which rotated the screw shaft by means of gearing. Although *China* appears to have been constructed to allow comparison with the paddle

An early screw Cunarder, Andes. (Harry Weston Collection.)

Calabria, the first Cunard screw driven mail ship.

driven *Scotia*, no similarity existed between the ships. The screw steamer's 326 ft length, 40 ft beam and 2,550 gross tonnage were no match for the 3,850 gross ton *Scotia*. There, however, the disparity between the ships in favour of the paddle steamer ceased. *China* had not been designed as a first class passenger mail boat, but was arranged for carrying some 753 steerage passengers as well as 150 in first class. Revenue would have compared very favourably with that from *Scotia*'s maximum 275 first class and second class passenger capacity. The absence of paddle boxes allowed passenger accommodation to be placed amidships and so more effective use could be made of all available space. Both ships had cargo capacities just in excess of 1,000 tons.

The major advantage *China* had over her rival lay in propulsive efficiency. She required only 2,200 horsepower to give a speed of 12.5 knots whilst *Scotia* needed engines of 4,200 horse-power to produce 13.5 knots. Daily coal consumption for the paddle steamer averaged at 164 tons, whilst for the screw driven vessel it was half that amount. The 'coal pile' certainly pointed out the economic advantages, but there was more than just fuel consumption to be considered. Lower powered engines cost less and reduced coal consumption required fewer stokers and trimmers. *China* had bunker space for 1,200 tons of coal but *Scotia* required much more of her valuable space to be set aside for fuel. The result was obvious and Cunard built no more paddle steamers.[6]

Oscillating engines were not new, many having been constructed to power paddle steamers, indeed the machinery installed in the *China* was not especially outstanding in an engineering sense. It was, however, the first of its type to be fitted in an Atlantic liner and it did reintroduce the surface condenser to the route. With this type of engine the pistons connected directly to the crankshaft, but to allow for crankshaft rotation, cylinders could oscillate and were attached

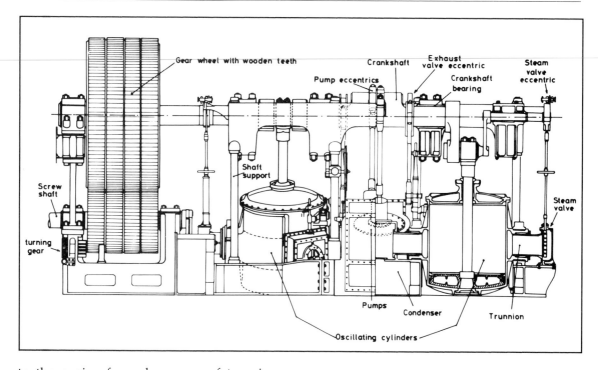

Overhead geared engine of the steamer China.

to the engine frame by means of trunnions. Steam supply and exhaust came through these hollow trunnions, thus avoiding the need for other steam connections. *China*'s two cylinders each had a bore of 80 in and a stroke of 66 in. Keyed to the after end of the crankshaft was a large spur-wheel with four sets of wooden teeth which engaged with teeth on screw shaft pinion. The use of gearing was considered more reliable and quieter than chains, but the cutting and lubrication of iron gear teeth in those days presented problems. Wooden teeth were easier to cut, caused fewer problems regarding lubrication and were quieter in operation. They did, however, wear quite alarmingly necessitating regular replacement and that was one of the reasons which prompted the widespread adoption of directly coupled engines.[7]

As mentioned in the previous chapter, surface condensation had its advantages but had fallen out of favour because tallow build-up caused tube blockage and thermal expansion resulted in tube leakage. The use of jet condensation meant that salt water feed for boilers continued and the associated problems of scale formation limited boiler pressure. Improved reliability of surface condensers and reduction in the amount of tallow carried over from the

engine by the use of mineral oils for lubrication removed most of the arguments against their adoption. Some people, however, considered that the pure water produced as a result of surface condensation caused rapid corrosion of the wrought iron boiler plates. It is true that in some cases increased corrosion had been experienced when distilled water was used, and that it had been reduced by the introduction of salt water to the boiler, but the premiss was incorrect. The nature of corrosion of iron plates due to oxygen dissolved in water was not then understood and the salt water had merely put a barrier layer of salt on the iron, isolating it from the water.[8]

Advantages of fresh water feed outweighed those of sea water feed, even though the surface condenser plant required more pumps and occupied greater space. Such advantages included a saving in fuel as boilers did not require frequent blowing down, less boiler cleaning and repair, a saving in fuel due to boilers being kept free from scale and the ability to operate boilers at higher pressure. The latter advantage was of paramount importance, for it ultimately allowed the development of compound engines. *China*'s four tubular boilers only operated at 25 psi, but after ten years service a Barclay Curle built two cylinder direct acting, compound engine was installed together with higher pressure boilers. The 51 in diameter high pressure and 86 in diameter low pressure cylinders each had a stroke of 48 in whilst the steam pressure was 62 psi. The change was not undertaken for speed but to improve fuel economy, and that it did.[9] Surface condensers had proved their worth.

Well satisfied with their first serious foray into the realms of screw propulsion, the Cunard Line managers decided upon a screw driven consort for the record breaking *Scotia*. The 2,950 gross ton *Russia* came from the favoured Cunard builders J. & G. Thompson of Clydebank. Some 350 ft long with a 42 ft beam, *Russia* was designed to carry 235 first and second class passengers across the rough Atlantic waters at a speed of 13.5 knots, the same as her paddle driven running mate. Her direct acting engine could produce 3,100 ihp from two 85 in bore by 45 in stroke cylinders. That machinery allowed the ship to achieve the distinction of being the first screw propelled holder of the much vaunted 'Blue Riband'. Purchased by the Red Star Line in 1880, *Russia* was renamed *Waesland*, lengthened by about 80 ft and given compound engines. She was re-engined again in 1890 and remained on Atlantic service until 1902 when she was lost off Anglesey following a collision with another steamer.

Her record eastbound crossing of 8 days 28 minutes between New York and Queenstown came in November 1867, some five months after she entered service. That 14.22 knot passage was the only record crossing she achieved. In direct competition was Inman's first *City of Paris* which entered service during March 1866. Built by Tod & MacGregor the Inman liner was similar in size to the Cunarder and there was little to choose between them in terms of speed, but her machinery was somewhat novel for a passenger liner. The Admiralty insisted that warships be propelled by machinery which was totally below the waterline, making it less vulnerable to damage in the event of projectiles penetrating the hull. To satisfy that need several designs of engine were developed including the horizontal trunk type and it was that form which was fitted in *City of Paris*. Her two 89 in bore by 42 in stroke cylinders could generate

2,800 ihp, but at 100 tons her daily coal consumption was 10 tons greater than that of *Russia*. Six flat sided multi-tubular boilers produced steam at 30 psi.[10]

City of Paris took the westbound 'Blue Riband' in November 1867 with a crossing just in excess of 8 days 4 hours between Queenstown and New York. Neither ship could improve on its passage, but they had both displaced the paddle steamer forever from Atlantic racing. Over the next two years arguments raged as to which vessel held the 'Blue Riband', but it was settled in 1869 when Inman's *City of Brussels* appeared. Slightly larger, more powerful and faster than *City of Paris*, the new Inman vessel put the issue beyond doubt when she crossed from New York to Queenstown in under eight days at an average speed of 14.66 knots. Her horizontal direct acting trunk engine differed little from that of her earlier sister apart from the fact that bore and stroke were slightly larger. The same form of machinery was adopted for the larger and slower *City of Montreal* in 1872, but all three vessels were re-engined with more economical compound machinery before that decade was out.

An interesting feature of the *City of Brussels* was her steam steering gear, the first installed aboard an Atlantic liner apart from the *Great Eastern*, if that ship can be classed as an Atlantic liner. The MacFarlane Gray steam steering gear was, in fact, similar to that fitted aboard Brunel's monster and very quickly powered steering became accepted steamer practice. No longer would crew members have to wrestle with the wheel in order to keep a vessel on course in Atlantic seas, but it was more work for the engineers.

At that time the engineer's role was still very much confined to his work with the propulsion engine and boilers, there being little other machinery for him to attend to. With the reintroduction of surface condensers it became standard practice to install separate pumps to circulate cooling seawater through them, these pumps being driven by small steam engines known as donkey engines. In some cases bilge and deck wash pumps would also be operated by donkey engines but, apart from the auxiliary boiler for supplying steam in port, everything else concerned propulsive plant. That should not, however, imply that the engineer's task was

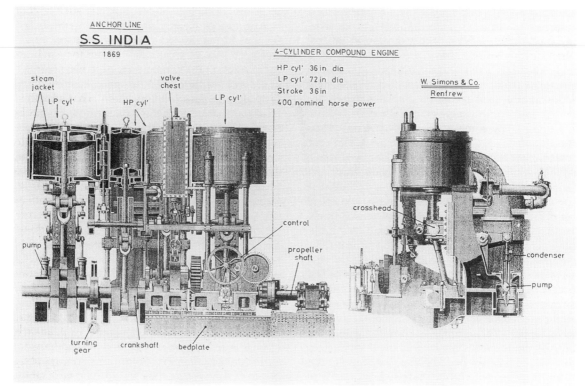

ANCHOR LINE

S.S. INDIA
1869

4-CYLINDER COMPOUND ENGINE

HP cyl' 36 in dia
LP cyl' 72 in dia
Stroke 36 in
400 nominal horse power

W. Simons & Co.
Renfrew

steam jacket

LP cyl'   HP cyl'   LP cyl'

valve chest

crosshead

control

propeller shaft

condenser

pump

pump

turning gear   crankshaft   bedplate

The first compound engines on the Atlantic.

a simple one, far from it. Machinery had to be under constant supervision, as did the firemen and coal trimmers! Machinery breakdown had to be rectified by those on board with the limited resources available. Machine tools did not exist and all equipment was hand powered, consisting basically of spanners, hammers and chisels, with ratchet drills aboard the better equipped vessels.

Safety of the ship and the lives of those on board frequently depended upon the skill of the engineering staff to keep the main engine turning or get it operating should it have failed, the cruel waters of the north Atlantic, especially in winter, being eager to devour any drifting vessel. Sails were still carried by ships of the period but in many cases afforded little means of propulsion, particularly as lack of use resulted in seamen and deck officers being unskilled at handling them and unfamiliar with their effects. In consequence of the increasing use of steam propulsion in Britain's merchant fleet and the high degree of responsibility vested in the engineers, the Merchant Shipping Act of 1862 required that all foreign going steamships of 100

nhp and upwards carried two certified engineers, a first and second engineer. The age of the recognized professional marine engineer had arrived.

The final year of that decade also saw the appearance of compound engine powered passenger liners on the western ocean. Expansive working of steam in an engine cylinder had been established practice since Brunel's *Great Western*, but the idea of expanding steam successively in cylinders of a larger diameter had been proposed in the eighteenth century. In 1781 the Cornishman Jonathan Hornblower patented a two stage pumping engine, but it was to be many years before a marine engine employing the same principle came into being. For effective expansion of steam higher initial steam pressures were required and so boilers had to be stronger. Gradually compounding was introduced with many different arrangements being developed as each engine builder tried to avoid infringing other patents. The economic gains possible with compounding were more readily appreciated on long sea routes rather than the relatively short 3,000 miles of an Atlantic crossing. The simple fact that a given quantity of coal went further reduced the need for maintaining a large number of expensive coaling stations on the routes to the east and Australia. It was with ships trading to these far away places that large compound engines proved their worth.

Compounding made its first appearance on the Atlantic early in 1869 aboard the 2,200 gross ton Anchor Line steamer *India*. She was not a major steamer as far as passenger ships go, being only 311 ft long with a beam of 35 ft, but she carried 60 people in first class and had space for 500 more in steerage. Her engine was of the vertical, direct acting in-line type with four cylinders, two high pressure (HP) of 36 in bore and two low pressure (LP) of 72 in bore. Her cylinders were steam jacketed, which means that low pressure steam was circulated through a space surrounding the cylinder wall in order to reduce power loss when incoming steam condensed on a relatively cold cylinder wall. The arrangement was common at that time, but never proved to be effective and was considered by many to be complicated and costly to provide.

Two cylindrical tubular boilers 12 ft 3 in diameter and 16 ft 6 in long provided steam at a pressure of 40 psi. The rectangular surface condenser had provision for sea water injection and so could be operated as a jet condenser should the need have arisen. To allow for such an arrangement it was necessary for the steam to surround the tubes and for the circulating cooling water to pass through them. That situation, which still exists today, also overcame the problem afflicting the early surface condensers where tallow would block tubes through which exhausting steam passed and deposits would fill the water section. *India* and her machinery were built on Clydeside by W. Simons & Co of Renfrew, being bought during construction by the Anchor Line. She cannot therefore be considered as the first compound ship laid down for the Atlantic, but her performance certainly left no doubt that her purchase was justified. An average speed of 11.47 knots during her maiden voyage on a daily average fuel consumption of 36 tons was good by prevailing standards.[11]

India marked a new beginning for powered Atlantic ships, but the experimental era was not over and many remarkable arrangements were to be devised before the marine reciprocating steam engine reached its zenith. The vertical in-line form, however, proved itself to be most effective and the Anchor Line steamer had set the pattern.

CHAPTER 3

Compound Engines

The Liverpool & Great Western Steamship Company, better known as the Guion Line, commenced its Atlantic service in 1866 with the single screw steamer *Manhattan*. Three other identical 2,900 gross ton vessels *Chicago, Minnesota* and *Colorado* quickly followed, allowing the concern to operate a regular service. It was no accident that the ships, and all others subsequently owned by the company, were named after American states or locations, for Stephen Barker Guion and his fellow directors were American citizens. Guion Line ships were built in Britain, probably due to the lack of suitable building capacity on American shores, and were registered there. Clydeside yards were to the forefront of passenger ship construction and marine engineering but Guion placed the order for his four ships with the Tyneside yard of Palmers at Jarrow.

There was nothing really special about these iron vessels in terms of size or power and their direct acting, surface condensing engines with two 60 in bore by 42 in stroke cylinders were typical for the period. Other similar, but slightly larger ships, followed from the same builder over the next three years but in 1870 two ships were delivered which, but for Anchor Line's purchase of *India*, would have been the first compound engined passenger liners on Atlantic service. As it was *Wyoming* and *Wisconsin* were the first compound engined ships actually ordered by an Atlantic company. These 3,250 gross ton ships, of length 366 ft and beam 43 ft, had engines which, apart from being compound, differed radically from those installed in earlier company ships.

The engines also departed from the vertical in-line format of *India*'s machinery and typified the period as designers strove to avoid infringing other people's patents and also to make powerful engines more compact, thus reducing the size of the engine room and increasing cargo capacity. The engines fitted to *Wyoming* and *Wisconsin* certainly went a long way to meet the latter point and easily complied with the first. They had a vertical 60 in diameter HP cylinder which attached to a crosshead and a horizontal 120 in diameter LP cylinder of trunk form. Both cylinders connected to the same crank and so had equal strokes of 42 in. Corliss drop valves were employed rather than the usual eccentric driven slide valves and steam supply pressure reached 70 psi. Such a cylinder arrangement reduced engine length considerably although it would have taken up a larger area; however, there were few auxiliaries requiring space in engine rooms of the period. A shorter machinery space had obvious advantages. Compared with the vertical in-line engine arrangement, these hybrids appeared odd but they must have been reliable for they remained with the ships until scrapping in 1893.[1] The same was not true of Palmer's next productions for the Guion Line.

Carriage of steerage passengers had been the company's original aim, but the cabin trade also offered potential and plans were soon laid for higher quality ships to cater for that market. Prestige value in holding the Atlantic 'Blue Riband' attracted passengers and Guion set out to capture that honour by building two 17 knot steamers. The order for *Montana* and *Dakota* went to Palmers, but responsibility for the hull and machinery was vested in John Jordan, the company's superintendent engineer. It would appear likely that Jordan also had a hand in the design of machinery for the earlier ships. A 17 knot ship of 4,300 gross tons with dimensions 400 ft by 43 ft and 33 ft depth of hold required considerably more power than had ever previously been installed in a screw steamer. Jordan set about his task with relish but adopted more new ideas than, in retrospect, was prudent.

The compound engines were of similar form to those of *Wyoming* and *Wisconsin*, but had three cylinders and two cranks. The 60 in diameter vertical HP cylinder connected to the forward crank, and also operated the pumps by means of crosshead driven levers. Two LP cylinders of 113 in diameter were placed horizontally and both connected to the after crank. A stroke of 42 in applied to all cylinders. In order to negotiate lock gates the beam was set at 43 ft, causing problems in the fitting of two such horizontal cylinders. The solution adopted was to connect both cylinders by means of two piston rods, one above and the other below the crankshaft. Such an arrangement saved space compared with two crossheads and connecting rods, but there were still limits on available room and the engine was a tight fit. In fact the crankshaft had to be placed slightly starboard of the ship's centre line. Whether the propeller was, there-

fore, off-centre or the shafting was aligned to connect with a centrally positioned propeller is unknown.

Corliss valves, which had performed successfully aboard the earlier vessels, were again adopted, but trouble was experienced due to bending of the valve rods during the delivery voyage of *Dakota*. The valve rods on both ships were made more substantial, but neither set of engines really lived up to expectation and design speed could never be achieved.[2] In order to help reduce water resistance the hulls were flush plated and, for some unknown reason, a tumblehome of 8 ft was provided on each side giving the ships a rather strange appearance.

In order to obtain the required power from the engines at reasonable economy of fuel, high pressure steam had to be employed. The design pressure fixed upon was 100 psi, compared with the 75 psi considered to be the safe marine maximum at the time. Jordan did not consider the oval and cylindrical type boilers then in use to be suitable for such pressures. Against the advice of Palmers he decided upon the use of water tube boilers, the first to be put in an Atlantic liner. Boiler design of that form was in its infancy and many practical construction difficulties existed. Each ship was to have ten boilers arranged back-to-back in two rows of five. Stokeholds were in the wings running the whole length of the 80 ft boiler room. There was

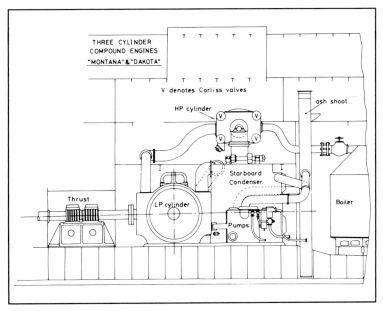

Three cylinder compound engine fitted in Guion liners Montana *and* Dakota.

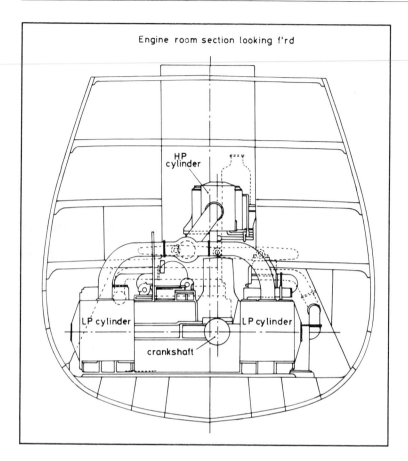

Engine room section looking f'rd

HP
cylinder

LP cylinder

LP cylinder

crankshaft

Left *Section through the engine room of* Montana *and* Dakota.

Below right *Water tube boiler as fitted in* Montana.

no dividing wall between the two rows of boilers, the flame space being common to each back-to-back pair, providing what would be classed as double ended boilers. A single uptake some 80 ft long extended the whole length of the boiler room and led to a single oval funnel.

A total of 35 tubes 15 ft long and 15 in diameter was fitted in each boiler, the tubes being in five rows with an inclination of 9 in. Vertical tubes connected the main tubes at their ends, allowing for water circulation and for steam to rise to the steam space in the top row. The two vertical sections nearest the boiler front were set apart for feed heating, cold feed entering at the top with warm feed passing to the main tube system at the bottom. At least that was the intention, but reality proved different. Three steam superheating drums 3 ft diameter and 30 ft long were positioned in the uptakes, two horizontally and one vertically.

Montana was the first ship completed and left

the Tyne for Liverpool on 11 June 1873. Only 13 hours later the first tubes began to fail, causing injury to a fireman. Within another 24 hours, five of the ten boilers were out of action and it was decided to make for Portsmouth in order to facilitate repairs. Eventually the ship made Liverpool, but before he would issue a passenger certificate the Board of Trade surveyor insisted upon a prolonged sea trial. On 26 August 1873 *Montana* left Liverpool for her trials in the Irish Sea. Early in the morning of the 28th tubes on one of the boilers cracked in the same manner as previously. Jordan had had enough and decided that the ship must put back to Liverpool. The boilers would just not do.

Without waiting for reports from those who had observed the trials, the owners of *Montana* decided that the boilers, and those of *Dakota* still under construction, had to be replaced. The total cost exceeded £60,000, but the loss of earnings and prestige must have been greater. Failures during the delivery voyage related to steam being generated in the feed heating tubes, thus forcing out water from those and some other tubes. These overheated, resulting in failure. Subsequent tube failure during the trials related to problems of even feed water supply throughout the tube system.[3] Had the boilers been thoroughly tried before they were put in *Montana* the problems might have been solved but the Atlantic 'Blue Riband' waits for no shipowner and that factor seems to have outweighed other considerations. Novelty deserves a try but John Jordan seems to have tried too hard, or maybe he was pressed too hard.

Reboilered, the *Montana* and *Dakota* commenced Atlantic service in 1875, but neither came anywhere near to accomplishing the expected 17 knots. Jordan's innovation deserved better but there were no prizes for just trying, competition on the Atlantic was too severe. It was probably a relief to the Guion Line when *Dakota* was wrecked off Anglesey in 1877 and her sister near the same spot three years later.

Whilst Guion made his play for fame, and possibly fortune, in the Atlantic, another shipping entrepreneur was similarly engaged. Thomas Henry Ismay took control of the White Star Line of sailing packets in 1867 and two years later, in

company with G. Hamilton Fletcher and William Imrie, launched the Oceanic Steam Navigation Company. Ismay's dream was the establishment of a high class passenger service across the Atlantic and he quickly set about raising funds for construction of his intended fleet. Earlier maritime contacts proved useful, in particular Gustav Christian Schwabe, who pointed him in the direction of the Belfast shipbuilders Harland & Wolff. Following suitable negotiations Edward Harland and Gustav Wolff both invested in the new company with the result that an order for four screw steamers was placed with them, the contract price being £110,000 per ship.[4]

Oceanic, first of the class, was launched in August 1870 and entered service the following year. Her major dimensions were length 420 ft, breadth 41 ft and depth 31 ft with a measurement of 3,707 gross tons. Harland & Wolff were given a free hand in the design, the White Star Line only laying down basic criteria regarding passenger capacity, decoration and speed. Other ships of the class, *Atlantic*, *Baltic* and *Republic*, appeared over the next year; two further ships of similar proportions, *Adriatic* and *Celtic*, were added to the initial order. They were all essentially the same and set a standard which hitherto had not been seen on the Atlantic Ocean. Much has been written about the accommodation

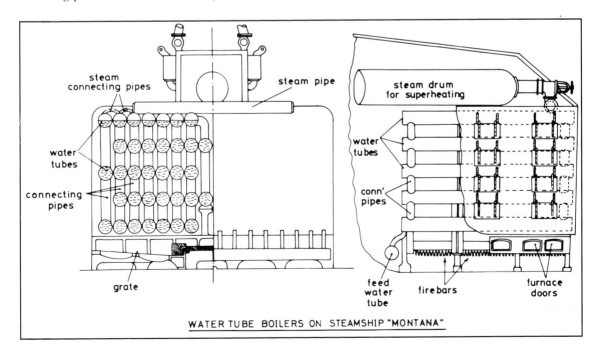

WATER TUBE BOILERS ON STEAMSHIP "MONTANA"

style of these pace setters and, indeed, they changed the traditional arrangements dramatically. Custom carried over from the paddle era disappeared as the saloon and better class cabins were sited in the central part of the ship. There was a good reason for such a move in that vibration due to screw propulsion was more pronounced in the after regions, but old habits died hard with many builders.

At that time Harland & Wolff had no facilities for engine construction and the work went to outside contractors. Although the ships were essentially identical there were slight differences in machinery. Maudslay, Sons & Field of Lambeth supplied the machinery for *Oceanic* whilst that for the second ship, *Atlantic*, came from the Liverpool firm of G. Forrester & Co. In each case the inverted, direct acting, compound engine consisted of two HP cylinders 41 in bore each arranged in tandem above a 78 in bore LP cylinder. The stroke was 60 in. An open distance piece separated the cylinders and gave access to piston rod glands. Slide valves for each HP and LP cylinder pairing were actuated by a single valve rod operated by a link motion from

White Star's pioneer Oceanic, *sections through boiler and engine rooms.*

eccentrics on the crankshaft. Expansive working of the steam was controlled by expansion valves situated in the steam line to the HP cylinders. A steam cylinder was used to alter the link motion for reversing the engine.

As was usual for engines of the period, boiler feed pumps and condenser air pumps were lever driven from the main crosshead. An independent condenser sea water circulating pump, of the centrifugal type, was powered by a small two cylinder steam engine. LP cylinders exhausted into a cylindrical surface condenser positioned between the cylinders. Live and exhaust steam lines were provided with bellows expansion joints in order to give some flexibility and so avoid high stresses due to changes in temperature.[5]

Twelve oval type tubular boilers having two furnaces each supplied steam at working pressure of 65 psi giving the engine a maximum rating of 2,000 ihp. That was sufficient to maintain a design speed of 13.5 knots although the class would often achieve more. Two members did produce record breaking crossings, *Adriatic* in 1872 with a westbound maiden voyage run at an average speed of 14.41 knots and *Baltic* the following year with an eastbound passage at 15.12 knots. Under normal operating circumstances the ships would burn about 65 tons of

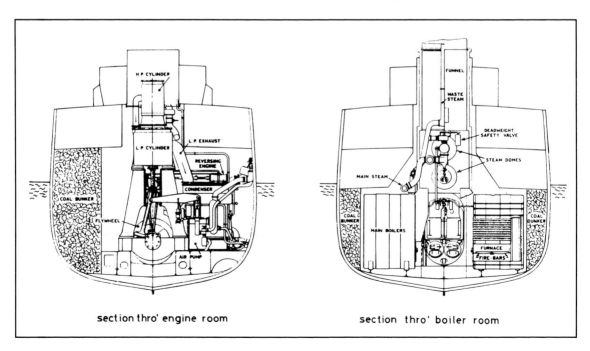

section thro' engine room   section thro' boiler room

coal per day, and each ship could carry nearly 800 tons. That consumption and bunker capacity were to figure in a tragic incident featuring the second member of the class, *Atlantic*.

Ships of the period frequently had to battle against foul weather and that increased voyage fuel consumption. It was not unknown for a vessel to run so low on coal that she was forced to put into the nearest port for further supplies. The Cunard secondary steamer *Cuba* was prone to such events, during a 12 month period in 1872–3 having to do so no less than three times.[6] Naturally a master did not like taking that action, but circumstances forced it upon him. Excessive use of fuel because of a prolonged passage was generally the reason, but sometimes poor quality coal or the taking of an inadequate supply could be blamed. Whatever the reason it caused problems and bad publicity.

The White Star liner *Atlantic* prepared for her 19th voyage to New York during March 1873 and took some 847 tons of coal to supplement the 132 tons which the chief engineer, John Foxley, estimated was already on board. That 979 tons should easily have been sufficient for the crossing under any reasonably expected circumstance. The average over the vessel's previous 18 voyages had been 744 tons, with 896 being consumed during the worst passage.[7] Departing from her anchorage in the River Mersey shortly after 3 o'clock in the afternoon of Thursday 20 March, *Atlantic* headed for Queenstown where she arrived 18 hours later. Within two hours the ship was on its way again and heading for the western ocean.

Company instructions insisted that the chief engineer inform the master as to the daily fuel consumption and the amount remaining on board. There were problems on both accounts unless an accurate count of the number of coal baskets brought to the boilers was kept. In addition the amount remaining on board depended upon an accurate value for the coal in the ship prior to bunkering, and that was always an estimate.

After a few fine days *Atlantic* ran into some severe weather which reduced speed below 5 knots at times. Nine days out of Liverpool the master, James Agnew Williams, became concerned about fuel consumption and instructed the engine room to be careful with the coal. On the morning of Monday 31 March he requested Foxley to check the amount remaining in the bunkers. Coal used was always estimated and then consumption rounded to the nearest 5 tons, such being common practice and reasonable under the circumstances of the time. That usually gave an over-estimate for consumption and so, as might be expected, visual sight of the bunker spaces indicated that there was more fuel on board than calculated. The calculation simply subtracted estimated consumption from bunkers at the start of the voyage.

Foxley wrote on a slip of paper the calculated value of 129 tons remaining on board. He did not wish to appear foolish having to explain the 140 tons which sight of the bunker spaces showed was actually on board. Upon personally delivering the slip he did mention to Williams that there was sufficient for two days' steaming, enough for the ship to make New York. The master either did not listen or chose to ignore the remark and decided to head for Halifax in order to obtain fresh bunkers. It was a fateful decision.

At full speed *Atlantic* raced towards the Canadian port and a coast of which those navigating had little knowledge. Through a gathering storm the ship battled on. Speed was determined by means of a common log rather than the Massey patent log which was on board. The common log consisted of a knotted line to one end of which was attached a triangular piece of wood. When the wood was thrown overboard line would be paid out and the length paid out in a given time provided a good estimation as to the ship's speed. An unknown factor during that dark stormy night of 31 March–1 April was the strength and direction of the local currents. *Atlantic*'s navigators underestimated their ship's speed through the water and shortly after 3 o'clock on the morning of 1 April 1873 she struck the coast of Nova Scotia at full speed.[8]

Dreadful loss of life occurred in the raging waters south of Halifax. The death of 562 people could have been avoided if those on board had been more aware of their ship's capabilities. Without doubt the master should have paid greater heed to the chief engineer's advice that coal for two days' steaming remained. The navigators seemed to be blissfully unaware of the machinery's capability for pushing the ship at high speed through the water.

An inability, or unwillingness, to comprehend the power that engines gave to a ship seemed to prevail amongst many masters and navigating officers of the period and even much later. Ships would be raced through fog and ice with an apparently total disregard for the safety of all on board. Before the advent of radio many steamers were lost without trace and a number of these must have been due to collision with other ships in foggy conditions or with icebergs. Despite warnings as to the conditions, and fully aware of the approaching ice fields, the *Titanic*'s master still pushed his ship on at high speed. That and many similar incidents were pure incompetence on the part of those who should have known better and were highly paid to do so. Unfortunately it was generally considered that a training 'before the mast' fitted a man for command of a large and powerful steamship. Regrettably many individuals lost their lives in proving that this was not the case. To know the capabilities of a powered ship, one must be fully trained aboard that ship.

Lighting of ships both in the accommodation and engine room was still by means of candles or oil lamps, both of which were inconvenient and presented a fire risk. Gas lighting had been tried ashore and although it did not eliminate the fire hazard, the inconvenience associated with attention to oil lamps and candles was reduced. White Star Line took the bold step of

Oil gas generator fitted in Celtic, *1872.*

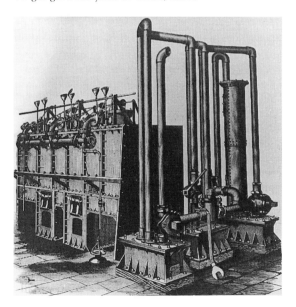

installing gas lighting plants aboard the second batch of 'Oceanics', *Adriatic* and *Celtic*, when they were constructed.

The system chosen was by Porter & Co of Lincoln and it could supply some 300 lights, about 30 of which were left burning night and day. Gas was generated by the vapourization of oil in a single unit which occupied 1,600 cu ft of space and weighed 22 tons. The apparatus consisted of retort stack, washer, condenser, scrubber and gas holder, there being three coal fired retorts in the stack. Two furnaces were so arranged that one, two or all three retorts could be operated in order to meet demand for gas. Oil supplied to the heated retorts was vapourized and then allowed to pass through a water washer, condenser and finally a scrubber where all impurities were removed. A gas holder, separate from the gas generator unit, stored the gas at a constant pressure until required for use and a gauge allowed the operator to see instantly the amount of gas in store so that he could adjust the retorts to suit demand.

A flow governor in the delivery line allowed the maintenance of uniform pressure at the burners. These produced open flames, the incandescent mantle not then being available, the light from which was equal to about 12 shipboard candles. Between 30 and 40 burners were employed in lighting the main saloon.[9] Unfortunately what started out as a good idea did not prove practical over a long period. Pipework in gas systems ashore remained rigid, but that aboard ship was subject to movement and vibration as the vessel operated. Pipe and joint failures resulted in gas leakage with the consequent increase in fire hazard as well as the annoyance to passengers who had to suffer the smell. Within a short period of time the experiment was discontinued, *Adriatic* and *Celtic* returning to oil lamp illumination.[10]

For a new concern the White Star Line was not reluctant to embrace new technology, and actively pursued innovation. Satisfied that Harland & Wolff had produced first rate liners in the 'Oceanics' the company returned to the same shipyard for a pair of larger and faster vessels within three years, the issue being forced somewhat by the arrival of Inman's new express steamer *City of Berlin*.

Britannic of 1874 and *Germanic* of 1875 were almost identical ships and essentially larger ver-

White Star liner Germanic, *1875.* (G. Charles Collection)

sions of their earlier sisters. There was no need to change the winning formula developed by Harlands, merely to enlarge it and increase the speed. Gross tonnage was increased to 5,004 on a length of 455 ft and breadth of 45 ft. The Belfast yard still had no facilities for engine construction and so the engine order went to Maudslay, Sons & Field. Needless to say the engines followed the same pattern as for *Oceanic*, although of greater power. HP cylinder diameter became 48 in and that of the LP 83 in, but the stroke remained the same at 60 in. With a steam pressure of 75 psi the engine, of 760 nhp, could develop 4,970 ihp. That was more than sufficient to give a speed of 16 knots on 110 tons of coal per day. In regular service the desired speed was somewhat lower.[11]

Eight double ended, oval boilers supplied steam but they were arranged longitudinally in groups of four across the ship. Each boiler had four furnaces, two at each end, and a cylindrical steam collector positioned in the uptake, this also acting as a superheater. Oval boilers marked the transition from the former box type

boiler which had a pressure limitation due to steam force on its flat sides. A cylindrical arrangement can withstand a higher pressure than a flat sided box for the same plate thickness and the oval form had some of the advantages possessed by the cylinder. A true cylindrical boiler was the next stage in development. In order to withstand high pressures on the flat front and rear faces, as well as on the flat sides, effective staying had to be provided. This usually took the form of stay bars or thicker walled stay tubes, whilst 3 in angle bars were rivetted to the side plating of *Britannic*'s boilers in order to increase the strength.

It took a little time for *Britannic* and *Germanic* to demonstrate their real potential, in the former's case an experimental propeller arrangement being the reason. Each vessel had a built-up screw, that being the only form of construction available for large propellers, with four blades giving an overall diameter of 23.5 ft and a pitch increasing from 28 ft at the blade roots to 31.5 ft at the tips.[12]

Aboard *Britannic* the screw could be raised and lowered whilst still being turned by the engine. This system had been devised by Harland & Wolff and fitted in its own small

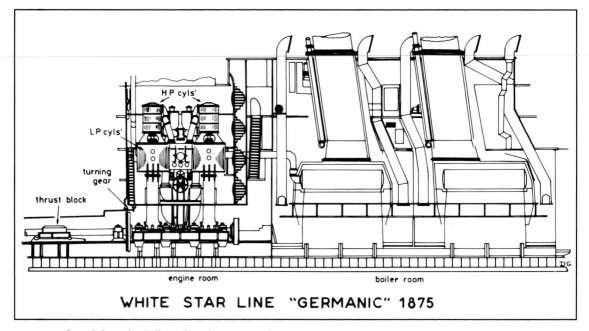

engine room   boiler room

WHITE STAR LINE "GERMANIC" 1875

steamer *Camel*, but the White Star liner was the first ocean going vessel so fitted, her owners appearing actively to encourage the experiment. The reasoning behind the arrangement lay in the fact that full propulsive efficiency is only obtained if the screw remains completely immersed. Atlantic weather caused long vessels to pitch heavily at times, resulting in the propeller coming partially out of the water so reducing the drive. With the engine and shafting tilted slightly down towards the stern the screw would be deeper in the water. In shallow waters the screw had to be raised in order to prevent it fouling the sea bed, hence the lifting arrangement.

A flexible coupling connected the main part of the shaft to the lifting screw portion, with a radial slot in the stern frame accommodating this movement. In order to seal the shaft tunnel a radial gland was provided in place of the usual stern tube gland. Lifting was accomplished by means of a small steam engine raising rods connected to an aftermost bush in which the tailshaft turned. The lignum vitae-lined bush was guided by cheeks in the slotted stern post.[13]

The novel arrangement was never satisfactory and caused severe vibration at times. After a short while it was discarded and a conventional system fitted. That required the engine and shafting to be realigned, resulting in time out of

Machinery layout of Germanic.

service and considerable expense. Once *Britannic* had been restored to normal condition she joined her sister in record breaking. For the next few years they vied with each other for the 'Blue Riband', taking it in turns to hold the record for the fastest crossings, east or west.

During this period of White Star ascendancy, Cunard was rather quiet in terms of liner construction and seemed determined not to compete. Compound machinery was introduced to the Line by way of *Batavia* in 1870, but this ship came from the yard of William Denny at Dumbarton and was not originally laid down for Cunard. A rather small ship of 2,550 gross tons and 327 ft long, she had space for 105 cabin passengers and 624 steerage. Bunker capacity amounted to 890 tons but her coal consumption was low, less than 410 tons on the maiden return voyage from New York to Liverpool. The main engine consisted of a 50 in bore HP cylinder and 80 in bore LP unit both having 48 in strokes. Steam at 60 psi came from two tubular boilers.[14]

There was nothing exceptional about *Batavia* save for its innovative position in the Cunard fleet, the machinery was typical of that being supplied to many ships of the period. She was, however, the first compound engined vessel built by Denny's. Cunard's management ordered another compound engined vessel from Denny's early in 1870, before *Batavia* was launched. With the order came the request that the new 3,150 gross ton ship, *Parthia*, be fitted with a similar two cylinder, surface condensing compound engine. Cylinder diameters were 56 in for the HP and 97 in for the LP with the stroke remaining at 48 in. *Parthia* remained 14 years in the Cunard fleet before being traded to Elder's in part exchange for *Umbria* and *Etruria*, a common practice at the time. Following service in the Pacific and Alaskan waters she became a towing barge and was only broken up in 1956.[15]

The only ship to actually challenge White Star's supremacy throughout the 1870s was Inman's *City of Berlin*, launched at Greenock in 1874. She was the longest Atlantic liner ever built in terms of length to beam ratio and had a length of 488 ft on a beam of 44 ft, with a gross tonnage of 5,500. A single inverted, two cylinder, compound engine provided the power, with steam at 72 psi being supplied by 12 tubular boilers. The 72 in bore HP cylinder and 120 in bore LP both had strokes of 66 in and these cylinders were amongst the largest ever fitted in a

ship to that time. During trials in 1875 the engine developed 5,200 indicated horse power giving the ship a mean speed of 14.825 knots, designed service speed being 14 knots. The boilers were somewhat extravagant, consuming around 120 tons per day during full power running. Bunker capacity of 1,400 tons was essential under such circumstances.[16]

City of Berlin produced record Atlantic crossings during 1875 with speed both ways in excess of 15 knots. She was provided with a number of separately driven auxiliary pumps and a MacFarlane Gray steam steering gear. In 1879 she became the first British Atlantic liner to be fitted with electric lighting when a Siemens' system was put on board for trial. That trial was a success and two years later an enlarged system was provided aboard *City of Rome*. William Inman had formed his company with the specific aim of meeting emigrant traffic needs. His belief that they deserved every possible convenience their fares would provide resulted in steerage quarters being amply supplied with electric lamps.[17]

City of Berlin was a fair sized modern vessel, but the pace of marine engineering development overtook her and as early as 1887 she was removed from service for renovation. Laird

Britannic's lifting screw mechanism.

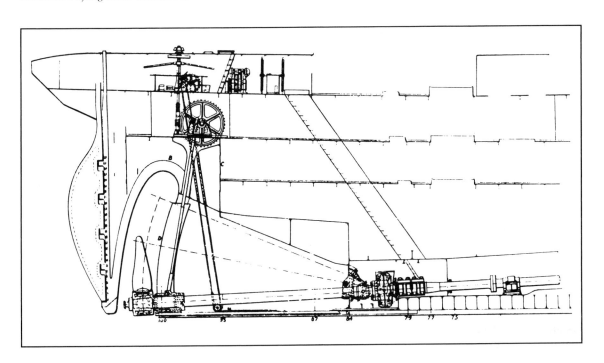

Brothers of Birkenhead were given the contract which included complete renewal of the machinery. Triple expansion engines were fitted together with higher pressure steel boilers employing forced draught. The entire ship was provided with electric lighting, steam winches installed, heating pipework fitted throughout the ship and an evaporator provided distilled water for the boilers. In 12 short years ships' machinery had changed dramatically.[18]

In 1879 Guion Line re-entered the fray with its 'Greyhound' *Arizona*. Following the fiasco of *Montana* and *Dakota* the order went to John Elder & Co at Govan on the Clyde. The hard won reputation of Clydeside for building first class liners was above reproach, and remained so for generations.

Launched in March 1879, *Arizona* was then the largest vessel to enter the waters of the Clyde and she was exceptional by any standards. Of iron construction, this 5,147 gross ton ship had accommodation for 140 first class, 70

second class and 140 steerage passengers although the lower cargo decks could be made available for 1,000 steerage passengers should it have been required. The low passenger figures are indicative of the price paid for speed—bunker space for 1,200 tons of coal had to be provided, expected daily consumption being in excess of 100 tons. A designed speed of 15.5 knots required powerful engines and the contract called for 6,000 ihp. On trials the plant produced a remarkable 6,357 ihp which forced the ship through the water at 17.3 knots. Elders had build an outstanding ship.

In order to limit cylinder diameter and so reduce manufacturing and operational problems, Elders designed a three crank compound engine with two LP cylinders connected to cranks either side of the HP cylinder. That HP cylinder was 62 in diameter whilst the two LP cylinders were each of 90 in bore; all had 66 in strokes. Cylinders were steam jacketed, with piston valves placed at the back of the engine

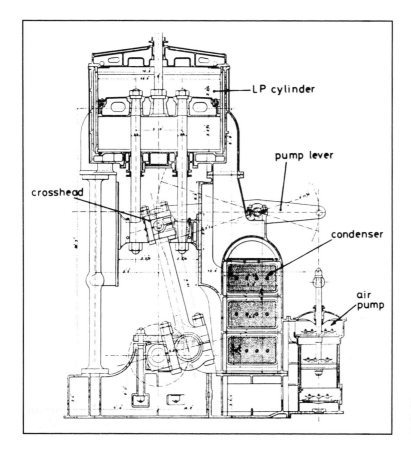

Section through City of Richmond's *compound engine. A typical arrangement of the early 1870s.*

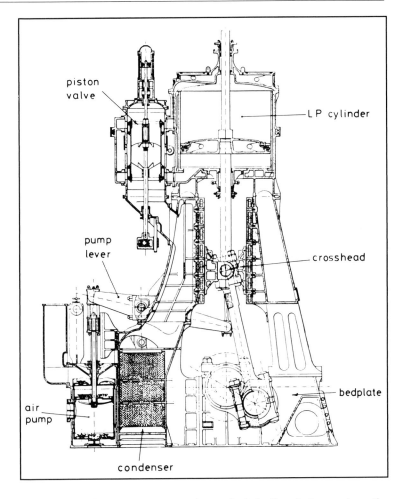

and operated from eccentrics by means of levers. That positioning of the valves, adopted by Elders some years earlier, allowed cylinders to be placed closer together compared with the arrangement of valves between the cylinders and so reduced engine length. That was important as it reduced the space required for the engine room, an important factor where large bunker capacity had to be provided. The usual arrangement of lever driven air pumps was employed but the condenser was in two parts, each being independent and taking steam from one of the LP cylinders. Boiler feed and bilge pumps were also worked by the main engine.

Cylindrical boilers of the type later to be known as 'scotch boilers' were employed, this form being the much stronger logical development of the oval boiler. One single ended and six double ended boilers supplied steam at 90

psi, the single ended boiler being primarily fitted for steam supply in port. Main boilers were arranged in groups of three with the stokeholds athwartships, these groups being separated by the single ended boiler. Each main boiler had six furnaces, the single ended one having three, giving a total grate area of 780 sq ft.

Elders provided an extensive array of steam auxiliary equipment. In the engine room they included the condenser circulating pump, sanitary water pumps for flushing water closets, auxiliary boiler feed pumps, main engine turning machine, ash hoisting engine and an extensive electrical plant. In addition there was a fresh water evaporator and the, by now common, steam steering gear. Deck machinery included steam winches for cargo handling, steam windlass and a steam crane for lifting the anchor on board after it had been raised.[19] Such auxiliary plant certainly helped the working of the ship and became essential as the size of ships increased. Some of the plant, like the ash hoists, was of direct benefit to engine room hands as it eased the burden of hauling ashes to an upper deck for disposal overboard. Most plant, however, increased the load on the engine room staff. Engineers had to maintain more equipment, whilst firemen worked harder to keep up steam pressure. As plant size and complexity increased so did the engine room staff, especially in the ranks of firemen and trimmers.

Arizona was by far the most advanced ship of her day. Not only was her accommodation first rate and her machinery more extensive than any competitor, but she was soundly built. She had to be. Her reputation was won whilst racing across the Atlantic, gaining the east and westbound records within months of entering service during May 1879. Fate and those in whose charge she lay, however, appeared to conspire at greater notoriety. Heading back to Liverpool in November 1879 *Arizona* raced at full speed

through a dense Newfoundland Bank fog and struck an iceberg. Only the skill of her builders and the fact that the collision was directly head on saved a tragedy. Her master and navigators again emphasized the inability of those in command of steamships to fully comprehend the power at their disposal.

Arizona's bow was stove in some 20 ft, to within a short distance of her collision bulkhead. After a temporary repair at St John's, Newfoundland the ship returned to the Clyde for reconstruction of her bow. But for the skill of Elders Fairfield shipyard workforce, the neglect of another ship master and his navigating officers might have produced another maritime disaster of major proportions. Rightly the master and second navigating officer had their certificates suspended, but for only six months—Fairfields workers had probably saved their careers as well as their lives. The incident enhanced the

Arizona's electrical generating plant.

Following collision with an iceberg, Arizona *remained afloat.*

Arizona's reputation as a safe ship and her passenger bookings increased.[20]

The success of *Arizona* prompted her owners to build a similar, but larger and more powerful, vessel. Again the Fairfield workforce produced a first class ship. Machinery fitted in the 6,950 gross ton *Alaska* differed little from that provided for the earlier 'Greyhound' except in size and power. She soon made crossings at average speeds in excess of 16 knots and within a year of entering service managed to cross from New York to Queenstown in under seven days. Once again speed was paid for at the price of coal consumption, which could amount to 250 tons per day during a fast run. The 'Greyhound' era had surely arrived.

The Cunard partners remained aloof. Not for them the race across, at least not yet, a period of thought was needed in order to contemplate changing technology. There was no point in rushing into construction of ships which would quickly date, but new tonnage was sorely wanted. The favoured shipbuilders, J. & G. Thomson of Clydebank, were approached and delivered the 4,800 gross ton *Gallia* in 1879. As was usual for the period, her builders were merely given instructions to construct a vessel to broad specifications regarding size, speed and passenger capacity, and the builders produced a design to suit. That is why ships from one builder for several different companies followed broadly the same design and layout.

Gallia was built of iron, with nine transverse watertight bulkheads. Seven of these extended to the spar deck, the others being the fore and after peaks. As a result of that strong and safe construction Cunard was able to satisfy Admiralty requirements in order that the ship might be employed for war or transport services. The three cylinder compound engine was arranged differently from the Elder form in that the 63 in diameter HP cylinder was placed forward of the two 80 in bore LP cylinders. Steam at 75 psi came from eight cylindrical boilers, whilst a

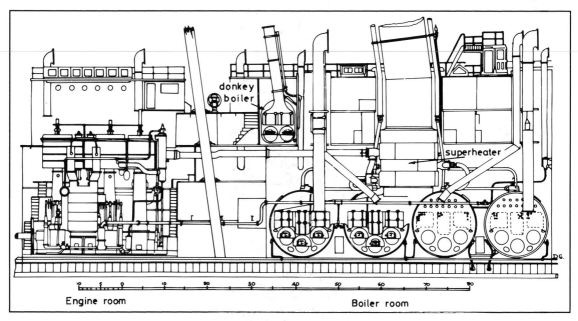

Engine room   Boiler room

small auxiliary or donkey boiler was provided for use in port.

Auxiliary equipment included pumps and steam steering gear, whilst a system of steam heating pipes was laid throughout the passenger accommodation, even in steerage. The propeller, as with others of the period, comprised individual blades bolted onto a separate boss. In the case of *Gallia* the boss was of iron and the blades of steel. The ship was built for comfort rather than speed but Cunard required a guarantee that she would be capable of 14.3 knots. In practice on the open waters of the Atlantic her speed ranged around 15 knots. Trials on the measured mile showed that 15.9 knots could be achieved with the engines developing 5,300 ihp. Service coal consumption at full speed never exceeded 100 tons per day.[21]

Gallia was also provided with a Dunlop pneumatic governor, designed to prevent the engine from racing when the propeller came out of the water. This device was novel in that it was not operated by the engine, but reacted to the propeller load. The more usual Watt and inertia type governors reacted to change in the engine speed and so some racing had to take place before the steam supply was reduced. In the Dunlop system an air vessel positioned in the shaft tunnel near the screw had connection with the sea by way of a valve. During normal immersion the head of water above the air vessel maintained pressure in that vessel. As a wave passed and the stern of the ship rose there would be less water covering the screw and hence the air vessel. Pressure in that vessel would then fall. A long pipe connected the air vessel with the space below a diaphragm on the receiver unit positioned next to the engine. As air pressure fell the spring would force the diaphragm downward causing a linkage to operate the steam throttle valve. Steam to the engine was reduced so preventing it from racing.[22] The Dunlop governor proved to be very popular with some builders but its use was not widespread, many favouring engine-operated governors.

The success of *Gallia* begat *Servia*, the first steel mail ship on the Atlantic. Steel had for a number of years been used in the construction of ships, but its quality and supply had been somewhat variable. Its use for boiler construction had been more widespread due to strength considerations and the greater suitability of the limited quantity of plates available. The merits of steel over iron were readily apparent to the shipowner; steel plates could be thinner than iron for the same strength thus reducing the weight of the hull and allowing more cargo to be carried. Despite the higher cost of steel compared with iron, its popularity grew as quantity

Left *Machinery arrangement aboard Gallia.*

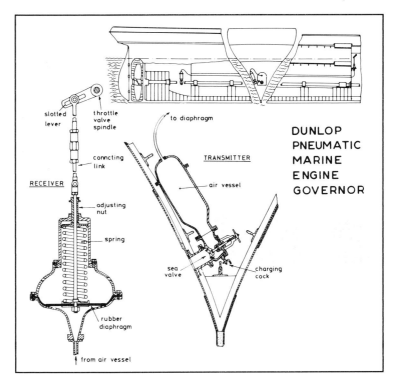

slotted lever

throttle valve spindle

to diaphragm

DUNLOP PNEUMATIC MARINE ENGINE GOVERNOR

connecting link

TRANSMITTER

RECEIVER

air vessel

adjusting nut

spring

sea valve

charging cock

rubber diaphragm

↑ from air vessel

Right *Dunlop governor.*

and quality increased. By 1885 most of the major shipbuilders were constructing solely in steel.[23] The problem of corrosion was a matter which had to be addressed, being greater for

steel than wrought iron.

Servia, 7,400 gross tons, was not designed as a record breaker, but she was powerful and fast. Her three cylinder compound engine was arranged in a more conventional manner with the two 100 in bore LP cylinders being positioned either side of the single 72 in diameter

Cunard's Servia *of 1881.* (Harry Weston Collection.)

HP cylinder. Slide valves regulated steam to the LP cylinders, but for the HP a piston valve was employed. Six double ended boilers and one single ended boiler, all constructed from Siemens' steel and employing Fox's corrugated flues, supplied steam at 90 psi. On trials *Servia's* engines developed 10,350 ihp at 53 rpm allowing her to attain a speed of 17.85 knots. Service speed averaged around 16 knots on a daily fuel consumption of 190 tons. That was lower than for the smaller, but slightly swifter, *Alaska*.

Though large and powerful the new Cunarder's main machinery illustrated few innovative ideas, but her auxiliary plant was extensive. As well as the usual array of pumps there was, in addition to the ice house, a dry air refrigerating chamber for preserving fresh meat. The Bell–Coleman air refrigerating plant was one of the first installed in any ship, let alone an Atlantic liner. Four distinct sets of steering gear were fitted, providing a fair degree of overkill. The steam gear was supplemented by a hand screw gear, a double purchase chain system and an arrangement for turning the rudder from an after positioned wheel through wire ropes acting on a quadrant. Corrosion of steel boiler plates was a greater problem than that for wrought iron and it was recognized that air, or rather oxygen, in the water was a major factor. *Servia* was provided with a patent de-aerator in the feed line in order to reduce the quantity of air likely to enter the boiler with the feed.

Electric lighting, the first such system in the Cunard fleet, employed 98 incandescent lamps, 50 of which illuminated the main saloon. A further 20 lamps provided light in the engine and boiler rooms whilst a further ten were fitted in the propeller shaft tunnel. Only public rooms had electric lighting, the passenger cabins had to wait for such luxury.

The ship was larger than any for which Lloyd's construction rules were available and so the builders had to devise values for scantlings using their own experience. Cunard never had any of its ships built to Lloyd's registry classification anyway and so Thomsons was on its own. The 4 ft 8 in deep double bottom was of cellular form and, apart from the section under the engine, could accommodate sea water ballast. Watertight subdivision matched that of any ship afloat and was of a high enough standard for the Admiralty to place *Servia* well up the list of auxiliary cruisers. Of her 12 watertight bulkheads, eight extended to the main deck and the ship would still float with two of her compartments flooded. An additional measure of the vessel's usefulness in the event of a conflict was the bunker capacity. If cargo spaces were included there would be coal for a 16,400 mile steaming range at full speed, 27,300 miles at 14

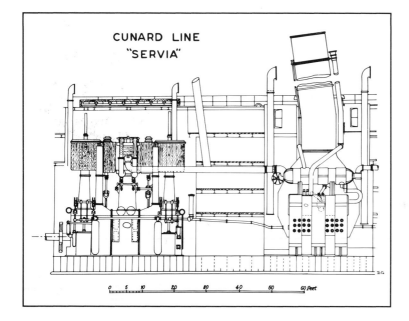

CUNARD LINE "SERVIA"

0 5 10   20   30   40   60   60 Feet

Left *Engine room of* Servia.

Right City of Rome, *the Barrow built Inman liner.* (Glasgow University Archives with permission of Mr W. Lind.)

knots or a staggering 35,700 miles at 12 knots.

Despite the high standard of design and construction, the position regarding life saving appliances left much to be desired, as it did on most ships until the *Titanic* disaster brought the point forcibly home. *Servia* could accommodate 500 first class passengers normally and 640 if stretched. Steerage space for 740 souls was provided, whilst the crew exceeded 200. With a maximum loading capacity of nearly 1,600 people the 12 lifeboats could hold at most 720. Fortunately they were never put to the test.[24]

A running mate, *Aurania*, was constructed by Thomsons in 1883. Of similar size to *Servia*, she had the same form of compound engines and auxiliary plant but a more extensive electric lighting system. Speed was still not the aim.

Whilst steel was recognized as the better shipbuilding material, many ships of the early 1880s were still constructed of wrought iron plate due to the difficulty in obtaining suitable steel plate. The Inman ship *City of Rome* became a victim of that shortage.

The Inman Line went to the Barrow Shipbuilding Company for its challenger to Guion's dominance, requesting construction of a fast luxury liner. Without doubt the builders fulfilled the second part of their brief, *City of Rome*'s accommodation being a match for any ship of the day. External appearance was also superb,

and she was acknowledged as one of the most beautiful ships ever to cross the Atlantic. In one notable aspect, that of speed, she failed to live up to expectation and that led to rejection.

The building contract specified steel construction but that was in short supply and so, in order not to miss an Atlantic season, agreement was reached for the use of wrought iron. From a length of 560 ft and beam of 52 ft she measured 8,400 gross tons, but the draught of 26 ft was greater than that expected from steel construction.

A six cylinder compound engine powered the single screw. In effect there were three tandem engines connected to the same crankshafts, which had cranks set at 120°. The 43 in diameter HP cylinders were positioned above their respective 86 in diameter LP cylinders, the stroke being 72 in. That arrangement resulted in a short engine, but a very tall one which extended above the main deck. Such vulnerability would not have been looked upon kindly by the Admiralty had the ship been intended for service as an auxiliary cruiser. The hollow steel, built-up crankshaft weighed 64 tons compared with 73 tons for an iron one and it illustrated why there was an increasing demand for steel machinery parts. Whitworth compressed steel as used for the shaft was subject to heavy hydraulic pressure whilst it was still molten in

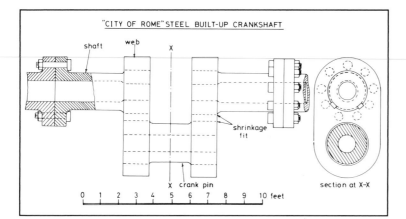

Left City of Rome's steel crank-shaft.

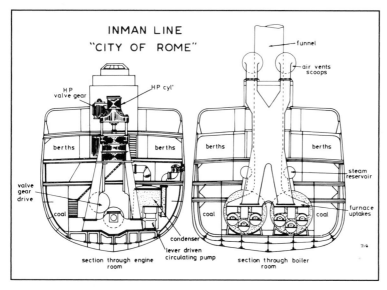

Left Engine and boiler room sectional views of City of Rome.

Below Section through the NDL liner Elbe.

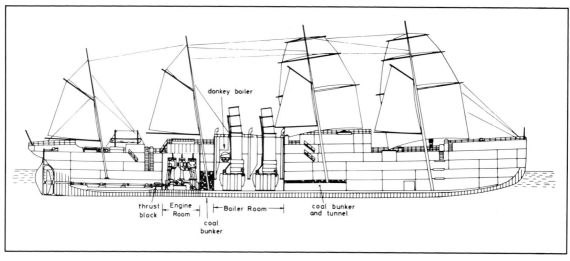

order to exclude gases which could produce weak spots.

Eight double ended cylindrical boilers, arranged in pairs, provided steam at 90 psi. The steel for these boilers was supplied by the firm of John Brown & Co which later acquired J. & G. Thomson, the Clyde shipbuilders. Each boiler was 14 ft diameter and 19 ft long with a steam receiver 13 ft long and 4 ft diameter. Such receivers were favoured at the time as they also acted as crude superheaters. The boiler room was divided into two sections by means of a transverse watertight bulkhead. An extensive array of auxiliary plant was installed including electric lighting and steam deck machinery.[25]

Intended as an 18 knot ship, City of Rome did not come up to expectation. Her engines could not reach the 10,000 ihp expected and the deeper draught due to iron construction increased her drag. After five voyages she was returned to her builders as unsuitable. Following alterations, which included removal of several cranky ideas insisted upon by individuals from the Inman management, and the addition of two boilers, City of Rome was placed back on the Atlantic under Anchor Line management. She achieved 18.5 knots on new trials, but despite changes in her rig could only carry 2,200 tons of cargo instead of the 3,800 tons specified in the original contract.[26]

From the events described in this chapter it might be supposed that only British companies operated Atlantic services but that was, obviously, not true. German and French concerns offered passages to America via the English Channel, but their ships came from British yards and usually from the Clyde. Naturally, the design of machinery followed closely that installed in contemporary vessels for other companies.

Compagnie Generale Transatlantique (French Line) had made use of Scotts on the Clyde for construction of paddle steamers in the 1860s and employed the same design for later French built ships. Two screw steamers came from Napiers in 1866, but they were no different to express mail ships already in service.

German companies Norddeutscher Lloyd (North German Lloyd (NGL)) and Hamburg-American Line, more correctly Hamburg-Amerikanische Packetfahrt Aktien-Gesellschaft (HAPAG) ordered almost exclusively from the Clyde until the end of the 1880s. Caird & Co received early orders from both concerns until Elders became the dominant Scottish builder at the beginning of that decade. Builders tended to design the ships and engines to suit an owner's basic requirements. For that reason Atlantic liners from a particular yard tended to follow the same pattern, although they varied in size and power. British companies may have held a monopoly on the record holders, but the German ships were all high quality, first rate vessels. They were, after all, products of the same Clyde yards which produced the 'Blue Riband' holders.

Typical of these ships was the NGL liner Elbe built by John Elder in 1881. Her three cylinder compound engine and boiler installation was similar to that installed in Arizona and Alaska, though less powerful. Of 4,900 gross tons Elbe had a 15.5 knot service speed and proved to be a profitable ship for her owners, so profitable that eight other 'River' class vessels of gradually increasing proportions were ordered from the same builders over the next seven years. During that period marine engineering techniques improved and the quality remained as high as ever. British shipbuilding and marine engineering served the Atlantic and the world.

CHAPTER 4

Greyhounds and Twin Screws

Success with *Arizona* and *Alaska* encouraged the Guion directors to consider a three ship weekly service, but finances were sorely strained. Not wishing to miss out on a possible construction contract the enterprising managers of the Fairfield yard made the Guion Line an offer it could not refuse, easy terms. Competition from Cunard was likely to be resumed through construction of express liners and the Guion board wanted to stay ahead of the field. Without apparently considering the financial implications an order for another liner, *Oregon*, was placed.

When delivered in October 1883 she was, at 7,400 gross tons, one of the largest commercial merchant vessels afloat, Brunel's *Great Eastern* being discounted on commercial grounds. If not the biggest ship then in service she was certainly the fastest. Despite the fact that steel was by then the accepted construction material, *Oregon* was built from iron. Why that should have been is difficult to say, for the Fairfield yard was constructing a large proportion of its ships from steel. The relatively high cost of steel may have inhibited the Guion directors or it may have been that, as with *City of Rome*, that material was in short supply.

In terms of engine and boilers the machinery was typically Elders, but bigger. Of three cylinder compound form, the propulsion engine was designed to produce 12,000 ihp with a steam pressure of 110 psi. Steel had been employed for the nine double ended scotch type boilers, which were provided with Fox's corrugated

flues and had been tested to 220 psi. The single HP cylinder had a diameter of 70 in whilst the two LP cylinders had diameters of 104 in, piston stroke being 72 in. For critical engine parts steel was essential and few parts are more critical than the crankshaft. Failure of that, or any section of the screw shaft, disabled the ship resulting in the need for sail power or a tow. Unless, of course, the ever resourceful engineers could rectify the fault by some ingenious means. *Oregon*'s crankshaft was of the built-up form and made from Vickers crucible steel, as were the tunnel and propeller shafts.[1]

Designed to carry 340 first, 92 second and 110 third class passengers, *Oregon* could also accommodate 1,000 steerage passengers in the cargo decks should that have been required. She was designed for 18 knots, but on trials managed to achieve average speeds of 20 knots with her engine developing 12,382 ihp and her screw turning at 62 rpm. During service on the Atlantic her speed was always creditable and on the third return crossing she took the 'Blue Riband' with an average speed of 18.05 knots.[2] Speed cost money in terms of coal and her average daily consumption exceeded 300 tons, the 'black gang' having to shovel over 12 tons each hour for six and a half days.[3] That coal also had to be

Above right *Typical double ended scotch type tubular boiler of the period.*

Right *Guion/Cunard liner* Oregon.

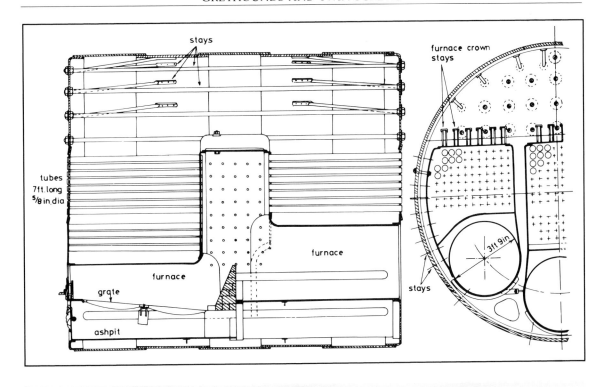

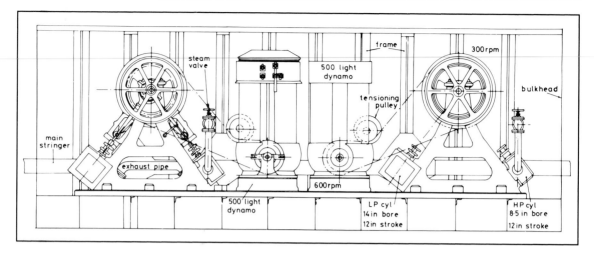

Oregon's electrical generating plant.

fetched from the bunkers and the resultant ash disposed of.

Steam was extensively employed for operating steering gear, winches, pumps and other auxiliary machinery but it was the Edison electrical installation which attracted attention. Two completely separate generating sets were provided, each capable of supplying 500 lamps, although only 460 were fitted. Such duplication ensured a power supply in the event of one machine failing. The Edison–Hopkinson dynamos operated at 600 rpm, generating electricity at 110 volts. Two cylinder diagonal compound steam engines, rotating at 300 rpm, drove the dynamos by means of belts. HP cylinders were 8.5 in diameter and the LP cylinders 14 in diameter. Mather & Platt of Salford manufactured the complete electrical generating sets which were positioned on the port side of the engine room at the lower level.[4]

Electric lighting had become standard equipment for Atlantic liners, not only because of its relative safety compared with oil lamps and candles but also because it was clean. Smoke from lamps caused discolouration of paintwork and curtains and left a smell which could be unpleasant in closed accommodation spaces, winter on the north Atlantic not being ideally suited to ventilation. Few who encountered electric lighting would ever wish to return to oil lamps and the liner companies had to meet passenger demand or suffer reduced patronage.

Electrical plant increased the engineers' work-

load and usually produced a demand for new skills, although qualified electricians were often appointed to larger ships. Putting equipment on board was simply a matter of cost, ensuring that it functioned correctly required knowledge and practical ability. Engineers were required to be masters of all plant, but frequently little or no training was offered or given by the shipowners. Fortunately there was a steady stream of willing young men eager to leave the shipyards for a life afloat. They soon learned to be resourceful and cope with the demands of marine engineering—safe return home depended upon it.

Cunard's reply to *Oregon* was not long in coming. Two fast ships were ordered from John Elder's Fairfield yard and they proved to be pace setters not just in terms of power, but with regard to their entire plant. Unlike the Guion ship, *Umbria* and *Etruria* were built from steel. Length between perpendiculars (bp) was 501 ft and the breadth just over 57 ft, producing a gross tonnage of 7,700. Operation draft was limited by the depth of water at the entrance to New York harbour and both ships were constructed to that limit. The harbour authorities at New York were quick to realize the implications of that restricted water and soon took steps to dredge the bar, increasing the depth by 2 ft.[5]

In terms of main propulsion plant the ships were of the usual Fairfield arrangement, comprising a three cylinder compound engine and scotch boilers. The steam plant was almost identical to that fitted aboard *Oregon*, but the engine was the most powerful fitted in a ship to that date. In order to obtain that high power HP and

LP cylinder diameters were made 1 in larger than those of the Guion ship. Although capable of developing close to 15,000 ihp the normal steaming power was somewhat less, but the ships were still able to achieve a steady 20 knots. Both *Etruria* and *Umbria* produced record Atlantic crossings during their careers, with the former proving to be slightly the faster. Coal consumption averaged about 315 tons per day, requiring 109 stokers and trimmers to feed and clean the boilers. There were 11 engineers and one electrician, the electrical plant being the most comprehensive ever put in a ship at that time.[6]

Cunard had investigated the economics of fast ships and decided that they were worthwhile. Not only was the publicity value of a record breaker invaluable, but the costings also proved to be favourable. Fast ships could command higher fares and less food was consumed by the passengers as they were on board for a shorter time. Additionally a larger number of voyages could be completed in a year, so crew and fixed costs like depreciation averaged out at less per crossing. Fuel consumption, although higher for increased speed, was a small price to pay for greater earning potential.[7]

The electrical plant, installed by Andrews & Co of Glasgow, comprised four steam driven Siemens dynamos and a system of 850 lights. Three of the dynamos had capacity for supplying 350 lamps, whilst a single smaller unit could light 200 lamps. The entire ship was divided into six independent circuits with the machinery spaces, having 90 lamps, being divided into sub-circuits. By means of a switchboard it was possible to connect any circuit to any dynamo, provided that the total load on the dynamo remained within its load limits. The switchboard consisted of a box with four rows of six holes in a wooden board. Each row was connected to a particular dynamo whilst each of the holes was connected to a particular light circuit. Inserting an insulated brass plug in a hole connected that lighting circuit to the dynamo supplying that row. Loads on dynamos could be adjusted to suit demand whilst dynamos could be taken off load altogether if the power demand was light or in order to allow for maintenance.

The first circuit, comprising 200 lamps, supplied the night system and machinery spaces. No 2 circuit supplied the after part of the ship,

No 3 amidships, No 4 and No 5 the saloon and major public rooms, whilst No 6 supplied all lamps forward of the saloon. Each lamp throughout the ship had its own switch and fuse but in addition certain groups of lamps, such as those in the saloon, could also be operated from a single switch. Fuses protected each main circuit and sub-circuit. Over 100 lamps illuminated the main dining saloon with 172 being fitted in state rooms. All wires conveying current to the lamps were insulated with india rubber, coated with a water resistant layer of wax or grease, then sheathed in iron wire to prevent damage. In machinery spaces electric cables were passed through tubes. Cables were only provided for the live connection to lamps, the return being through the ship's structure. In all the plant far exceeded any which had hitherto been applied to a ship.[8]

Both *Etruria* and *Umbria* complied with Admiralty conditions for use as auxiliary cruisers, but their primary function was the carriage of passengers, and cargo, across the Atlantic. Passengers paying high fares insisted upon quality service and first rate conditions. Effective ventilation was always essential for a comfortable and healthy crossing and the Fairfield designers incorporated the latest devices to ensure an adequate air circulation.

Both ships had two rather large diameter funnels, but the entire space was not employed for boiler waste gas. Surrounding the central uptake section was an annular casing through which flowed air from the accommodation spaces. This not only provided a suitable ventilator unit, but also served to form an insulating jacket around the boiler uptake, thus avoiding chilling of the gases in cold Atlantic winds which might affect boiler performance. However, accommodation air circulation was not dependent upon natural draught as a forced ventilation system was provided. Instead of employing fans, the designers fitted Green's patent ventilation system which had previously been employed aboard several passenger liners including a number belonging to North German Lloyd.

The system made use of the fact that a jet of high velocity air would draw some of the surrounding air along with it, thus inducing a positive air flow. It was not necessary, therefore, to provide large amounts of air ducting, only small bore pipes had to be fitted to carry high pressure air around the ship. Holes in these pipes allowed jets of air to issue from them and those jets induced the air flow. This system served only the lower deck areas, the upper deck regions making use of opening ports.[9]

Etruria and *Umbria* were single screw ships and, although constructed to the highest standards, were not immune to the scourge which afflicted such vessels, namely broken shafts. A broken crankshaft or propeller shaft immobilized the single screw steamer and a vestige of sail was always provided as a safeguard. Such sails were usually totally inadequate for propulsive purposes and the services of another vessel had to be called upon for a tow. Both ships were affected by shaft problems throughout their service years, but the incident involving *Umbria* at the end of 1892 is worthy of mention as it illustrates the ingenuity and resourcefulness demanded of marine engineers. During a violent storm on 23 December, about 760 miles east of New York, the propeller shafting failed at the thrust block. To have called for the services of another vessel in towing *Umbria* to New York would have incurred a salvage claim in the order of £60,000.[10]

As a propeller rotates it exerts a thrust which is transmitted along the propeller shafting. That thrust must be transferred to the ship's structure in order to force the ship through the water. Hence the fitting of a thrust block where such transfer takes place. Because the shaft is rotating, and the ship's structure is not, some form of bearing must be provided. Low powered engines produce a relatively small thrust and so a single bearing thrust face could be employed, as with Brunel's *Great Britain*. For higher powers a large thrust area is required if the lubricating oil film which separates the rotating and stationary parts is not to be damaged. With engines of the period that area was provided by a number of collars on the thrust shaft, although in more recent times the Michell tilting pad thrust has proved to be better suited. In a multi-collared thrust block each collar transmitted some thrust to a horseshoe shaped block faced with white metal. A general rule governing thrust areas was that there should be 0.6 sq in per engine ihp. To avoid the use of large diameter collars, which presented manufacturing problems, a large number of smaller diameter collars were used.

It was fortunate that failure of *Umbria*'s shaft did take place at the thrust block, as it presented an opportunity for repair using two of the thrust collars as coupling flanges. A number of thrust pads were removed in order to gain access to the cracked section of shaft. The 25 in diameter shaft was not completely severed, but was so weakened that it could not be relied upon to transmit load. Under instructions from the chief engineer, three slotted holes were cut in the thrust collars either side of the crack in order to allow the fitting of bolts. The holes had to be slotted as other collars prevented the bolts from being pushed into place. These slots were just over 4 in wide and nearly 5 in deep, the collars being 3.25 in wide. With only the aid of ratchet drills, chisels and hammers, and in a confined space aboard a rolling ship, it took from the evening of 23 December until the morning of 27 December to complete the repair. Some Christmas for the engineers who worked in shifts throughout that period!

In order to hold the shaft sections together and prevent the bolts from coming out of their slots, collars were also manufactured. All parts were duplicated in case those fitted failed. At a speed of 10 knots, which was the maximum the chief engineer would allow, *Umbria* made New York safely on 31 December. There a more complete repair was effected, which comprised cutting out the cracked portion of shaft and fitting a new section. Back at Liverpool a new complete thrust block shaft had to be installed.[11]

Etruria also suffered a disabling incident in the Atlantic during 1902, but there was no chance of any repair at sea. Failure of the ship to arrive at Liverpool at her appointed time gave cause for concern and that grew as the ship became more and more overdue. Five days after her expected arrival a cable from the Azores informed Cunard that she was being towed there by the Leyland steamer *William Cliff*. During passage she lost her propeller, rudder and part of her stern post. How the loss occurred was a mystery, but it would be reasonable to assume that the propeller shaft fractured freeing the screw which then impacted with the stern post and rudder. Whatever the reason it left *Etruria* helpless.

Cunard chartered three tugs to bring the ship back from the Azores but the absence of a rudder made her difficult to handle and in stormy weather the tugs let her drift for their own

Above *Cunard's* Umbria.

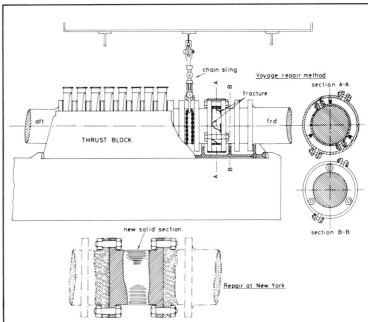

Right *Diagram of* Umbria's *thrust block, showing the voyage repair and repair carried out at New York.*

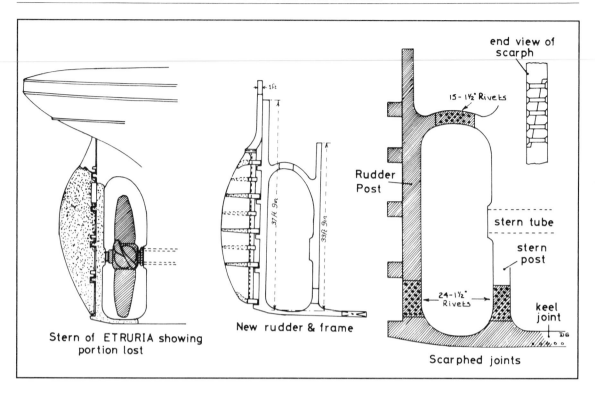

Stern of ETRURIA showing portion lost

New rudder & frame

Scarphed joints

end view of scarph

15-1½" Rivets

Rudder Post

stern tube

stern post

24-1½" Rivets

keel joint

Etruria's stern frame repairs.

safety. The 1,400 mile tow took 17 days. At Liverpool new parts were fitted, the rudder and stern post sections being connected by means of scarphed joints. A complete stern frame had been manufactured and then cut to suit the sections of old frame which remained.[12]

Incidents of this nature serve to illustrate the problems ships faced in the days before radio. A vessel might drift helplessly for many days before chanced upon by another ship. In severe weather loss of engine power could prove fatal.

Whilst Cunard planned its pair of liners, other companies were also engaged in modernizing their fleets or attempting to take records. In 1883 the National Line took delivery of its only vessel of note, a ship which stretched the company's resources. Built of steel at Clydebank by J. & G. Thomson, the 5,528 gross ton *America* was a radical departure from the National Line's previous policy of building smaller slower steamers for the secondary market. She was, in effect, a typical Thomson product of the period, employing a three cylinder compound engine with two 91 in bore LP cylinders and a 63 in

diameter HP cylinder. Steam at 95 psi came from seven cylindrical boilers, six double ended and one single ended.

In terms of main and auxiliary machinery *America* was nothing special, but she was fast and economical. The 6,500 ihp engine produced record crossings each way during her maiden voyage in May and June 1884, with average speeds in excess of 17.5 knots. Compared with other express liners of the period *America* was small but she was also more economical in terms of fuel consumption, despite her speed. Fine lines and a well proportioned hull contributed greatly to that economy. Her length to beam ratio was 8.5 to 1 and the block coefficient 0.55. Bunker space for 1,650 tons of coal had been provided but she would consume only 1,300 tons on a voyage; daily fuel consumption averaged about 185 tons, 115 tons less than *Oregon*.[13] Owners did not consider it economical to carry bunkers for the complete round trip as that limited cargo capacity. American coal was not suitable and so fuel would be shipped from Britain to New York for burning on the return voyage.

The National Line soon learned that a first

class express service could not be operated by a single ship, even a 'Blue Riband' holder. Although popular and fast, *America* lost money and was sold to the Italian navy in 1886.

French interests in the Atlantic blossomed during the early 1880s when the Compagnie Generale Transatlantique (French Line) set about replacing its rather ageing fleet. Five first class ships were ordered for delivery between 1883 and 1886, the first of these coming from a British yard. The Barrow Shipbuilding Company, later to be taken over by Vickers, built the 6,283 gross ton *La Normandie* and fitted a main engine similar to that constructed for *City of Rome*. Unlike the ill-fated ship Inman ordered, the French vessel was constructed from steel and she performed admirably. Construction and operating subsidies were essential to most express liner companies and the French Line was no exception. Money was sought from the French Ministry of Marine and Post Office as the ship was to carry mails and be suitable for

Engine room and after boiler room arrangements for the French owned and Barrow built Normandie.

conversion to an armed cruiser. Naturally, both of these government departments wished to supervise construction in order to ensure suitability. When delivered *La Normandie* was the most powerful ship in the French merchant fleet.

La Normandie's three crank tandem compound engine had HP cylinders of 900 mm diameter and LP cylinders of 1,900 mm diameter, the stroke being 1,700 mm. Metric dimensions had actually been specified by the French Line. Steam jacketing, an arrangement falling into disfavour at about that time, was applied to the LP cylinders only. In effect, as with *City of Rome*, each set of tandem cylinders constituted an independent engine for separate condensers, air pumps and condensate pumps were also provided. That arrangement allowed any set to be cut out should that prove necessary due to malfunction of items such as valve gear, the engine continuing to function on the other sets. Failure of shafting, such as experienced by *Umbria*, would have still proved disastrous.

A number of steam driven pumps were provided, including three powerful centrifugal pumps for circulating sea water around the con-

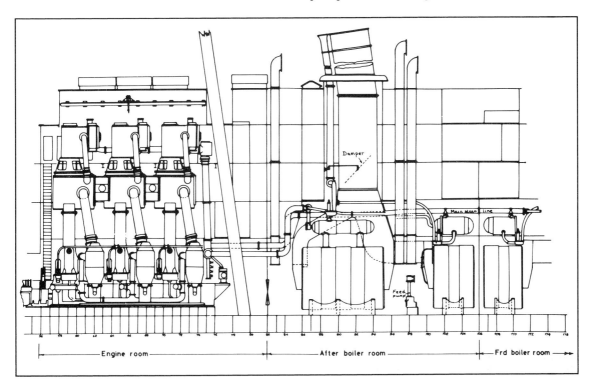

densers. In addition to reciprocating pumps which could be employed for pumping out the bilges, three steam ejectors were also fitted for that purpose. These worked on the principle that a condensing steam jet could create an effective suction and force water through a pipe, the same principle as employed on steam locomotives for forcing water into the boiler. These devices enabled the bilges to be emptied in the event of pumps being made inoperative due to flooding or mechanical damage. So long as there was a steam supply they would function.

Eight cylindrical boilers, four double and four single ended, supplied steam at 85 psi, the double ended boilers being 13 ft 9 in diameter and 18 ft 6 in long. Separate steam drums were provided for each of the double ended boilers and two for the single ended boilers. These were outside of the gas flow and could not be employed for superheating. Surprisingly iron was used for boiler construction and that possibly explains the rather low steam pressure. A watertight bulkhead divided the boiler plant into two separate rooms, each containing two double ended and two single ended boilers. Dampers in the uptakes provided a means of

regulating furnace combustion. Two donkey boilers working at 60 psi provided steam for operating pumps and other auxiliaries such as dynamos. *La Normandie*'s engines developed a steady 8,000 ihp on trials and gave the ship a respectable 17.25 knot average speed.

Wing coal bunkers protected the boiler rooms from direct connection with the ship's side whilst a transverse bunker was arranged between boiler rooms and engine room. Further bunker space was provided on the port side of the engine room.[14]

The four other ships in the series were constructed in France, as were all future vessels ordered by the French Line. *La Champagne* and *La Bretagne* came from St Nazaire whilst the slightly larger *La Bourgogne* and *La Gascogne* were built at La Seyne. All four were slightly larger than the Barrow built ship, but they employed the same design of engine, obviously built under licence from the Barrow Shipbuilding Company. Cylinder dimensions showed a small increase, HP being 1,007 mm diameter, LP 2,003 mm and stroke 1,776 mm. On trials *La*

La Gasgogne, *French built sister to* Normandie.

Gascogne's engine developed 9,800 ihp and the ship achieved a speed in excess of 19 knots, however, service speed was limited to 17.5 knots. Steam was supplied by 12 boilers, but pressure remained at a relatively low 85 psi.[15]

La Bourgogne and *La Gascogne* could accommodate 221 first class, 72 second class and 906 steerage passengers. They were of 7,972 gross tons with a length of 492 ft, beam 52 ft and loaded draught 24 ft. During the period 1894–96 triple expansion engines were fitted to all five vessels in the series, thereby improving their fuel economy. Although not in the 'Greyhound' league these five French vessels were popular and established the French Line as a major force on the Atlantic.

The German companies also had plans for improving their respective positions with regard to Atlantic traffic. HAPAG built the rather small iron steamer *Hammonia* at Thomson's on the Clyde in 1883, but she was no competitor for the big ships and that concern remained inactive until the end of that decade. NGL, however, built on the success of its Elder's constructed 'River' class and returned to the Fairfield yard in 1886 for a trio of 5,300 gross ton liners with triple expansion engines. *Aller*, *Trave* and *Saale* were the first express Atlantic liners with that type of engine.

Although the construction contract for the ships had been won by Fairfields it was NGL's custom to issue a second contract for fitting and furnishing. That went to a German concern which shipped men and materials to the Clyde in order to complete the ships. The engines had three cylinders in line: HP 44 in diameter, intermediate pressure (IP) 70 in diameter and LP 108 in diameter, all with a stroke of 72 in. Apart from the fact that there were three stages of expansion the basic engine form followed very much that of earlier three cylinder compound engines produced by the same builder. A single large condenser was provided, but air and condensate pumps were lever driven by the engine.

The whole point of triple expansion machinery was to further improve on fuel consumption and that this trio did. Although nominally designed to produce 7,000 ihp, the engines could easily develop more. During her trials *Saale* managed 8,000 ihp at 63 rpm, giving a speed of 18 knots. Her coal consumption on that trip was 1.4 lb/ihp/hr.[16] That worked out at 120 tons per day, not bad for a 5,000 gross ton ship at such a speed. Even though they were trial trip figures, they served to confirm the results obtained from triple expansion machinery installed aboard other ships. Once more there would be no turning back.

NGL returned to Fairfields in 1888 for what turned out to be its final British built ship. *Lahn* was larger and more powerful than the three earlier vessels, although she was similar in appearance with four masts and two funnels. Engine builders of the time were experiencing problems with castings for large diameter LP cylinders and the balancing of these also presented problems. As had been the case with compound engines it made sense to form two smaller LP cylinders rather than one of large diameter and that was the approach adopted for the engines fitted in *Lahn*. There was, however, a further development in that two HP cylinders were also provided, these being in tandem with, and above, the LP cylinders. Such an arrangement was similar to the Barrow built engines and it increased the height, but reduced the length, of the engine.

The HP cylinders were 32.5 in diameter, LP cylinders 85 in diameter and the IP cylinder 68 in diameter, all having a stroke of 72 in. Steam was supplied at 150 psi, an improvement on contemporary installations which allowed full use to be made of expansive capability. The engine had been designed to produce 9,500 ihp in order to give *Lahn* a speed of 18.5 knots, but it was capable of developing more. In terms of the passenger comforts of heating and ventilation the ship compared favourably with any then afloat, but it was for her main propulsion plant that she was most widely known.[17] Marine engineering developments quickly dated the plant as far as express liners were concerned, but that had happened so often in the past, such was progress in the marine field.

With each passing year there appeared to be a demand for bigger and faster ships—competition on the north Atlantic was becoming keener. Fortunately shipbuilders and marine engineers were capable of meeting that demand, but the machinery itself imposed certain limits. Engine power was transmitted to the screw by means of shafting and, theoretically, it was simply a case of increasing shaft diameter when larger powers were developed. In practice problems with shaft construction limited its maximum diameter and hence power transmission capabilities. For high powers twin screws had to be employed, but there were other advantages to such an installation. A ready argument put forward by protagonists of twin screws was that engine failure would not disable the ship as it did with a single screw. There was, they so rightly stated, another engine to propel the ship. Regrettably they forgot to seek Neptune's approval and an early incident in the era of twin screw liners soon illustrated that in maritime affairs nothing could be taken for granted.

In view of the fact that the Inman Line had been to the fore with Atlantic screw propulsion, it was fitting that the same concern should also be first with twin screws. Following its bitter experiences with *City of Rome*, the proprietors had steered clear of new construction for some time. Re-engining *City of Berlin* with triple expansion machinery in 1887 illustrated what fuel savings could be made. Laird Brothers of Birkenhead reconditioned the ship and installed

the new propulsion plant. Eight cylindrical steel boilers working at 150 psi and operating on the Howden forced draught system were fitted. The space occupied was less than the original set, allowing increased passenger accommodation. The new triple expansion engine, capable of developing 5,500 ihp, also occupied less space than the original although of greater power.[18]

Even before this work was set in hand the Inman Line decided to re-enter the Atlantic races and sought tenders from a number of British yards for the construction of two ships. In the spring of 1887 the directors reached agreement with J. & G. Thomson. All particulars of the design were to be left to the builders, only three conditions having to be fulfilled: the ships were to be unsinkable, as comfortable as any hotel and as fast as possible consistent with the first two conditions.[19] It is obvious that the directors still had faith in the infallibility of ship design-

Triple expansion engine for the re-engined City of Berlin.

Inman Line's City of Paris *on trials in 1889.* (Glasgow University Archives with permission of Mr W. Lind.)

ers, probably having read about Guion's *Arizona*. Without doubt the Clydeside shipbuilder would make the ships as strong as humanly possible, but nobody could design for the incompetence of those responsible for their operation.

City of New York entered service in 1888 and the identical *City of Paris* the following year. To say that they revolutionized north Atlantic shipping is an understatement. From an engineering viewpoint they were nothing short of remarkable. A fast and safe ship, the designers considered, had to be long and large but the size of docks imposed limits on length, draught and beam. Locks at Liverpool restricted length to 525 ft at the load water line and beam to 63 ft. At 10,650 gross tons they were the largest commercial ships built to that date.

Thomsons made the ships as 'unsinkable' as they possibly could, providing 15 watertight compartments, three of which comprised the boiler space and two the engine room. Each main engine was actually in its own watertight compartment, a longitudinal bulkhead being fitted for that purpose. No compartment exceeded 35 ft in length and the ships were designed to remain afloat with three compartments flooded. A 4ft deep double bottom space also extended over most of each vessel's length, this space being kept dry or used for water ballast as appropriate.

An innovative feature lay in the provision of anti-rolling tanks. Such tanks had been provided in large warships of the period but they were a novelty in merchant ships and had never before been fitted in an Atlantic liner. The tank roll stabilizing system was a primitive form of the Frahm tanks which later found popularity, especially with German owners. Each ship had a tank 35 ft long which extended the full width of the vessel but had a constricted section amidships. When partially filled with water the tank could be used to moderate rolling of the ship. As the ship rolled, water would wash from side to side but this lagged behind the ship, thus helping to control the roll's amplitude. Model tests had been carried out in order to determine the most effective shape of tank for Atlantic service.

Electric lighting was fitted throughout the ship in passenger, crew and working spaces, some 1,000 lamps being employed. The 100 volt system was not only employed for lighting, a number of electric motors were used for driving ventilation fans in the main passenger compartments. This was the first time electricity had been used for ventilation purposes in any ship. Each fan had a capacity of 250,000 cubic ft of air per hour.

With some 2,000 people on board, passengers and crew, *City of New York* and her sister had to have an adequate fresh water and food supply. Although evaporators were fitted they found full employment in producing boiler feed water, so fresh water for domestic consumption had to be obtained in port and stored in suitable tanks. For flushing water closets sea water was quite adequate. Food presented problems, particularly perishables. Although a crossing occupied only six days under normal circumstances, vast quantities of food were still required, the cow house and chicken coop of earlier days were no longer sufficient. An ammonia refrigerating plant provided by the Kilbourn company of Liverpool allowed food to be stored frozen or just chilled. All such non-engine room plant still fell under the engineering department's control.

Twin screw propulsion allowed the use of a novel design of rudder which was entirely below the waterline and blended in with the ship's lines. It was also of semi-balanced form, with part of its area being forward of the axis about which it turned. That arrangement reduced the force needed to turn the rudder. Two hydraulic cylinders provided power for turning the rudder and variations of that ram steering gear, developed by Brown Brothers of Edinburgh, are still applied to ships today. The actual engines which powered the hydraulic pumps were also novel in that, although of compound form, they were automatically made non-compound for the first half stroke in order to make starting easy.

Each main engine occupied its own watertight room and was essentially independent of its neighbour. Manufactured to the highest warship standards the engines were a triumph of

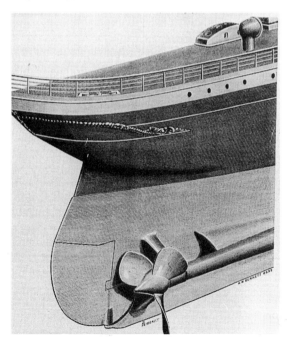

Propeller supports for the twin screw City of Paris.

Clydeside skill, only the best quality materials being employed. These ships were not just for Inman Line services, they were a floating advertisement for J. & G. Thomson.

Three cylinder triple expansion engines were common, but *City of New York* and *City of Paris* had two each. The total power capability exceeded the 20,000 ihp demanded for a 19.5 knot service speed and, as expected, they both produced record Atlantic crossings during their careers. Cylinder dimensions were HP 45 in, IP 71 in, LP 113 in and stroke 60 in. All valves, eccentric operated using Stephenson link motion, were of the piston type with two being provided for the IP and four for the LP. So large were the engines that the equilibrium valve, for regulating the steam supply, had to be powered by its own steam engine to which a Dunlop governor was also connected. That little steam engine made manoeuvring of the main engines a relatively easy task. Air pumps were the only auxiliaries driven by the main engines, all other pumps having their own power unit.

Steam supply came from three boiler rooms, each containing three double ended scotch boilers working at 150 psi. These boilers were 19 ft long, 15 ft 6 in diameter and had six furnaces, opposing furnaces being connected to a common combustion chamber. In order to increase boiler steam output it was necessary to burn more fuel, but that required an increase in air supply. Forced draught was needed. The new Inman 'Cities' were high powered vessels and their engines needed steam in vast quantities. Increasing the number of boilers was a solution, but that took up valuable space so a higher output from each boiler provided the answer.

A closed stokehold form of forced draught was fitted in the ships, the first of its type on the Atlantic. Each boiler room had to be enclosed and air was supplied by means of fans, four to each room. Air locks were needed to allow access to what became pressurized chambers when the ship was operating. That the fans had a diameter of 66 in gives some idea as to their air capacity.

Two fire and bilge pumps in each engine room were also capable of acting as boiler feed pumps and could be employed for pumping ballast from the double bottoms. Hydraulic power, for which pump units were situated in both engine rooms, was used to operate six

Three cylinder triple expansion engine for City of New
York.

hoists, nine derrick winches, two warping
winches, two warping capstans and a windlass.
The system was the most extensive ever fitted in
a ship. In fact the engineering arrangements
read like a catalogue of all that was new and best
in British maritime achievement.[20]

The engine room complement for each ship
consisted of a chief engineer, 18 assistant engineers, three electricians, three refrigerating
engineers, three donkeymen, three storekeepers,
33 greasers, 54 firemen, 57 coal trimmers and
one clerk.[21]

In praising *City of New York, The Engineer* for
27 July 1888 made the statement: 'The startling
feature about the practice of Atlantic steam navigation is that it is perfectly well understood that
the *City of New York* will probably be obsolete in
five years'. Obsolete was a strong word to use,

but the sentiments were correct. Progress in the
maritime field was rapid and Britain led the
world.

A strong argument in favour of twin screw
installation was that loss of one engine or shaft
did not disable the ship. *City of Paris* soon
proved that nothing could be taken for granted
where the sea was concerned. At 5.20 on the
afternoon of 23 March 1890, whilst the engines
were apparently working well at their normal
speed in the region of 82 rpm, the starboard
engine suddenly raced for a few seconds then
returned to normal speed. The relief watch-
keeping engineer checked that engine, then
returned to the port engine room. No sooner
had he done so than the starboard engine completely collapsed and the wreckage fractured
sea water and steam pipes. Other engineers
rushed to attend and all watertight doors were
closed.

A damaged sea water pipe caused flooding of

Above *The wrecked starboard engine room,* City of Paris.

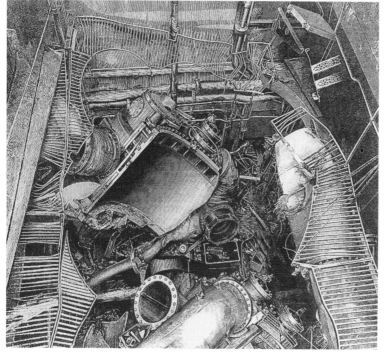

Left *Another view of* City of Paris's *damaged starboard engine room.*

Right *Howden forced draught system fitted in* City of Paris.

the starboard engine room, but the longitudinal bulkhead should have protected the port engine room. Unfortunately wreckage from the collapsing engine had also punctured the bulkhead and, despite attempts to plug leaks, water entered the port engine room faster than the pumps could cope with. Within a short time both engine rooms were completely out of action. A twin screw ship had been disabled by a freak accident.

There was no risk of the ship sinking, she just couldn't go anywhere. A boat was sent out to seek assistance and encountered the White Star ship *Adriatic*. Having been informed that *City of Paris* was in no danger, *Adriatic*'s master refused to attend, but said he would inform any other ship he met. Eventually the steamer *Aldersgate* took the stricken Inman ship in tow. The short passage to Queenstown did not take long and there divers were employed to plug leaks and make good damaged ship's side connections. With engine rooms pumped dry, *City of Paris* was able to make Liverpool under power from one screw.

Detailed investigations ensued, to be followed by a searching enquiry. The conclusion drawn from these was that the starboard engine had raced out of control after her screw shaft fractured. Consequent high engine speed caused the LP piston to hit its cylinder cover and that resulted in fracture of the cover, piston and rod. These parts then collapsed back on the remainder of the engine causing further damage. What caused the screw shaft to fracture in the first place was the subject of much conjecture. Opinion eventually settled on the view that a brass sleeve on the section of shaft passing through the stern tube had split. The resulting sharp edge planed away the stern tube's lignum vitae lining. Bending of the shaft followed as its support point had been worn away and resultant high alternating stress caused fatigue failure.[22]

A new engine and shaft were constructed for *City of Paris* and she resumed service during May 1891. During the ship's time out of service the opportunity was taken to change her boiler forced draught arrangements. The Howden system was chosen as it not only allowed open stokeholds, but was very effective and provided for air heating. Each of the six stokeholds had an air trunking passing across the fronts of the boilers and that trunking was supplied with air from two fans, one on the port side and the other on the starboard. These steam engine driven fans were 6 ft diameter and situated in compartments two decks above the boiler room.

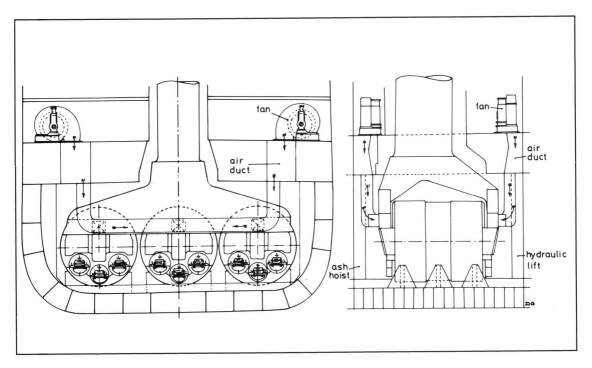

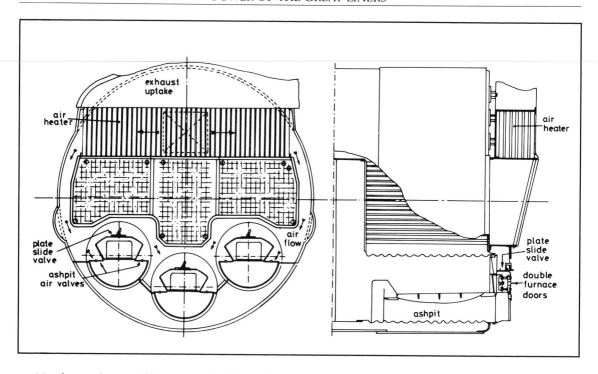

Air from the trunking passed through a heater at the front of each boiler and then via ducting to the furnace fronts. Gas exhausting from the boiler passed through tubes in the heater and thus the boiler heated its own air. A plate slide valve allowed control of air to the space above the fires, through a space between double furnace doors, whilst two valves regulated air supply to the ashpit. Variation of above and below fire air supply enabled combustion to be adjusted to suit conditions of firing. Whilst

Boiler with Howden forced draught system.

firing, the air valves would be closed in order to avoid blowback of the fire.[23]

City of New York and *City of Paris* had set the pace with their twin screws and powerful machinery, but others quickly caught up and passed the sleek Inman ships. The 1890s were to see even more powerful and extensive installations, but it is doubtful if any other ships incorporated so many engineering innovations.

CHAPTER 5

Bigger, Better and Faster

Whilst the Inman directors enjoyed their success another company was busily engaged in plans for re-establishing itself on the Atlantic. *Britannic* and *Germanic* were performing well for their owners and proved themselves to be popular with passengers. In 1888, despite being nearly 15 years old and ancient by contemporary standards, both ships were still able to achieve crossings in little over seven days. The time for newer tonnage was fast approaching if the White Star Line was to remain in the Atlantic vanguard. There was also the added incentive that money could be obtained from the Government for new ships constructed to act as auxiliary cruisers.

White Star liner Teutonic *in the River Mersey.* (Harry Weston Collection.)

The close relationship which existed between the proprietors of White Star and the Belfast shipbuilders Harland & Wolff had resulted in designs for new ships being prepared as early as 1880. The shipowner preferred to wait, and six years later a favourable opportunity presented itself. Successful negotiations with the Admiralty produced funding to assist in the construction of two large and fast steamers which could act as armed merchant cruisers should the need ever arise. *Teutonic* and *Majestic*, as the ships were called, became the first vessels to be especially constructed and retained by the Admiralty. Local strengthening was arranged so that a dozen 5 in guns could be positioned aboard each vessel.[1]

To serve the purposes of Admiralty and owner, these ships had to be fast. Twin screws

offered the only solution, but Harlands adopted a rather unique arrangement. The 19 ft 6 in diameter, four bladed manganese bronze screws had their shafts positioned so close that they actually overlapped each other by 5 ft 6 in. The intention was to improve propulsive efficiency and protect the screws by keeping them within the overhang of the stern. In order to allow for such an arrangement it was necessary to position the starboard propeller some 6 ft astern of the port one. How effective the system was is difficult to judge, for it was never repeated by White Star. Both ships were fast and efficient but the screw arrangement did not fit in with conventional practice and required shafting of different lengths. It was considered that the vibration experienced by *Majestic* was due to screw positioning, although *Teutonic* did not suffer from vibration to the same extent.

A representative from the journal *Engineering* was on board *Majestic* during 1890 when a well respected engineer carried out some improvized experiments in order to analyse the hull vibration. Using a menu card pinned to the wooden section of rigid handrail and a pencil fitted to a more flexible support, several cards of vibration were taken over intervals of one minute. These cards showed that vibration amplitude gradually increased to a peak, then diminished again. That peak, it was discovered, coincided with the time when the heavy LP pistons of the engines were synchronized. It was almost impossible to have both engines running at identical speeds and so one would gradually overtake the other. The result was that, for a short period of time, the LP pistons of both engines were moving up and down in unison. Such large out of balance masses caused the vibration.[2]

Designers took great care to minimize the risk of vibration, but it could never be eliminated. Three crank triple expansion engines were particularly difficult to balance dynamically and twin screw installations posed problems. Some years later the Yarrow–Schlick–Tweedy balancing system was devised. That required four cranks and its effectiveness popularized the four crank engine.[3] (See Appendix 1.)

View across the tops of Majestic's *engines. The scale is somewhat incorrect regarding the size of the engineer.*

Teutonic's *middle level engine platform.*

The engines of *Teutonic* and *Majestic* were designed to develop some 8,500 ihp each, but would frequently produce more without being pressed. From the outset it was the builders' and owners' intention that the ships would be fast, and they were. Within a year of entering service each of these 9,950 gross ton ships had reduced the record for Atlantic crossing with speeds in excess of 20 knots.

Each engine had three cylinders of 43 in, 68 in and 100 in diameter with a stroke of 60 in. As with the Inman ships, longitudinal subdivision of the engine room produced two watertight compartments for the engines, these being some 50 ft in length. There were 12 double ended main boilers of scotch type which supplied steam at 180 psi. The total grate area of these was a modest 1,163 sq ft, compared with 1,293 sq ft for nine boilers aboard the Inman twin screw ships. Four single ended boilers were fitted for use in port and to supplement the main boilers.

These steel ships had a length of 582 ft and

breadth of 57 ft 6 in. They had accommodation for 300 first class, 150 second class and over 750 steerage passengers, as well as a crew of some 400. The engine room staff accounted for 168 crew members, 60 firemen and 48 trimmers being employed in handling the coal.

A modified Howden forced draught system operated for boiler air supply with fans on the bridge deck supplying air to the stokehold. Further fans took air from the hottest parts of the stokehold and, after passing it through heaters at the base of the funnels, delivered it to the furnaces at a temperature of 250°F. Such an arrangement helped to ventilate the stokehold and so keep temperatures reasonable. By employing air heated to that temperature a daily saving of 20 tons of coal was claimed, compared with a system using cold air for combustion. As it was, coal consumption amounted to over 320 tons per day. Efficient high temperature forced draught did allow smaller grate and heat transfer area to be employed.

Contemporary journals were not above producing statistics in order to emphasize the enormous proportions of any new ship and this

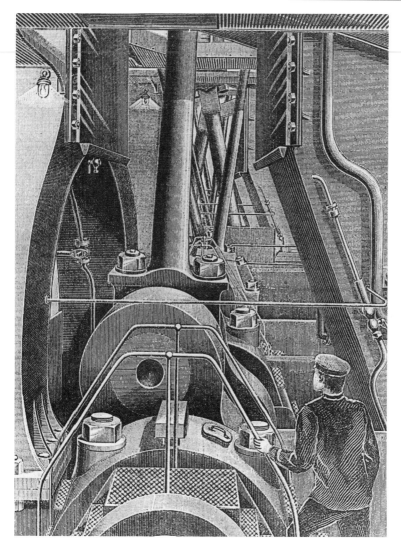

Right *Refrigerated hold arrangements for* Teutonic *and* Majestic.

White Star pair proved to be no exception. Unless details of specific cases were given some of the statistics were meaningless, but others served to emphasize the machinery's power and size. During normal service the 13.5 tons of coal burnt each hour required an incredible 270 tons of air and that needed powerful fans. Steam was generated at the rate of 120 tons each hour and so boiler feed pumps had to supply that amount of water to the boilers. Energy expended in forcing water into the boilers was over 57 horse power, even neglecting friction losses in pipework. That same quantity of steam had to be returned to a liquid state in the condensers and to achieve that over 4,000 tons of sea water

had to be circulated around the condensers each hour.

During a round trip between Liverpool and New York the circulating pumps dealt with over 1,000,000 tons of water. Such figures serve to illustrate how important the auxiliary equipment had become to a large liner. The two Tangye condenser circulating pumps aboard *Teutonic* and her sister were of the centrifugal type and had impellers 5 ft diameter, water pipes being 20 in bore. Each pump was powered by two compound engines with cylinders of 8 in and 15 in diameter and 14 in stroke.

The electrical plant was equally impressive, with four steam driven 400 light dynamos being located in two separate rooms. The entire lighting system was arranged in 11 circuits, each of which could be connected to any of the dynamos. As electrical installations became more complex and larger it was necessary to employ more specialist electricians to ensure efficient operation and safety. That latter point was important because electrical installations ashore were not common and many passengers, including those in first class, would be unfamiliar with electricity and its dangers.

Refrigerating plant for keeping passenger provisions fresh was standard aboard all first class liners of the period, but these new White Star ships were also fitted for carrying refrigerated cargo. Two meat holds of 40,000 cubic ft capacity were provided, there being a good premium paid for carriage of frozen meat from America to Britain. Each hold had its own refrigerating plant, but they could be worked together or one plant used to refrigerate both holds. Ammonia was employed as the refrigerant in the Linde designed systems fitted. Steam driven compressors compressed the ammonia gas which was then cooled in order to produce a liquid. Expansion of the liquid ammonia was

regulated by means of an expansion valve, the expanding gas passing through coils. Air circulating around the holds and provision rooms would be cooled on passing over the coils and that cold air then kept the meat cargo and provisions cold.[4]

Although other ships had refrigerated hold space, that provided aboard *Teutonic* and *Majestic* was the most extensive then fitted in an Atlantic liner. Such was the demand for refrigerated cargo space, and so lucrative the cargo, that White Star took *Britannic* and *Germanic* out of service in 1892 so that they might be similarly fitted. Instead of using ammonia as the refrigerant CO_2 was employed. The reason lay in the use of brine for cooling the holds. Ammonia attacked copper, of which the brine pipes were made, but CO_2 did not. Because these installations were actually conversions it was found to be more convenient to cool the holds by means of brine pipes fitted along bulkheads.[5] The same basic refrigerating principle applied to the Hall's CO_2 system as to the ammonia. An expanding liquified gas, CO_2 or ammonia, extracted heat from its surroundings as it changed from liquid back to gas. The surrounding media, brine or

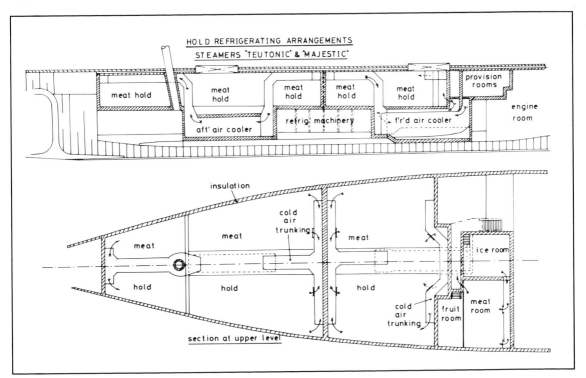

The last single screw express Atlantic liner, NGL's Spree.

air, would then be pumped around the chamber to be cooled.

Neither of the German north Atlantic companies was slow in meeting the challenge for bigger and faster tonnage. North German Lloyd ordered two 6,950 gross ton Atlantic ships from the Vulcan Company of Stettin, marking the end of its connection with British shipbuilders; *Kaiser Wilhelm II*, ordered at about the same time from Stettin, was primarily intended for the Australian service. Although twin screws had become accepted practice for express liners, *Spree* and *Havel* both had single propellers. The owners claimed that there was insufficient experience available to justify the change from single to twin screws, but the real reason may have lain in beam restrictions due to existing Bremerhaven dock gates.

The engines were similar to the five cylinder triple expansion engines. *Augusta Victoria* came earlier steamer *Lahn*. Power was slightly higher at 12,500 ihp and both ships could maintain 18.5 knots. In no way was the machinery outstanding, boiler pressure even being a relatively low

165 psi, but the ships indicated a growing trend, German built ships for German owners.[6] The folly of adopting single screws was quickly illustrated when, in 1892, *Spree* was disabled with a fractured shaft. The same thing happened in 1895. New vessels constructed from 1896 onwards all carried twin screws.[7]

NGL's Hamburg rival, HAPAG, was not so slow in adopting twin screw propulsion. In 1889 two almost identical vessels were delivered to its fleet and both had two propellers driven by triple expansion engines. *Augusta Victoria* came from Stettin and *Columbia* from Laird Brothers of Birkenhead. Engines of some 12,500 ihp could drive these 7,500 gross ton ships at about 19 knots under normal conditons. As with the NGL pair there was little innovative about the machinery, but these ships further illustrated the growing power of Germany's Atlantic merchant fleet.[8]

The success of *Augusta Victoria*, correctly renamed *Auguste Victoria* in 1897, and *Columbia* prompted an immediate order for two larger ships along similar lines. Again one was constructed in Germany at Stettin and the other in Britain, this time at Fairfields. The Scottish built 8,250 gross ton *Normannia* was slightly smaller and 4 ft shorter than her 8,850 gross ton, 504 ft long sister, *Furst Bismarck*. Both vessels had beams of 57 ft and similar three cylinder triple expansion engines, those of the German built ship being marginally larger and more powerful. Dimensions of *Normannia's* engines were 40 in HP, 67 in IP, 106 in LP and 66 in stroke. Engines for both ships were rated at 8,000 ihp, but contracts only called for 14,000 ihp per ship. That reserve of power allowed speed in excess of the service 19 knots to be readily achieved. On trials both ships averaged 20.7 knots with *Normannia* producing a maximum of 21.25 knots.

Nine double ended scotch boilers arranged in three groups athwartships supplied steam at 160 psi. Each boiler had eight corrugated furnaces, four at each end, and that differed from the more usual arrangement of three at each end. Total grate area amounted to 1,450 sq ft

Sectional view through HAPAG's twin screw steamer Normannia.

which was larger than that of *Teutonic's* main boilers, but the German ships did not employ forced draught. A large auxiliary boiler was provided in the forward part of the middle boiler room. Auxiliary plant for port operation consisted mainly of electrical generators and so a single auxiliary boiler would have sufficed. That electrical installation comprised four 100 volt, 360 ampere dynamos, each capable of supplying 600 lamps, there being some 1,100 lamps aboard each ship.[9]

The large White Star vessels had extensive refrigerating space which needed to be cooled prior to loading cargo and kept cold during discharge. An abundant steam supply had to be maintained in port to keep that plant operational, hence their larger number of auxiliary boilers than their German rivals.

Normannia and her sister had three boiler rooms separated by cross bunkers and watertight bulkheads, of which there were ten. In addition a longitudinal watertight bulkhead divided the engine room and all such bulkheads extended to upper deck level. Such protection would not have saved *Normannia* from tragedy during her maiden voyage, only fortune did that. On 27 June 1890 the ship encountered an iceberg claimed to be 100 ft taller than her main

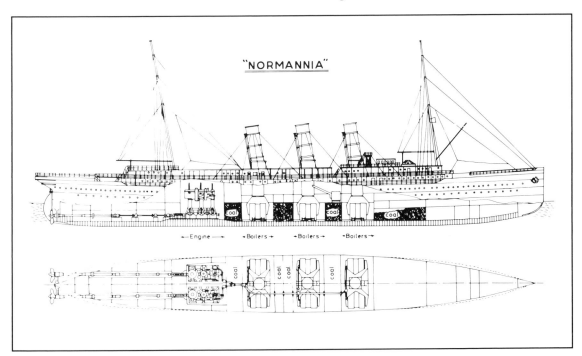

mast and had to take immediate evading action. If the ice was really that high it is difficult to imagine how *Normannia* could have come so close before it was noticed! By putting the helm hard over and stopping, then reversing the starboard engine while keeping the port one full ahead it was possible to turn the ship quickly to starboard. That ease of turning demonstrated another advantage of twin as against single screw. An impact collision with the iceberg was avoided, but it was struck a glancing blow of such force that some 20 tons of ice were deposited on the deck. Fortune smiled on *Normannia*, little damage occurred and no leaks resulted. Under similar circumstances 22 years later *Titanic* was not so lucky.

Once again the cause was neglect and incompetence. Steaming at full speed through waters where 23 icebergs had been sighted between longitudes 42° and 48° west was just asking for trouble.[10]

Despite the fact that *Etruria* and *Umbria* were barely five years old, it became evident to Cunard directors in 1890 that the pride of their fleet were already outdated. If the company was to compete it had to invest in bigger and faster tonnage. Negotiations with Fairfields resulted in a contract for two ships being signed during August 1891 and design work commenced immediately. Not only were they large ships, 12,950 gross tons, 598 ft between perpendiculars and 65 ft beam, but they were also fast with a minimum design speed of 21.5 knots. That sort of speed from a large ship required powerful engines, over 28,000 ihp from the two

engines. After a short running-in period the engines developed some 30,000 ihp allowing both ships to achieve average Atlantic crossing speeds of around 22 knots. Over a 3,000 mile trip that took some effort. *Campania* and *Lucania* were exceptional and their construction excited the maritime world.

Each triple expansion engine had five cylinders, the 37 in diameter HP cylinders being in tandem with and above 98 in diameter LP cylinders. These groupings were positioned either side of the single 79 in diameter IP cylinder. The stroke of each piston was 69 in. As might be expected with such high reciprocating masses formed by tandem HP and LP piston groupings, there were problems with vibration. At normal operating speeds of 78 to 79 rpm there was little evident vibration, but at slightly slower speeds of 75 rpm it became very pronounced. At this speed there was obviously some natural frequency of the ship's structure, hence the vibration, but avoidance of that speed could not always be guaranteed. The triple crank engine presented problems of balance and large masses present in the reciprocating parts only served to aggravate the situation.

These Fairfield engines were amongst the largest triple expansion marine engines ever made, but in many respects they were merely enlarged versions of earlier types. That does not, however, detract from the engineering skill required in their design and manufacture but

Normannia on trials off the Clyde. (Glasgow University Archives with permission of Mr W. Lind.)

Right *Propulsion engine as fitted in* Campania *and* Lucania.

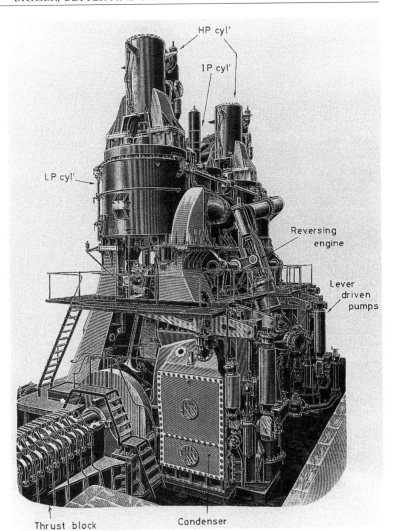

Below *Upper section of* Campania's *engine room. The top of the longitudinal bulkhead can be seen.*

serves to illustrate that triple expansion engines, and reciprocating steam engines in general, had practically reached the limit of their basic development. Quadruple expansion, better control of steam flow and more accurate regulation of valves would all help improve efficiency for future engines, but the basic concept could not really be developed further in isolation. Nothing could detract from the size, power and craftsmanship of the plant, however, it was magnificent and fully deserved the praise offered by maritime commentators on both sides of the Atlantic.

Well aware of the problems which afflicted *City of Paris* when one of its engines raced to destruction, Fairfields played safe and provided three governors for each engine. A Dunlop governor regulated steam when the screw's immersion was reduced, whilst a rotating ball weight governor kept maximum engine speed within limits during normal operation.

The Dunlop governor could not protect against racing in the event of shaft fracture and the rotating weight governor was too slow to react under such circumstances to prevent engine damage. For such protection an inertia governor was fitted and that operated on the cylinder slide and piston valves rather than the main steam supply valve. Shutting off steam supply did not cause the engine to slow immediately, as steam would still be flowing through IP and LP cylinders. Should engine speed rise too high a spring loaded inertia weight, reciprocating with part of the engine, would move outwards and actuate the reversing engine's steam valve. That engine was simply a steam cylinder connected to the expansion linkage on the main valve gear. With steam applied, the reversing cylinder would shift the expansion link to mid-position, instantly preventing piston and slide valves from admitting steam to any cylinder. Racing was avoided.

Fairfields employed steam jackets on all cylinders with the drains being returned to a hotwell. Harland & Wolff did not adopt that arrangement for the engines of *Teutonic* and *Majestic*, considering it to be wasteful and ineffective. A system of liners and air jackets was employed, an air space serving to insulate the cylinder.[11]

A number of lever driven pumps were fitted to each engine, but most pumps were operated by their own steam engines. Thrust block shafts had 14 collars and the shafting was 24 in diameter,

illustrating the high power which had to be transmitted. Three bladed propellers were employed rather than the more usual four bladed type. They were of the built-up type, each 8 ton manganese bronze blade bolting onto the steel propeller boss. In adding to the already impressive statistics, several journals repeated the claim that it would have taken the metal in 5.5 million pennies to cast all six blades for each vessel.

Main boiler plant consisted of 12 double ended scotch boilers 18 ft diameter and 17 ft long. Eight Fox corrugated furnaces were fitted to each boiler, four at each end, with common combustion space for opposing furnaces. Groups of three boilers were fitted athwartships with a set of six boilers occupying each independent boiler room. As each set of boilers discharged into its own double cased funnel the two funnels were placed some 130 ft apart. Bunkers occupied space fore and aft of each boiler room and also above them. Coal could be fed to the stokeholds from the bunkers by means of chutes at the sides of boiler groups. Daily fuel consumption exceeded 550 tons.

Strangely no forced draught arrangements were provided, that not being Fairfield's practice. A form of closed pressurized stokehold did allow increased air flow to the boilers, 12 large fans being provided for the purpose. There was, however, no attempt to regulate air pressure in the stokehold, the fans only serving to ensure an adequate supply. In other respects the builders did attempt to improve operating performance and efficiency by using Weir's feed heaters. Feed water sprayed into a chamber was heated by steam bled from the IP cylinder casing and by auxiliary engine exhaust. Mixing of steam and water not only heated the water, but also liberated oxygen from it which helped reduce boiler corrosion, oxygen being a prime cause of corrosion.

As might be expected with large ships carrying over 1,600 passengers, 1,000 of them in steerage, the electric lighting systems aboard *Campania* and *Lucania* were extensive. Some 1,350 lamps, with a total power consumption of 42,000 watts, illuminated each ship. Duplicated generating capacity was provided in two identical but separate dynamo rooms, each containing two generating sets. By this time electric lighting was well established and expected by passengers,

Campania *at speed on trials*. (Glasgow University Archives with permission of Mr W. Lind.)

so provision of back-up was essential.

Throughout the extensive accommodation a system of steam heating pipes ensured a comfortable environment, even in the most cold of Atlantic winters. All steam pipes were covered with a polished brass casing in order to maintain the illusion of opulence. The same conditions were not afforded to officers and crew—their accommodation could only be heated in port when no passengers were aboard as the heating system did not have sufficient capacity to provide warmth throughout the ship. Possibly the owners and builders believed that crew members would generate their own heat whilst they worked.

As ships became bigger and passenger accommodation more extensive, the problem of providing adequate ventilation began to tax ship builders. Forced air circulation was an answer but it could be noisy, create draughts and go wrong. Traditional ports in the ship's side remained ever popular with passengers as they allowed for individual cabin ventilation. The major problem with these was keeping the sea out whilst letting air in as passengers could not be relied upon to close ports when heavy, or even moderate, seas were expected. To avoid the inconvenience of wet cabins several patent ports were developed, most proving to be cumbersome and ineffective. One of the more reliable types was installed aboard the new Cunard pair.

Traditional ship's side ports were paired with Utley ports, thus allowing each cabin a supply of fresh air in all conditions. The Utley port consisted of a valve unit fitted inboard of and above the usual port. A glass sidelight in front of the port allowed light in, but the air came via the valve unit mounted above. If the port became submerged then water would enter through the port but would lift the valve and seal it, thus preventing water from entering the cabin. When the wave passed the valve would drop allowing air free access to the cabin once more. Similar valve units regulated ventilation in other parts of the ship. Although the system functioned it was expensive and the experiment was never repeated aboard other Cunard ships.

Like the new White Star liners, *Campania* and *Lucania* were provided with refrigeration plant for passenger and crew provisions as well as cargo holds. An ammonia system with circulating brine met hotel demands and could still supply 560 lb of ice each day. The much larger cargo system also worked on ammonia compression, with circulation of cold brine for keeping the chambers cold. Three refrigerated chambers with a capacity of 20,000 cu ft could accommodate 2,700 quarters of beef. Although shipment of live beef from the USA was a growing trade, there was still money to be made in carriage of frozen carcasses in fast passenger ships. Live animals would disturb the passengers but dead ones did not and the trade was too good to miss, there being little else of high value to be shipped eastward.

Campania and *Lucania* each required a crew of some 415 for normal working. Of these 61 supplied the needs of the deck department,

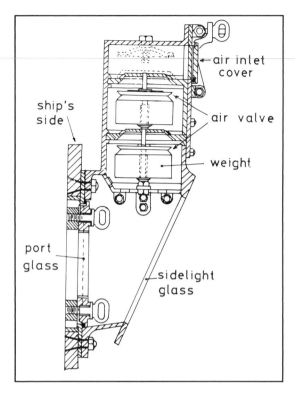

Patent Utley port allowing ventilation without water entering the cabin.

including a purser and a surgeon. 159 were needed for hotel services, there being 105 stewards, eight stewardesses, 45 cooks and bakers, plus one chief steward. As might be expected aboard such large vessels the engine room complement was the biggest, comprising one chief engineer, 21 assistants, two refrigerating engineers, eight electricians, one deck engineer, two storekeepers, one 'donkey' man (to tend the donkey engines and donkey boiler), 18 greasers, nine leading firemen, 75 firemen and 57 coal trimmers. That list of 195 souls serves to indicate how extensive the engine room domain had become. Not only had the number of engineers and firemen increased with machinery power, but the employment of refrigerating engineers and electricians had increased to meet expanding use of technology.

Ship and engine construction may have been in the hands of a single concern, in this case Fairfields, but the growth of shipbuilding in general, and large passenger ships in particular, had spawned a massive support industry. Fur-

nishing, decorative and other outfitting trades were essential, but on the engineering side many concerns specialized in particular items. Brown Brothers of Edinburgh had become specialists in steering gear, Siemens specialized in electrical plant and G. & J. Weir of Cathcart, Glasgow developed a reputation for the manufacture of boiler feed pumps and ancillary equipment. Others supplying equipment for these ships included W. H. Allen & Co of London the stokehold ventilator fans and engines, Napiers of Glasgow the windlass and winches, Muir and Caldwell of Glasgow the capstans, with Sterne of Glasgow supplying domestic refrigerating plant and Kilbourn of Liverpool the cargo refrigerating equipment.[12]

Although most of the engineering concerns were centred on ports in order to supply repair and back-up facilities, there was a marked effect on the economy nationally by the placing of orders for large ships. Cunard received an annual operating subsidy from the Admiralty of £19,000 for each of these two ships in order that they might be available to act as auxiliary cruisers. In many respects it was money well spent, for it not only ensured that ships were available but it stimulated differing sections of the economy in many parts of the country. The subsidy amounted to less than £1 per week for every job on board.

Most countries with ships operating Atlantic services provided subsidies in one form or another, it simply became standard practice. Even the United States of America joined the club when a subsidy for construction of two liners was offered to the newly formed American Line in 1893. That concern had taken over most of the Inman Line ships including *City of New York* and *City of Paris*, which were renamed simply *New York* and *Paris* (later to become *Philadelphia*). Congress insisted that the two ships be built in the USA and the order went to William Cramp & Sons of Philadelphia. In terms of deep sea trading America had a comparatively small fleet, whilst its shipbuilding and marine engineering industries were not as developed as those on the eastern shores of the Atlantic. They did, however, come of age in constructing *St Louis* and *St Paul*.

These 10,250 gross ton, twin screw ships were practically identical and both entered service in 1895. Of length 535 ft (bp) and beam 63 ft they were by far the largest vessels constructed in

America up to that time. Their speed of 20 knots was marginally below the fastest Atlantic liners, but they were well able to maintain an express service.

Messrs Cramp adopted a quadruple expansion arrangement for the engines, the first such installation aboard any express Atlantic liner. Cylinder groupings were somewhat unusual in that two 28.5 in HP cylinders were connected in tandem with two 77 in LP cylinders, these driving the forward two cranks. On the third crank was positioned a 55 in diameter IP cylinder with the 77 in second IP stage connected to the fourth crank. All cylinders had 60 in strokes. Only the two low pressure cylinders were steam jacketed, asbestos and hair-felt lagging being liberally applied to the others. Each engine could develop some 8,000 ihp.

Six double ended and four single ended scotch type boilers supplied steam at 200 psi, showing how independent and adventurous the American marine engineers were prepared to be. All boilers were 15 ft 7.5 in diameter, with the double ended ones at 20 ft being nearly twice the length of the single ended units. A British concept was adopted in the use of Howden's forced draught. Boiler tubes were fitted with retarders, twisted strips of metal which produced a turbulent action in the gas flow, so that more efficient heat transfer from gas to water might take place. As was usual for the period the boilers were housed in two separate watertight compartments, but against the normal trend there was only bunker space for eight days' steaming. Coal capacity of 2,500 tons did not leave much margin for delays or emergencies.[13] American coal was not of such good quality as British steam coal, but being American ships there would be pressure on the owners to take local fuel. However, with such small bunker space fuel also had to be taken aboard in Europe. The reduced bunker space gave increased cargo capacity.

Despite the success of these ships in an engineering sense, American entrepreneurs failed to take advantage and left European owners to dominate the Atlantic scene for decades to come.

In Germany there was no such reluctance and, following his visit to the Spithead Naval Review in 1889, Kaiser Wilhelm II determined that his country would dominate the Atlantic waters. His intentions were both military and

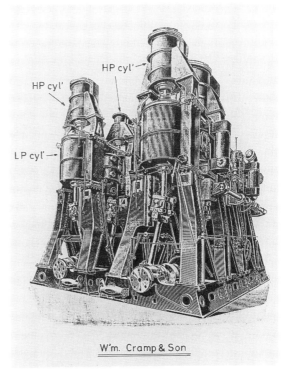

Twin engines fitted by Cramp in the American vessels St Paul *and* St Louis.

merchant, but as far as commercial enterprise was concerned the two major Atlantic shipping companies, HAPAG and NGL, had to be encouraged with subsidies. It was the latter which first jumped at the bait and set in motion plans which culminated in construction of the first German 'superliner'.

Kaiser Wilhelm der Grosse entered service in 1897, but she was not the immediate result of the Kaiser's plans as several slightly smaller ships had been constructed for the Australian and Atlantic trades. These 'Barbarossa' class ships were of 10,600 gross tons and propelled by twin quadruple expansion engines. All were built in Germany, for it was also part of the plan that the German shipbuilding and marine engineering industries would become world leaders.

Built at the Vulcan Works, Stettin, *Kaiser Wilhelm der Grosse* became the first non-British holder of the 'Blue Riband' since the Collins Line ships of the 1850s. She was, at 14,350 gross tons with a length (bp) of 625 ft and beam 66 ft, the largest ship in the world and remained so for two years. Designed to carry 554 first class, 324 second class and 800 steerage passengers, she required a crew of 458. Her appearance was radically different from other vessels engaged on Atlantic service due to the fitting of four funnels arranged in two distinct groups. That came about due to the positioning of her boiler rooms, a large coal bunker separating the two pairs. Total coal capacity amounted to 4,596 tons.[14]

In order to compete with other ships, the accommodation was equal to that of the best liners then in service. Utley ventilators were fitted to most ports in the ship's side, whilst deck level cabins had sliding ventilators. Electric lighting was fitted throughout the ship, with 1,712 lamps consuming a maximum 90 kW when all were in use. Four steam driven 100 volt dc dynamos not only provided current for lighting, but also powered a number of electric motors. The 16 stokehold ventilation fans were driven by motors of 6 horsepower whilst other electrically driven fans provided air circulation for the engine room, galleys and public rooms. Lifts (elevators) were fitted for moving provisions and mail, but not people, between decks. These

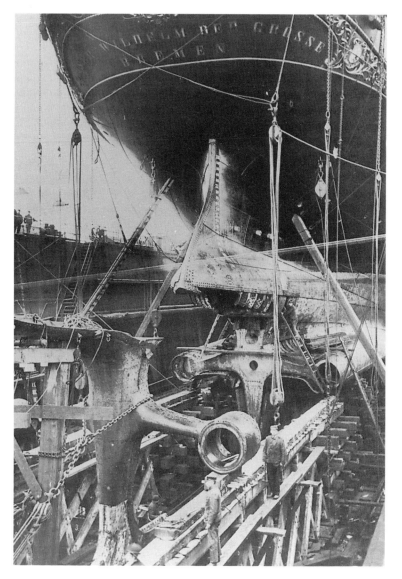

Left *Stern post and brackets of the German* Kaiser Wilhelm der Grosse.

Right *Bridge panel diagram showing the positioning of watertight doors aboard* Kaiser Wilhelm der Grosse.

required motors of 3 horsepower and could raise loads of up to 800 lb through 36 ft in 15 seconds. Automatic stops were fitted to prevent damage in the event of operators not controlling the lifts correctly.

Electricity was also employed for heating, cooking and other purposes, including cabin radiators, water heaters and even a cigar lighter in the smoking room. Electrically driven fans were also used for circulating cold air from the ammonia refrigerating plant around the provision rooms, but there was no refrigerated cargo space. Without doubt it was the most extensive use of electricity aboard any ship to that date.[15]

In terms of main propulsion plant *Kaiser Wilhelm der Grosse* was nothing unusual, just big. Triple expansion engines were stipulated, although quadruple expansion had already proved itself to be effective aboard the 'Barbarossa' class ships. There were, however, four cranks instead of the customary three of British ships. That four crank arrangement allowed balancing on the Yarrow–Schlick–Tweedy system, which resulted in an absence of any noticeable vibration even at high powers. The 51.875 in (1,320 mm) HP and 89.75 in (2,280 mm) IP cylinders were arranged next to each other in one forward group with the two 96.5 in (2,450 mm) LP cylinders in the after group. Stroke of all cylinders was 68.875 in (1,750 mm). Apart from an emergency sanitary and bilge pump which was main engine driven, all pumps were provided with their own steam engines.

Scotch type boilers, 12 double ended and two single ended, supplied steam at 175 psi. The main boilers were fitted in groups of three athwartships, each group having its own watertight compartment. The two single ended boilers

for harbour use were positioned in the after part of the after boiler room, a large coal bunker separating that compartment from the engine room. No forced draught was provided, it being considered that natural draught from the 106 ft high funnels, assisted by stokehold ventilator fans, would be sufficient for combustion purposes. Boiler flues remained distinct up through each funnel. Each double ended boiler had eight furnaces and at full speed these consumed considerable quantities of coal. In order that coal might be moved to the boilers as quickly as possible a little railway system was arranged between bunkers and stokeholds. Ash was removed from the stokeholds by means of water powered ash ejectors.[16]

Each three bladed 26 ton screw was just over 22 ft diameter and they overlapped by some 8 in. As with the White Star *Teutonic* and *Majestic* it was necessary to cut out the dead space in the after part of the hull and position one screw in front of the other. With *Kaiser Wilhelm der Grosse* the port propeller was 35.5 in forward of the starboard one.[17]

Safety had high priority and the ship was divided by 17 watertight bulkheads, 15 of which extended to the upper deck and two to the lower deck. A longitudinal bulkhead divided the engine room. She was designed to remain afloat with any two adjacent compartments flooded. With a ship of this size it was essential to have communication through these bulkheads, especially in the machinery spaces, and so an effective system of watertight doors had to be fitted. On the bridge an indicator panel showed which doors were open or closed. Coloured discs, red for starboard and green for port, showed at each watertight door position when a door was open. A closed door showed a white

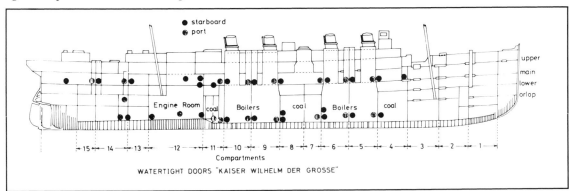

WATERTIGHT DOORS "KAISER WILHELM DER GROSSE"

disc. The disc system operated electrically, being actuated by switches at each of the doors.[18]

Kaiser Wilhelm der Grosse's engines could develop 30,000 ihp under normal circumstances and more if pressed. That sort of power produced a service design speed of 22.5 knots. To maintain such average speeds over a six day Atlantic crossing required power in reserve and that the ship had. In November 1898 *Kaiser Wilhelm der Grosse* smashed her own record time with a crossing from Southampton to New York at an average speed of 23 knots.

During the latter 1890s HAPAG had constructed four 13,300 gross ton ships for its secondary services to the USA, but the success of NGL's express liner cast a shadow. With subsidies still being offered it made sound sense to re-enter the express trade. *Deutschland* was ordered from the same Stettin shipyard and had a similar profile, but was some 4,000 gross tons larger than *Kaiser Wilhelm der Grosse*. With a length (bp) of 662 ft and beam 67 ft, the new

ship was also intended to be faster and that required even higher power. Instead of four cylinder triple expansion engines the decision was made to adopt a six cylinder quadruple expansion arrangement, employing four cranks in order to take advantage of the Yarrow–Schlick–Tweedy system of balancing.

Two HP cylinders, 36.61 in (930 mm) diameter, were mounted in tandem above each LP cylinder, 106.3 in (2,700 mm) diameter. These combinations occupied the centre cranks in order to give the heaviest weights for balancing, whilst the first IP cylinder, 73.6 in (1,870 mm) diameter, was placed forward and the second IP cylinder, 103.9 in (2,640 mm) diameter was positioned on the aftermost crank. All cylinders had a 72.8 in (1,850 mm) stroke. Piston valves applied throughout. Each engine set had been designed to develop 16,500 ihp, giving a ship total of 33,000 ihp, but in service the plant had produced an output of 37,000 ihp. With that power it was obvious that high speeds would result, and they did.[19]

Upon entry into service in 1900 *Deutschland* soon showed the speed of which she was capable

Diagram of an engine fitted in Deutschland.

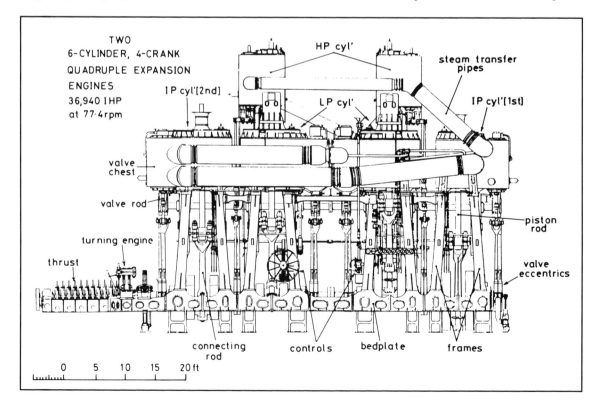

Deutschland's engines erected at the works, but without the HP cylinders.

and captured the 'Blue Riband' during her first few voyages. In that first year she produced a crossing between New York and Plymouth at an average speed of 23.36 knots. That speed had to be paid for, and not only in terms of coal consumption, for the ship suffered from severe vibration. Although the engines had been balanced it would appear that the ship's structure was very much tuned to their operating revolutions at full speed and so the ship would vibrate 'from stem to stern' at anything near designed speed. No amount of stiffening could solve the problem and her reputation for discomfort began to influence passenger figures. High speed was always an attraction,

but passengers did not take kindly to being shaken continuously throughout a five day crossing.

HAPAG soldiered on with its rather lame duck, but by 1910 they admitted defeat and *Deutschland* was re-engined with less powerful machinery to become a specialized cruise liner. It was a sad end for a ship which showed so much promise at its conceptual stage but she was constructed in something of a hurry, delivery being only some six months after launch. A grounding during the voyage from Stettin prevented any real trials which would have demonstrated the vibration problem before she entered service. No solution would, however, have been forthcoming, as numerous modifications during ten years in service failed to cure the defect. *Deutschland* was effectively an enlarged

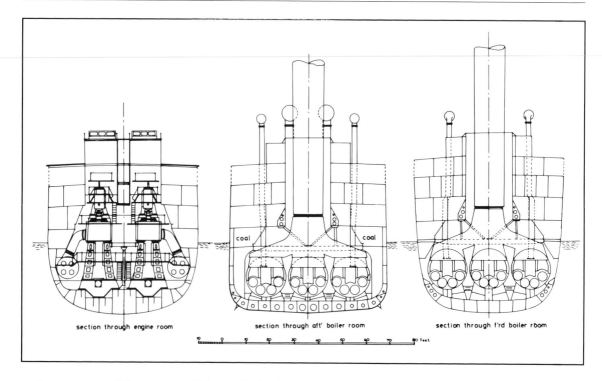

section through engine room   section through aft' boiler room   section through f'rd boiler room

Sectional views through Deutschland's *machinery spaces.*

and more powerful version of *Kaiser Wilhelm der Grosse*, but shipbuilding is not simply a case of increasing dimensions to make things bigger. Naval architecture and ship construction are complicated sciences where, despite rigorous analysis, the unexpected can happen, even with modern computer aided techniques. The real test comes when the ship is in service and by then only modifications can be made, redesign and reconstruction being impractical. *Deutschland* was just unlucky.

In order to generate sufficient steam for her engines *Deutschland*'s 12 double and four single ended boilers operated with Howden forced draught. Boiler pressure of 220 psi showed a considerable increase over the earlier NGL ship, but the actual grate area from a larger number of boilers was less: 2,188 sq ft against 1,618 sq ft. The use of forced draught allowed for such a reduction because the boilers could burn coal more effectively. With these large express ships it became evident that boiler space was critical to power and speed. Boiler rooms and cross bunkers occupied some 285 ft of the ship's 662 ft length. The engine room took up just under 90 ft.

The 110 volt dc electrical system was supplied by three 77 kW dynamos and two of 44 kW. In addition to the very comprehensive lighting circuits, these dynamos also supplied power to 25 electric motors, aggregating 36 kW, eight electric stoves, two water heaters, two egg boilers, 70 small ventilator fans and 375 curling iron sockets. In addition to lighting, domestic use of electricity aboard ship was increasing steadily but it was the growth in electric motor use which produced the major demand for power. Electric motors powered boiler forced draught as well as engine room and bunker ventilation fans, these being more readily controlled than their steam driven counterparts. For the mail and provision hoists only electric motors were really suitable. Power was available at the push of a button or flick of a switch.[20]

NGL was not content to let HAPAG take the honours without a fight. An order for a 14,900 gross ton vessel of similar design to *Kaiser Wilhelm der Grosse* was placed with Stettin even before *Deutschland* had entered service. *Kronprinz Wilhelm* was powered by two six cylinder four crank quadruple expansion engines similar to those of *Deutschland*, but with dimensions slightly less. Speeds of both vessels were comparable, but the NGL ship could never quite beat her HAPAG rival. Despite that she proved to be a more popular ship due to the absence of any noticeable vibration.

With an engine similar in size to *Deutschland* it was not unreasonable that *Kronprinz Wilhelm* should have a similar boiler installation, comprising 12 double ended and four single ended boilers working at 213 psi. NGL did not, however, favour forced draught and the ship operated on a natural draught system. Boilers were arranged in four banks with a funnel to each bank. Bunker space was provided at the sides of each boiler room, but the main bunker was positioned between the second and third boiler rooms. That produced the characteristic funnel groupings of the class, allowed for more even weight distribution and provided a degree of safety in the event of one set of boiler rooms being made inactive by a collision. Watertight bulkheads separated all boiler and engine compartments.

In terms of auxiliary plant and fittings *Kronprinz Wilhelm* followed her earlier sisters from the same builder, but improvements were incorporated in the light of operating experience or recent developments. The Brown Brothers' steering gear was also duplicated by an additional set in the poop, the main gear being below the waterline as was usual in a ship intended as a military auxiliary. Although these ships were German designed and built, several items of British equipment were incorporated. Brown Brothers had become world leaders in steering gear, but Weirs were equally well known for pumps and feed equipment, whilst Napiers had an unequalled reputation for windlasses and winches. The Germans only fitted the best and these companies provided it.

Whilst the electrical plant supplied normal lighting and power needs, electricity was also employed for the extensive system of steward call bells in the cabins. All clocks were electrically controlled and a telephone system operated throughout the ship, including many cabins. As far as safety was concerned only bulkheads in the machinery spaces had doors below the waterline. These doors operated hydraulically with electrical control from the bridge. A pressurized fire main was installed with pipes going to all parts of the vessel, thus allowing water

under pressure to be available whenever and wherever it was needed.[21]

Success followed success, and *Kaiser Wilhelm II* appeared in 1903. NGL had also ordered her from the Vulcan Works at Stettin, but she was a larger and improved version of the earlier ships. The basic shape and concept were as before, but tonnage and power had been increased. At 19,500 gross tons and some 40,000 ihp *Kaiser Wilhelm II* was the largest and most powerful vessel in the world. If her overall layout was similar to her predecessors, the same cannot be said for the propulsion machinery.

Each of the twin screws was, in fact, driven by two essentially independent engines coupled in line, thus the ship had four main engines. These were of four cylinder three crank form, the 37.4 in (950 mm) HP cylinder being in tandem with and above the first IP cylinder of 49.1 in (1,250 mm) diameter. On the adjacent crank was connected the 74.7 in (1,900 mm) second IP cylinder with the 112.2 in (2,850 mm) LP stage on the end crank. Engines were coupled with tandem cylinders next to each other, but separated by watertight bulkheads. This, in effect, produced eight cylinder six crank engines, but controls and auxiliaries like condensers were duplicated for each three crank set. That allowed the after engine only to be operated should the forward room become flooded, or vice versa. It never proved necessary to do so.

The 12 double and seven single ended boilers working on open stokeholds supplied steam at 225 psi. These were arranged in four boiler rooms with pipework so connected that the engines could be supplied with steam from any combination. German designers were evidently ultra cautious, or else they had an eye to naval use of these ships. The overall length of 706 ft 6 in was divided into 19 watertight compartments, with the main engines occupying four of these.[22]

For the first six years of the twentieth century a unique fleet of German express liners raced across the Atlantic and other nations could only watch in amazement. An almost identical ship to *Kaiser Wilhelm II* was planned, but the order did not come immediately and when *Kronprinzessin Cecilie* entered service in 1907 she was already a part of maritime history. The turbine era had arrived and ocean travel would never be the same.

CHAPTER 6

Turbine Power

White Star Line still entertained aspirations as a high speed Atlantic operator, even though the relatively new *Teutonic* and *Majestic* had been outpaced by the Cunard pair and by *Kaiser Wilhelm der Grosse*. Encouraged by Harland & Wolff, the ageing Thomas H. Ismay decided upon a final fling and two express steamers were planned. Only one, *Oceanic*, was actually built, the other proposed vessel, to have been named *Olympic*, being cancelled when Ismay withdrew money from the yard in order to leave his son, J. Bruce Ismay, sufficient funds to meet anticipated death duties.[1]

When delivered in 1899, *Oceanic* became the first ship to exceed *Great Eastern* in length, although her gross tonnage of 17,250 was slightly less than that of Brunel's giant. Length to beam ratio of 10 to 1,685 ft (bp) by 68 ft, was chosen to suit high speed running, but service speed was never much in excess of 20 knots. It has been suggested that vibration limited the maximum speed, but that is now difficult to prove or disprove. Whatever the reasoning for her speed she became an exceptionally popular vessel with accommodation for 410 first, 300 second and 1,000 third class passengers. Lack of speed was more than made up for by the exceptional standard of her cabins and public rooms.

Her main engines were of four crank triple expansion form, with cylinders 47.5 in HP, 79 in IP and two 93 in LP. All pistons had 72 in strokes. Designed power of 28,000 ihp was rather conservative, considering the dimensions and steam pressure of 192 psi. That underrating did allow a reserve of power to make up for any delays, thus giving *Oceanic* an enviable record

for timekeeping. A strange feature of the engines lay in the fact that each was provided with two thrust blocks. The reasoning behind that is difficult to understand as engines of similar power had managed with single multi-collared blocks, each 14,000 ihp rated engine of *Campania* and *Lucania* managed with single 14 collar thrust blocks. It does suggest, however, that the maximum engine power was greatly in excess of the nominal rating and two blocks were considered more suitable for high power transmission.[2]

Engines were balanced on the Yarrow–Schlick–Tweedy system and if that was accurate any vibration, if it existed, could have been due to the hull design which caused resonance at certain higher speeds. Claiming that vibration restricted maximum speed presupposes a desire to operate at high speed. *Oceanic* had been intended to run in consort with a fast sister ship, but that plan was abandoned shortly after her launch. Her running mates were the 19.5 knot *Teutonic* and *Majestic*, so it was only necessary to match their speeds. These ships left Liverpool on a Wednesday afternoon and were timed to arrive at New York the following Wednesday morning.

With machinery well under construction at launch there would be no economic justification for starting again, so the original engines were fitted and run at below maximum rating. Reserve power could always be useful on the Atlantic. At a luncheon prior to the maiden voyage Bruce Ismay stated that '*Oceanic* will not be a record breaker with regard to speed'.[3]

Oceanic's propellers had three manganese bronze blades bolted to gun metal bosses, their

Oceanic *of 1899.* (Harry Weston Collection.)

overall diameter being 22 ft 3 in. Although there was a cut-out space in the hull structure between them, the propellers did not overlap and so shafting could be of the same length. Fifteen double ended scotch boilers of the common combustion chamber type were arranged in four boiler rooms. Those in the forward boiler rooms were smaller in diameter and had three furnaces instead of four due to space limitations. Assisted draught was employed, with fans supplying air to the open stokeholds. As

was the case with many ships of the period, windlass and capstans came from Napiers. The presence of chains and rope required space in the vicinity of these devices to be kept clear for safety and operational reasons. Napiers arranged for driving engines and gearing to be positioned on the deck below with drives being through vertical shafting.[4]

Oceanic of 1899 was powerful and of sound construction, her two very tall funnels creating an impression of elegance and majesty. She showed that the pursuit of speed could be a false goal, passengers were just as keen on high standards and assurance as to arrival time. A reserve of power allowed *Oceanic* to cross and

Sectional view of Oceanic *showing machinery positioning.*

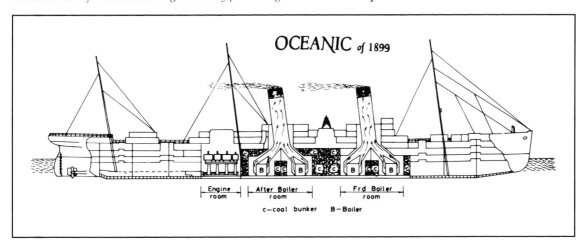

recross the Atlantic with a regularity of timing which verged on the monotonous. She was, as far as White Star was concerned, the perfect 'one week' boat.[5] As *Engineering* so rightly stated, 'It is useless making great sacrifices to save a few hours in order to spend them at anchor in New York or the Mersey'.[6]

For any ship leaving Liverpool or Southampton an afternoon or early evening departure allowed passengers to arrive from London by train the same day. From Liverpool the call at Queenstown would be made next day, whilst from Southampton a Cherbourg call might be made the same evening. It was pointless to arrive at New York after dark as passengers had then to be kept on board until next day in order to complete immigration formalities. In the case of White Star a crossing from Liverpool in six and a half days made sense. Arrival during an afternoon instead of the following morning required a passage some 15 hours shorter. That needed an average speed over 2 knots faster than the nominal 19.5 knots. Speed cost fuel and fuel cost money. In general passengers preferred morning arrivals as formalities could be completed and journey to final destination commenced. White Star seemed to know its market and catered for it with economy.

Success with *Oceanic* prompted construction of further ships to update the fleet, but the de-

cision had been made to go for comfort rather than speed. During the period 1901 to 1907 four large but, by 'Blue Riband' standards, slow ships were constructed, also by Harland & Wolff. 'The Big Four', as they became known, set standards for comfort for all passengers which had hitherto only been available to the very rich. Speed was not the prime consideration and a 3 knot reduction compared with *Oceanic* required a daily fuel consumption of 260 tons, about 140 tons less than the faster vessel. *Celtic* was first of the class, entering service during 1901, and at 20,880 gross tons was then the world's largest ship.

Following market research into the relative number of first and second class passengers crossing the Atlantic, White Star arranged space for 347 first class, 160 second class and 2,352 steerage. Although passage rates were lower than aboard faster ships it was argued that a relatively full ship would be economical, especially as she consumed less coal and had space for 13,000 tons of cargo. The era of the economic secondary liner had arrived and over the years these big ships illustrated how successful their operation could be.

Celtic and *Cedric*, of 1903, were 680 ft long (bp) by 75.3 ft in the beam and were practically identical, especially with respect to machinery.

One of White Star's 'Big Four', Celtic.

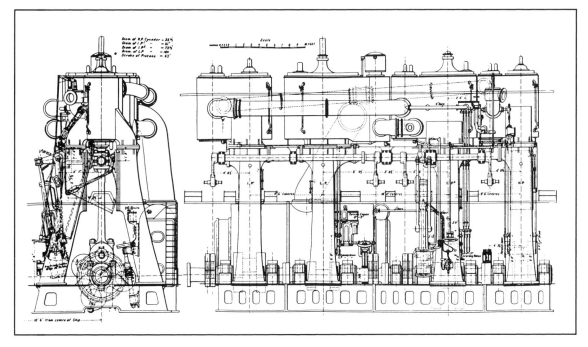

One of Adriatic's *quadruple expansion engines.*

The twin engines were four crank quadruple expansion and balanced in order to minimize vibration. At the 16.5 knot service speed they developed a total of 14,000 ihp. Eight double ended scotch boilers, 19 ft 6 in long by 15 ft 9 in diameter, supplied steam at 210 psi, the funnel height of 120 ft above the grates ensuring adequate draught without the need for any forced arrangement. The three bladed propellers were 20 ft diameter with their shaft centres only 20 ft 9 in apart. As with *Oceanic*, a clearance aperture had to be provided in the hull structure in way of the screws to allow adequate water flow.[7]

Baltic of 1904 was slightly larger and more powerful than her earlier sisters, but had the same type of machinery installation. *Adriatic* was last of the quartet and did not enter service until 1907. Reasons for the delay have never been fully explained as the original order was placed during December 1903. It is probable that White Star's new owner, International Mercantile Marine (IMM), was taking stock of its position and delayed construction until the Atlantic operating situation became clear. Due to her increased dimensions *Baltic* proved to be slightly slower than expected and so engines for *Adriatic*, 24,555 gross tons, were made more powerful

but still of the same quadruple expansion type. She was also to have a speed of 18 knots in order to allow operations in consort with *Oceanic*.

Cylinder dimensions for *Adriatic*'s engines were as follows, with the figures for *Celtic* given in brackets for comparison: HP 35.5 in (33 in), first IP 51 in (47.5 in), second IP 73.5 in (68.5 in), and LP 104 in (98 in) with the stroke 63 in (63 in). Performance was in the region of 17,000 ihp. For these larger engines an increased steam supply was required and that came from 12 boilers, eight double ended the same as for *Celtic* and four single ended 11 ft long by 15 ft 6 in diameter. Throughout these ships extensive use was made of electricity, especially for ventilation fans.[8]

Whilst White Star dallied over the construction of *Adriatic*, an event of considerable maritime significance was taking place across the harbour from Harland & Wolff at the yard of Workman, Clark & Co. Ever since Charles Parsons had startled Queen Victoria's admirals by his high speed dash through the fleet with *Turbinia* at the Spithead review in 1897, the dream had been of a turbine driven ocean liner. Turbines were not new in marine practice, several being employed for electrical generator drives. The Inman liner *City of Berlin* was provided with two steam turbine powered generators, which

The Allan liner Virginian. (Glasgow University Archives with permission of Mr W. Lind.)

found favour with the engineers as no attention was usually required throughout a crossing.[9] It is likely that they were fitted during the ship's re-engining of 1887.

Turbine propulsion had to wait a number of years, but after *Turbinia's* triumph few people had any doubts that, if properly developed, it had considerable potential. Although turbine technology was not so advanced as that for reciprocating engines, the turbine was better balanced and offered reduced risk of vibration. In addition a turbine installation could occupy less space. First to take the plunge was the Allan Line with two ships, *Victorian* and *Virginian*, for its Canadian services. Originally both were to have been constructed by Workman, Clark & Co and reciprocating engines had been specified. Only after some progress had been made on *Victorian's* hull was the decision made to change to turbines. That required certain structural alterations, but a far more difficult task lay in construction of the turbines, the largest and most powerful constructed to that date. *Victorian* was destined to be the first turbine driven liner on the Atlantic, or any ocean for that matter.

Change of mind caused a delay, resulting in the order for *Virginian* going to Alexander Stephen & Co of Glasgow, regular builders for the Allan Line. Both ships were practically identical and turbines were provided by Parsons' own company. In order to drive these 10,700 gross ton steamers through the water at 17.5 knots, engine output of some 12,000 horsepower was required. Turbines had to be directly connected to the screw shafts, but in order to obtain a reasonable propulsive efficency at the ship's designed speed the propeller rotational speed, and hence that of the turbine, had to be 290 rpm maximum. Steam velocity through a nozzle is high and so turbine blade speed must be high. In order to allow for a relatively low rotational speed it was necessary to fit turbines of large diameter and that system remained with all directly connected turbines.

Three turbines, one HP in the centre and two LP either side, connected to individual drive shafts giving a triple screw arrangement. Because turbines cannot be reversed it was necessary to fit separate astern turbines, but these were only provided on the two wing shafts. When working ahead the astern turbines rotate in the partial vacuum generated by the condenser, but there was still some windage loss due to the low pressure and that reduced the effective output slightly. Within the three turbines were 1.5 million blades, half being fitted in the rotor and the remainder as nozzles in the casing. The smallest for the HP stage were 0.75 in long whilst the largest in the LP stage were 8 in long. Each low pressure turbine weighed about 100 tons, whilst the high pressure unit was some 60 tons. That compared favourably with a reciprocating plant of similar power and the turbines occupied less space.

In comparison to the turbines the eight scotch boilers working at a pressure of 185 psi were nothing unusual, nor was the remaining plant.[10] *Victorian* and *Virginian* proved to be popular with passengers because of their comfort and freedom from vibration. In later years conversion to oil burning and the fitting of geared turbines improved their efficiency, with the result that they remained economical ships to operate. *Virginian* remained in service for 50 years, serving later as the Swedish liner *Drottningholm*, before age finally took its toll. Both ships deserve their place in marine engineering history, and the Allan Line praise for its bold decision.

Cunard was not so far behind, but acted more cautiously. With the high speed German ships in service concern was expressed at Britain's position, especially as White Star had fallen under control of the American owned IMM. Following lengthy negotiations an agreement

was reached between Cunard and the British Government for a loan which would finance construction of two steamers capable of maintaining at least 23.5 knots. The loan of £2.6 million was to be supplemented by an additional £150,000 per annum to help meet running costs.[11]

Model tests were carried out at a number of establishments in order to determine the optimum hull form for the new vessels. Eventually a suitable hull form was decided upon and Cunard placed orders with two of the shipbuilders who had co-operated in the initial investigations. John Brown & Co, formerly J. & G. Thomson, of Clydebank set about constructing what was to become *Lusitania* whilst Swan Hunter and Wigham Richardson of Wallsend on Tyne were to build the sister ship, later to be known as *Mauretania*. Early tank tests indicated that some 68,000 shaft horse power would be required to propel the ships at the intended speed and serious thought had to be given to the ideal form of engine, reciprocating or turbine.

With little information available at that time, 1903, regarding marine turbine performance

Victorian's partly bladed LP rotor and casing.

and efficiency Cunard appointed a commission of leading engineers to investigate the matter. Members of the commission included J. Bain from Cunard, Engineer-Rear-Admiral Oram and J.T. Milton from Lloyd's, together with representatives from shipbuilders and engine builders including Andrew Laing of the Wallsend Engineering Company. Charles Parsons also offered advice and assisted in tests aboard turbine driven steamers already operating on cross channel services. The commission reported during 1904, but in December 1903, when tendering for a sister ship to the twin screw 19,500 gross ton *Caronia*, John Brown & Co proposed the use of turbines instead of reciprocating engines. Cunard agreed with the idea and, early in 1904, placed an order with John Brown & Co for construction of *Carmania*.

As the same concern was to build both ships and they were to be identical in size and dimension, the exercise would provide valuable comparative data. It was a bold step by Cunard to agree to such construction as the ships required engines of some 21,000 shaft horsepower (shp) in order to achieve the desired speed. That sort of power had been obtained from reciprocating engines, but never before from turbines. It was nearly double the power of the Allan Line ships. Before *Carmania* entered service and any information could be obtained, the commission submitted its report. With remarkable foresight the members decided that turbines offered the solution to high power requirements for large and fast ships. The engine builders, John Brown & Co and the Wallsend Engineering Company, displayed considerable enterprise in taking contracts for the turbines of *Lusitania* and *Mauretania* as it

was a major step beyond the bounds of known technology. Meanwhile the performance of *Carmania*'s machinery would be watched with interest.

With respect to accommodation and hull design *Caronia* and *Carmania* were identical, save for the fact that turbine propulsion of the latter demanded a triple screw arrangement rather than twin screw for the reciprocating engine drive. Externally they were attractive ships with two raked funnels, one for each of the two boiler rooms, and soon became known as the 'pretty sisters'. Over the years demand for passenger accommodation had increased and builders met the demand by providing extra decks. That became possible through the employment of steel for construction which was lighter than iron, thus reducing the risk of the ship being top heavy, and the elimination of sails. Until the advent of twin screws it was still customary to carry sails of some form and clear deck space had to be provided. *Caronia* and *Carmania* had eight decks, the boat deck being 45 ft above the waterline. Most of the 310 ft length of the boat deck was set aside as a first class passenger promenade, but a small area aft was, commendably, partitioned off as a fresh air area for the stokers. A protective screen was arranged, according to contemporary publicity, in order to protect stokers from the wind but it was more likely that it was to keep the 'black-gang' out of sight from first class passengers.

Accommodation was provided for 330 first, 350 second, 1,000 third and 1,000 steerage pas-

One of Cunard's 'Pretty sisters', the twin screw Caronia. *(Harry Weston Collection.)*

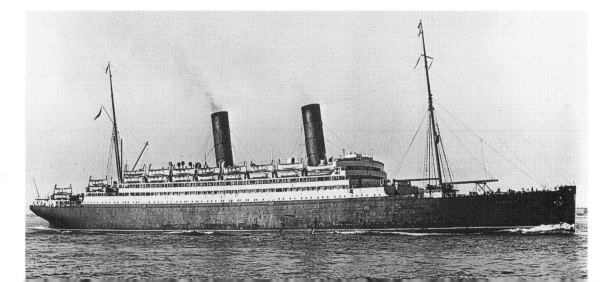

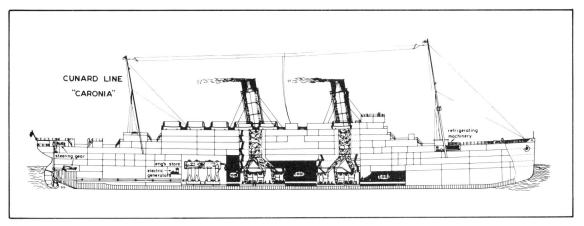

Sectional view of Caronia's hull.

sengers. That, together with a crew complement of some 450, resulted in 3,100 souls on board whenever the ships were full thus catering, ventilation, toilet and washing facilities had to be extensive.

Electricity met not only the lighting demand, but also that of ventilation. There were 12 thermo-tanks with electrically driven fans supplying fresh air to third class and steerage quarters, that air being heated to a minimum of 65°F during even the coldest of weather. The fans allowed for a complete air change seven times each hour. Separate fans provided air circulation in the main public rooms as well as ventilation in first and second class cabins. These cabins were steam heated with individual control. Public rooms employed electric heaters, generally with decorative disguises.

Electric motors were, at the time, displacing steam engines from many duties due to their simplified power supply and control arrangements. In addition to the ventilation fans already mentioned there were two winches on the boat deck which employed electric drives for raising the lifeboats. Several electrically powered hoists made the movement of food, mail and coal easier. Galleys remained coal fired, hence the necessity for a coal hoist to supply the first class galley high up in the accommodation.

For automatic operation of the whistles during foggy conditions, an electrical system was provided with three control switches at the centre, port and starboard parts of the bridge. An additional item of electrical apparatus was the submarine signalling system. In basic terms it

consisted of microphones positioned below the waterline on port and starboard sides of the hull. Underwater bells at the approaches to Liverpool and New York could be detected by these microphones, allowing the ship's position to be easily determined during foggy conditions.

Except for the main engines, most items of engineering plant aboard *Caronia* and *Carmania* were the same. Eight double ended and five single ended scotch boilers supplied all steam at sea and in port. Steam pressure for *Caronia* was 210 psi whilst for the turbine ship it was only 195 psi. Forced draught on the Howden system applied in each case. The two elliptical funnels exhausted at a height of 135 ft above the furnace bars.

Condensing plant had to be slightly different in order to suit exhaust conditions from each type of engine. With reciprocating engines practical difficulties relating to exhaust port size prevented the employment of high vacuum in the condenser and that limited the load on air pumps, allowing them to remain engine driven. With turbines independently driven air pumps had to be employed in order to produce a high vacuum during running and prior to starting. By installing separate condensate extraction pumps it was also possible to fit recently developed Weir's regenerative condensers. In such condensers the condensate was heated by incoming exhaust steam and so it could be delivered directly to the boiler as feed.

Caronia's four crank quadruple expansion engines were the largest of that type ever fitted in a Cunard ship. All cylinders had strokes of 66 in and, from forward to aft, diameters of 39 in (HP), 110 in (LP), 77 in (second IP) and 54.5 in (first IP). Unlike with similar twin screw instal-

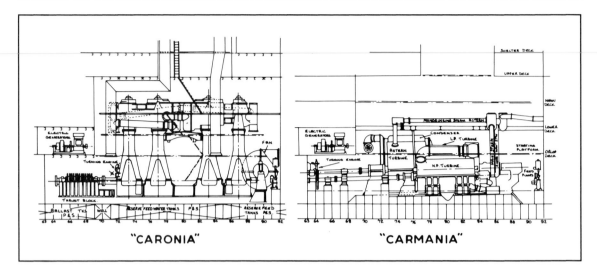

"CARONIA"   "CARMANIA"

lations of previous years, no longitudinal bulk-head divided the engine room.

Carmania's turbines occupied the same space in the engine room, but overall there was a roomier appearance due to the lower height. As with the Allan Line turbine steamers her drive employed triple screws with the centre screw being connected to the HP turbine and the two wing screws to LP turbines. Only the LP units had astern turbines. Direct connection to propellers turning at 175 rpm, compared with *Caronia*'s 80 rpm, necessitated large diameter turbine wheels in order to achieve the correct blade speed. Hollow drums, 2.5 in thick, were forged at John Brown's Sheffield works, those for the LP turbines being 11 ft diameter whilst that for the HP was 8 ft 6 in diameter. In all there were 1,115,000 blades, rotating and stationary, in the complete set of turbines.

As no turbines of the magnitude required had ever been built before, John Brown constructed an experimental three screw set which could develop 1,800 ihp. Using that test system connected to dynamos which absorbed the power, valuable information was obtained towards the design of *Carmania*'s set and those for the express Cunarders. That enterprise put the Clydebank yard well ahead of its competitors in terms of marine turbine construction.

Carmania's turbine plant showed a weight saving of some five per cent compared with that of her sister and she showed less inclination to vibrate, as well as producing a higher trials speed by nearly 1 knot. Both ships were well

Comparison of the engine spaces aboard Caronia *and* Carmania.

built and well engineered, whilst their different propulsion plants set them apart from any other class of sister ships. Unique is a word which is often overworked, but in terms of Atlantic liners it can be reasonably be used to describe *Caronia* and *Carmania*.[12]

It has been claimed that the 'pretty sisters' demonstrated the superiority of the turbine and that was why *Lusitania* and *Mauretania* were so engined, but in fact *Carmania* did not enter service until 1905 by which time a decision as to type of engines for the express ships had long been made. Long term running of *Caronia* and *Carmania* actually produced contrary evidence. Leonard Peskett, Naval Architect to the Cunard Company, drew the conclusion after eight years in service that *Carmania*'s coal consumption was considerably greater than that of *Caronia* and that service results did not warrant the adoption of direct drive turbines in ships of their type and speed.[13]

Clearly the turbine was not a universal solution and only with gearing or turbo-electric drives could propeller speeds be reduced to more effective proportions. In the meantime Cunard pressed ahead with its express liners.

In engineering respects *Lusitania* and *Mauretania* were identical vessels, although there were slight differences in terms of other fittings. Most noticeable was the absence of ventilator cowls aboard the Clyde built ship compared with her

Tyne constructed consort. These ventilator shafts served the engine and boiler rooms and the trunking was the same for both ships, it's just that John Brown seemed to prefer low housings on the deck house top to the more visually striking air scoops.

Quadruple screws had to be employed in order to obtain the desired speed, and each was directly connected to a turbine. High pressure turbines turned the wing shafts, whilst tandem low pressure units powered the inner shafts. For astern running two high pressure turbines were attached to the inner shafts. The ahead HP rotor drums were 8 ft diameter and the blades varied in length from 2.5 in to 12 in. The LP drums of 11 ft 8 in diameter contained blades ranging in length from 8 in to a remarkable 22 in. Blades on the 8 ft 8 in diameter astern drums had lengths of between 2 in and 8 in. Gradual increase in blade length was required as steam expanded across successive rows of blades on its way through the turbine. Although drum diameters were similar to those for *Carmania*'s turbines they were of greater length and contained many more blades.

Manufacture of the blades differed between the two contractors. For *Lusitania* the bronze blade material was drawn through dies in order to give the required section. Blade lengths were then caulked into slots cut in the rotor drums,

distance pieces providing necessary spacing. For longer LP blades stiffness was provided by three rows of shrouding which connected adjacent blades at three points along their lengths. Wallsend Engineering adopted a different approach in that segments of blades were constructed and these then inserted in the rotor. Blade length still had to be cut from bar, but by forming segments away from the rotor it allowed final assembly to take place much more quickly.

Steam at 195 psi came from 23 double ended and two single ended scotch boilers of the four furnace type. They all operated on Howden forced draught system with air being supplied by electrically driven fans. Four separate rooms housed the boilers, six in each except for the forward one which contained five double ended and the two single ended boilers. Bunkers occupied the space between boiler rooms and the ship's sides. That not only made full use of the sections at the side of the ship, but coal provided protection for the boilers during enemy action; these ships were, after all, built under subsidy to act as merchant cruisers. The arrangement also provided a system of longitudinal and transverse bulkhead which, Cunard considered, was best suited to its requirements for strength and safety. Coaling ports at the side of the ship also reduced the time taken in bunkering, as well as the manpower needed for trimming.[14]

At times of high output it was not only essential to keep boilers fed with coal, but also to remove ashes from the stokehold area in order

Lusitania belches black smoke during trials off the Clyde. (Glasgow University Archives with permission of Mr W. Lind.)

The majestic Aquitania. (Glasgow University Archives with permission of Mr W. Lind.)

that efficient working might proceed. Eight See's ash ejectors were fitted aboard each ship and it was only necessary for the firemen to shovel the ashes into a hopper in the stokehold after which the apparatus dealt with disposal. High velocity water jets forced the ashes clear of the ship's side some 6 ft above water level. Ash hoists were fitted for use in port as the discharge of ash into harbour waters was not permitted.

Electrical demand on the ships was high, requiring the fitting of four 375 kW Parsons turbo-generators. In addition to the expected lighting, fans, heaters and motors, electrical power also operated four cranes each capable of lifting 30 cwt. Mail, baggage and provision hoists had become common aboard large passenger mail ships, but these ships also had two passenger hoists. The first Atlantic liner to be fitted with such a convenience had been HAPAG's Harland & Wolff built *Amerika* of 1905. Additional decks increased passenger capacity, but it also made life difficult for passengers, so aboard *Lusitania* and *Mauretania* passengers could be electrically transported the 36 ft 3 in which separated the boat and main decks.

Both at their construction and subsequently much has been written about these fine ships, many contemporary journals publishing special editions. Full accounts of construction, machinery and fittings, as well as the accommodation, were provided in a 1907 special number of *The Shipbuilder*, whilst the same year *Engineering* published commemorative editions for both ships. These have been reproduced by Patrick Stephens Ltd and a complete record regarding the engineering of the ships can be found in these publications.[15]

Immediately on entry into service these 760 ft (bp) by 87 ft 6 in beam, 30,396 gross ton (30,704 gross ton for *Mauretania*) ships began to prove themselves, their 72,500 shp engines winning both ships the 'Blue Riband'. *Mauretania* proved to be marginally faster, but both ships could make crossings at almost 26 knots. A crew of 850 for only 2,140 passengers and a high coal consumption, some 1,000 tons per day for all purposes, was the price of fame. However, the Government paid much of that cost by way of its £150,000 per annum subsidy for each ship.[16]

Although the express ships were extremely popular, a need arose for the provision of a consort in order to operate a weekly schedule. Different economic criteria influenced the design as the operating subsidy only applied to *Lusitania* and *Mauretania*. Cunard alone had to finance construction and operation of the third ship and she needed to make as much profit per voyage without a subsidy as the express ships made with one. In order to allow sailings every three weeks from terminal ports, a speed of 23 knots was required, allowing some margin for delays. Such reduced speed allowed for savings on the fuel bill, but the remaining difference had to be made up by increased passenger and cargo revenue. A larger ship was required.

By a process of trial and error Cunard arrived at the approximate dimensions and proportions of a ship to achieve the desired financial return. Discussions with Lloyd's Register concerning scantlings allowed more detailed plans to be drawn up before tenders for construction were requested. Only after model tank tests by John Brown & Co during July 1910 could dimensions for the new ship be finally decided upon.[17] The Clydebank yard received the order and *Aquitania* was laid down in June 1911.

Considerably larger than her running mates, 45,647 gross tons, 868 ft long (bp) and 97 ft beam, she only required engines capable of delivering 60,000 shp; indicated power was slightly larger than that, shaft power being the useful work produced. Passenger capacity of 618 first, 614 second and 1,998 third class, with a crew of 972 illustrates the advantage of her size compared with the subsidized steamers. Choice of triple expansion direct drive turbines indicates what advances had been made in the five years since construction of *Lusitania*'s engines. As with the reciprocating engines before, movement to triple expansion turbines produced an increase in economy.

Low pressure ahead and astern turbines were fitted to the centre shafts whilst an HP ahead powered the port outer shaft and an IP turbine the starboard outer shaft. Both outer shafts also had HP astern turbines, illustrating the need for higher astern manoeuvring power with the larger ship. Design of the turbines had to be carried out very carefully in order to obtain the same power on each of the outboard shafts. A single room 84 ft long housed all main turbines. Thrust blocks fitted at the forward end of each turbine shaft had 17 collars. Construction of the turbines followed closely the form adopted for the earlier ships, but because of the lower overall power drum diameters and blade lengths

were somewhat less, however, their rotational speed of 180 rpm was the same.

A total of 21 double ended scotch boilers with eight furnaces, each having its own combustion chamber, provided steam at 195 psi. Howden forced draught applied to all boilers, which were arranged in four boiler rooms. The forward three rooms contained six boilers whilst the aftermost, separating auxiliary and refrigerating machinery spaces from the turbine room, contained the remaining three. Four funnels, one for each boiler room, of elliptical cross-section carried away flue gases. In order to preserve appearance all measured 24 ft by 17 ft, but No 4 only had three boilers to exhaust and so the remaining space could be utilized as an uptake ventilator for the turbine room. Because of her lower power, but despite greater hotel demands, *Aquitania* consumed less coal than her consorts, under 900 tons per day for all purposes.

Transverse watertight bulkheads separated the boiler rooms with longitudinal bulkheads forming the side bunker spaces. In addition coal and auxiliary machinery spaces were positioned between boiler rooms providing even greater protection in the event of one or more compartments being flooded. Longitudinal bulkheads kept wing turbine rooms apart from the centre room which contained the low pressure turbines.

With such a large ship an increased electrical demand could be expected and four Westinghouse turbo-generators were provided, giving a total capacity of 1,600 kW. In addition there was a 30 kW emergency generator driven by a 45 brake horsepower (bhp) Mirrlees diesel engine, certainly one of the first aboard an Atlantic liner. Internal combustion engines could also be found in two of the lifeboats. Fitted with the intention that they could tow the ordinary rowing lifeboats from the scene of any disaster, these boats had 30 bhp Thornycroft paraffin engines and wireless telegraphy. Even with the longitudinal and transverse watertight subdivision, Cunard appeared to be taking no chances with the safety of its passengers.[18]

Passenger comfort also came high on the list, and not only in the heating and ventilating arrangements. In order to minimize annoyance caused by rolling, *Aquitania* was provided with a Frahm anti-rolling tank located below G deck between No 2 and No 3 boiler rooms. The feature, common aboard German ships, was not new to

Cunard as the intermediate liner *Laconia*, delivered two years earlier in 1912, had been a test bed for the system.

Franconia (1911) and *Laconia* (1912) were built by Swan Hunter for Cunard's Liverpool to Boston service as well as Mediterranean cruising from American ports. These twin screw 18,100 gross ton ships only required a speed of 16.5 knots and so the owners did not consider turbine machinery to be essential. Tried and trusted four crank quadruple expansion engines, built by the Wallsend Slipway & Engineering Co, were installed. Because of the lower power requirement, some 12,000 bhp, these engines, balanced on the Yarrow–Schlick–Tweedy system, had smaller cylinder dimensions than those of *Caronia*: 33 in, 47 in, 67 in and 95 in diameter with a stroke of 60 in. The number of boilers was also less, only six double ended, 210 psi scotch boilers, working under natural draught, had to be provided. Positioning the two boiler room centres, and hence the funnels, about 90 ft apart gave a well proportioned appearance to the ships. Coal bunkers occupied the space between the boiler rooms.

In terms of the propulsion machinery these ships did not introduce any new ideas, but they did serve to show that reciprocating engines still had a part to play in powering the slower and smaller liners. Despite their size some 2,800 passengers could be accommodated, nearly 2,000 of these in third class. A 400 kW electrical

The twin screw Franconia *of 1911.* (Harry Weston Collection.)

system, supplied by three compound reciprocating engine driven dynamos, kept the ships well illuminated and powered many electric motors. Thermotank systems provided warmth throughout both ships, but heating for public rooms aboard *Laconia* was on the Nuvacuumette system, the first time it had been installed in any ship. The arrangement employed radiators through which exhaust steam from auxiliary engines flowed, thus making use of what was normally waste heat. Water condensing in the radiators was removed by means of a vacuum pump connected to the outlets from each radiator. Regulation of inlet steam came by way of a thermostatic valve set to allow steam into the radiator if the surrounding temperature fell below 60°F. By employing a vacuum in the radiator return line it was possible for steam to flow to the most distant heater and through small bore pipes. In addition leakage of water out of the system was prevented by the vacuum inside.[19]

The Frahm anti-rolling tanks which *Laconia* introduced to British shipping were a refined version of the anti-rolling tank which had been employed for *City of New York* many years earlier. Passenger discomfort through ship rolling occupied the minds of many naval architects, with long hours in design being spent on possible ways to alleviate the condition. Bilge keels could counter small angles of roll, but north Atlantic conditions generally defeated them. Only when the German inventor Dr H. Frahm devised a system for controlling movement of water in anti-rolling tanks was a satisfactory arrangement available.

It had long been understood that maximum rolling of any ship would occur when the time interval between wave crests was the same as the time for a complete roll. Under such conditions the motion of the ship lagged behind that of the wave crest by exactly one quarter of the time period for that roll—the ship would be vertical when midway between crest and trough, reaching maximum angle when on the crest or in the trough. Anti-rolling tanks employed a third oscillating system, namely water held in an enclosed tank, the first and second oscillating systems being the waves and ship.

Careful design of the tank, shaped in the form of a 'U' across the ship, allowed the time period of the water which it contained to equal the roll period of the ship. However, motion of the water lagged behind that of the ship by one quarter of the roll period and behind that of the wave by one half. Action of water in the tank thus opposed the wave action, tending to reduce the roll. Movement of water in the tanks could be regulated to some extent by means of valves in the air trunking which connected the air spaces of those tanks. With valves closed the tanks would be put out of action as water displacement could not effectively take place. Only if air could move between the upper parts of the tanks could water be displaced in the lower parts of the 'U'. With valves partly open the period of water in the tanks might be adjusted to suit that of the waves.

Laconia had two adjacent tanks occupying the lower portions of her forward cross bunker. These tanks, 23 ft 7.5 in and 15 ft 9 in long respectively, could be operated together or as individuals in order to obtain stability under

Franconia's reciprocating engines in the erecting shop.

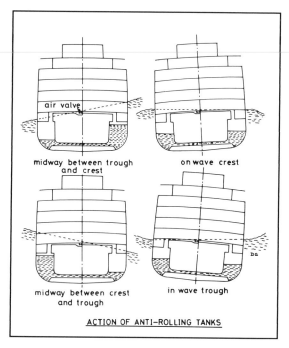

Frahm anti-rolling tanks, principle of operation.

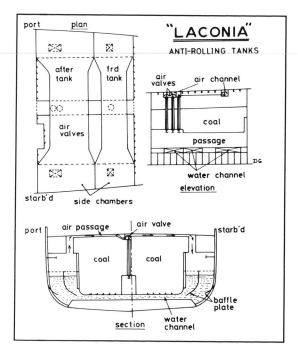

Frahm tank arrangements aboard Laconia.

various conditions. In both tanks side chambers were 12 ft 6 in wide and normally contained water to a depth of 9 ft 6 in. Because the connecting water channel could not be less than 2 ft deep it was necessary to reduce the width of the channels in order to maintain the desired water velocity. Air valves of 20 in diameter had to be employed so that air flow did not become restricted.[20]

Although these tanks reduced *Laconia*'s effective carrying capacity they did prove to be most useful in countering the effects of rolling. Reduction in rolling amplitudes averaged at 60 per cent during a series of trials and the results

encouraged adoption of the system aboard *Aquitania*.[21] With such large beam ships the amount by which passengers were vertically displaced whenever the ship rolled became appreciable and increased the discomfort. Unfortunately no results for the system installed in *Aquitania* were ever released by Cunard and it is unlikely that the arrangements turned out to be successful. The tanks remained, but following conversion to oil firing became part of the fuel oil bunker system.[22] No other British Atlantic liner was fitted with Frahm tanks but the practice persisted aboard German vessels, Blohm & Voss of Hamburg holding the Frahm patent rights.

CHAPTER 7

The Big Ships

During the early years of the twentieth century most shipping companies still relied upon shipbuilders for help and advice when it came to deciding the type of machinery for particular vessels. Indeed that situation prevailed until the end of their existence as far as many liner companies were concerned. The close association existing between Harland & Wolff and White Star resulted in the Belfast concern being given very much a free rein when it came to ship design and machinery installation. Harlands had similar understandings with its other 'privileged' clients and always produced ships of the highest quality.

Notwithstanding the fact that its reciprocating engines were a match for any then being built, Harland & Wolff could not close its eyes to the steam turbine, but it had no access to that technology. However, unlike John Brown, Harlands did not have any immediate need to invest in turbine construction. With a White Star order for two 14,900 gross ton liners in 1907 that need arose. *Carmania* had proved that a direct drive turbine installation was not then suitable for a ship of its size and speed.[1] However, turbines did have advantages over reciprocating engines where low steam pressures existed and so Harlands' engineers decided to develop a hybrid system employing steam reciprocating engines and a low pressure exhaust turbine. A comparative trial with two otherwise identical ships was considered to be prudent. Like Cunard's 'pretty sisters', only one of the ships, *Laurentic*, would have the new machinery system, the other, *Megantic*, being provided with quadruple expansion engines. As with the Cunard pair these ships were to provide data for engining of larger and more powerful vessels.

In order to gain access to turbine technology Lord Pirrie offered a merger between Harlands and John Brown which the Clydebank yard eagerly accepted. Browns purchased a major stake in Harlands and as part of the agreement undertook to share its turbine technology as well as provide any necessary parts. *Laurentic*'s low pressure turbine was immediately subcontracted to John Brown & Co.[2]

Both ships, for the newly acquired Canadian service, were identical apart from machinery. Their size, 550 ft (bp) long and 67 ft beam, provided space for 260 first, 430 second and 1,000 third class passengers, as well as a large amount of general and refrigerated cargo. Although accommodation could compete in opulence with any of the day and, by now standard, features such as electric lifts had been provided, it was the machinery which attracted attention amongst the shipping fraternity. A speed of 16.5 knots had been specified.

Megantic's plant consised of two four crank quadruple expansion engines driving twin screws. Cylinders 29 in, 42 in, 61 in and 87 in, all with 60 in strokes, worked at an inlet steam pressure of 215 psi to develop some 10,000 ihp. That steam came from six double ended scotch boilers, 19 ft long by 15 ft 6 in diameter, each containing six corrugated flues. All boilers exhausted through a single funnel which had an insulating air space surrounding the flue. An identical steam system applied to *Laurentic*.

In order to employ low pressure steam in a turbine it was necessary to adopt a triple screw arrangement for *Laurentic*. Two four crank triple expansion engines turned the outer propellers whilst the low pressure turbine powered the one in the centre. In contrast with *Megantic*'s engines these had HP cylinders of 30 in diameter, IP cylinders 46 in diameter and two 53 in diameter LP cylinders, all with 54 in stroke. Although the HP diameter was somewhat larger than in *Megantic*'s engines, the smaller stroke meant that less steam was employed and the power developed amounted to 3,600 ihp at 81 rpm. Both engines fed steam to the exhaust turbine capable of generating some 3,300 shp at 235 rpm.[3]

Although these ships were as much a test-bed for two different engine systems as *Carmania* and *Caronia* they did not receive the same attention. Both ships entered service during 1909 and comparative data on performance must have been obtained but little was published, even notable journals such as *The Engineer* and *The Shipbuilder* being unable to obtain any figures. Unofficially it was believed that coal consumption for *Laurentic* was about 12 to 15 per cent less than that of her sister.[4] The fact that such a propulsive system was adopted for the larger 'Olympic' class ships would lend credence to the figures.

The hybrid arrangement had considerable merit, at least at the time. It allowed steam to be expanded to a lower pressure than was possible with a straight reciprocating engine installation, thereby improving overall fuel economy. At slower ship speeds the reciprocating engine was more effective than the direct drive turbine as the propeller turned more slowly. Of equal importance was the fact that a reciprocating engine could be directly reversed whereas the turbine needed separate astern wheels which produced a windage loss whilst going ahead. Harlands' hybrid system only used an ahead turbine, reversing being accomplished by means of the reciprocating engines alone.[5]

When Ismay placed the order for *Laurentic* and *Megantic* he also informed Harlands that White Star would soon be in a position to order two 46,000 gross ton ships intended to compete with *Lusitania* and *Mauretania*.[6] Naturally the Belfast yard won the contract and almost as naturally the machinery decided upon was an enlarged version of that installed in *Laurentic*.

Olympic and *Titanic* were essentially the same design although the latter proved to be slightly larger. A sister ship, ordered later and called

Olympic. (Harry Weston Collection.)

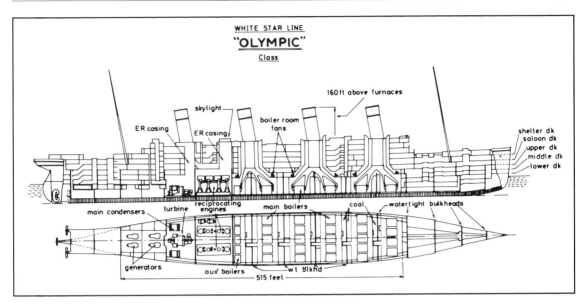

WHITE STAR LINE
"OLYMPIC"
Class

160ft above furnaces

skylight

ER casing

ER casing

boiler room
fans

shelter dk
saloon dk
upper dk
middle dk
lower dk

main condensers   turbine   reciprocating   main boilers   coal   watertight bulkheads
                              engines

generators

aux boilers   wt Blkhd
            515 feet

Machinery layout for White Star's 'Olympic' class.

Britannic, was larger still. These 850 ft long (bp) by 92 ft 6 in beam ships were never intended to compete with the express Cunarders in terms of speed, only in quality of service. With White Star being under American control no building or operating subsidy could be expected and so the owner had to provide all finance. To drive ships of such size through the water at speeds of 26 knots would result in coal consumption way beyond economic sense. A service speed no greater than 21.5 knots need be provided in order to allow for weekly sailings from three ships.

Without doubt *Olympic* and *Titanic* were large and spectacular ships, in turn the biggest in the world upon entry into service, but from a marine engineering viewpoint their propulsion plant was a blind alley, an interesting system destined to become quickly obsolete. That does not, however, detract from the designers' ability nor the skill of the craftsmen who fashioned the metal, it merely illustrates the technological advances to be brought about by introduction of the turbine. At the time, however, there appeared to be little choice as a full direct drive turbine installation was uneconomic both for the owner who had to foot the fuel bill and, to a great extent, for the builder whose engine plant was fully equipped for reciprocating engine construction. In operational terms the installation

devised by Harlands was almost as economic on fuel as that fitted in *Aquitania*, 1.4 lb of coal/shp/hr for all purposes, compared with 1.38 lb/shp/hr for the Cunarder. The high speed *Lusitania* and her sister averaged 1.43 lb/shp/hr.[7]

In order to maintain an engine output of 56,000 hp it was necessary to provide an abundant steam supply, some 700,000 lb/hr. The ships had 24 double ended and five single ended boilers, located in six separate boiler rooms. These produced steam at 215 psi. All boilers were 15 ft 9 in diameter, the double ended being 21 ft long and the single ended 11 ft 9 in. White Star preferred forced ventilation to forced draught and so air supply came by way of two electrically driven fans for each boiler room. Unlike the Cunard ships, *Olympic*'s and *Titanic*'s boiler rooms extended to the ship sides.

Bunkers were positioned transversely between the boiler rooms and also in 'tween deck spaces at the ships' sides just above the boilers. Stokers only obtained coal from the cross bunkers immediately opposite the furnaces, coal in the 'tween decks feeding into those cross bunkers. As each cross bunker, and associated 'tween deck, carried sufficient coal for its set of boilers, each bunker could be an isolated unit. There was, therefore, no necessity for watertight doors in the bunker ends, but such doors had to be provided in the transverse watertight bulkheads to allow connection between the boiler rooms.

In concept the plant for *Olympic* and *Titanic* followed that for *Laurentic*, but on a much bigger scale. Each reciprocating engine had been designed for balance on the Yarrow–Schlick–Tweedy system with cylinders 54 in, 84 in, 97 in and 97 in diameter for a 75 in stroke. Designed for an output of 15,000 shp at 75 rpm, each engine could produce much more. On trials *Olympic*'s port and starboard engines developed 18,700 ihp and 18,900 ihp at 78 rpm and 79.3 rpm respectively. Inlet steam pressure of 215 psi fell to 9 psi absolute at exhaust, less than atmospheric pressure.

At such conditions the steam entered the low pressure turbine whilst going ahead, but if running astern the steam passed directly to the condensers. Energy in the steam was lost, but that arrangement removed any necessity for an astern turbine thus simplifying the system and reducing its cost. Even so, large and expensive components had to be employed. Massive change-over valves directed steam from both reciprocating engines to the turbines when running ahead, but to the condenser whilst running astern. The operation was automatic and by hydraulic means actuated through the same linkage which reversed the engine valves. A strainer fitted in the steam line prior to the turbine removed water droplets which otherwise might have caused damage to turbine blades.

Parsons' reaction design had been chosen for the turbine which, because of the amount and low pressure of steam involved, was of massive proportions. A rotor drum 12 ft diameter and 13 ft 8 in long contained blades which varied in length from 18 in to 25 in. John Brown & Co constructed turbines for the first two ships, but Harlands designed and manufactured that for *Britannic*. Similar in form to those built at Clydebank, *Britannic*'s turbine was slightly larger and more powerful. With a bladed rotor weighing 155 tons the unit was the largest marine turbine ever made, although by no means the most powerful. Some 18,500 shp could be developed at 169 rpm. A measure of the size of that low pressure system may be gathered from the fact that electrically operated sluice valves which connected the turbine to its condensers had a clear opening of 10 ft 6 in by 8 ft 6 in. Overall the plant was engineering on a massive scale, but the balance was precise and the performance unequalled by any ship afloat.

In comparison the remaining plant might be classed as fairly ordinary, except that for ships of such size there was plenty of it. Four steam reciprocating engine driven generators of 400 kW capacity provided electrical power at 100 volts. W.H. Allen & Son of Bedford provided the generators which were situated in their own watertight compartment aft of the turbine room. Two 30 kW auxiliary generating sets, also powered by steam reciprocating engines, had their own room within the engine casing on the saloon deck.[8] It was this plant that *Titanic*'s courageous engineers fought bravely to keep operational whilst others evacuated the stricken liner. As successive boiler rooms became flooded their rearguard action maintained lighting until the very end, both of the ship and their own lives.

Little further needs to be said about that tragedy which need never, and should never, have happened. By the merest of chances a slight scrape against an iceberg sheared rivets and sprung plates just in the wrong places. Any other form of impact and the ship could have survived, but there should never have been an impact had those in positions of responsibility acted competently. Innocent people and brave men died not because of machinery failure, but because of human failure.

Britannic never entered Atlantic passenger service, becoming victim of human conflict in the Mediterranean during 1916. Only *Olympic* carried the torch for a proud trio. These ships were not, however, the only vessels to employ this hybrid propulsion system, but they were the largest. *Justicia*, a 32,000 gross ton 18 knot vessel originally intended for Holland America Line as *Statendam*, had been launched during 1914 but war prevented completion as originally planned. Her machinery developed about 20,000 shp, but German torpedoes ended a brief career in 1918.

The only other Atlantic steamers of any note with Harlands' hybrid propulsion system were Red Star Line's *Belgenland* and White Star's second *Laurentic*. *Laurentic*'s only claim to fame lay in the fact that she was the final Atlantic passenger liner to have either reciprocating engines or be coal fired, a classic anachronism when she entered service during 1927. The reasoning behind the choice of such an outdated plant cannot easily be explained, and nobody made any real attempt to do so at the time. It was claimed that coal firing provided some degree of safeguard against an oil shortage, oil firing then being the norm for passenger tonnage. That might reasonably have been true, but no oil shortage had been promised or expected. Geared turbines easily outperformed any reciprocating plant then available so the choice of such a hybrid could not be readily explained. It is even more difficult to explain when consideration is given to the fact that the boilers produced superheated steam which suited turbines admirably.[9] At the time Harlands were enjoying great success with diesel engines and the choice of that system would have made more sense.

Belgenland was also somewhat out of place in that she did not enter Atlantic passenger service until 1923, having been laid down in 1914. Ordered by the Red Star Line, part of J.P. Morgan's International Mercantile Marine combine, the ship became caught up in the First World War and, in partially completed condition, was turned over to White Star to operate as a cargo and troop carrier under the name *Belgic*. Cessation of hostilities saw her once more at Belfast where, in late 1920, work commenced on completion as originally intended. In engineering terms there were few changes, but the accommodation was organized to suit the 1920s rather than 1914. Provision of a third, dummy,

Machinery layout aboard the Red Star steamer Belgenland.

funnel to act as an engine room vent greatly improved her profile.

One significant change came about through the introduction of oil firing to replace her coal burning equipment. Oil burning had shown itself to be both economical and convenient during the recently ended conflict and its use quickly spread to merchant ships. That applied especially to passenger liners, where the inconvenience of coal dust during bunkering caused cleaning problems. Ten double ended scotch boilers as originally fitted were retained, these were of the same diameter as those fitted in the 'Olympic' class vessels but had a length 1 ft shorter. Boiler pressure remained the same at 215 psi. Even when converted to oil burning the assisted draught arrangement employing eight electrically driven fans was retained.

Consequent upon the change to oil it became necessary to fit a more effective fire fighting system in the boiler rooms. Oil with a flash point of 240°F and at a pressure of 80 psi had to be treated with caution, early extinguishing of any conflagration being essential. Each boiler room contained a Foamite patent fire extinguishing system consisting of two large foam storage tanks, the foam being discharged by means of air pressure from a pressurized line. Auxiliary units containing 34 gallons of foam were also provided in each stokehold, these being discharged by steam at 100 psi. A coal fire

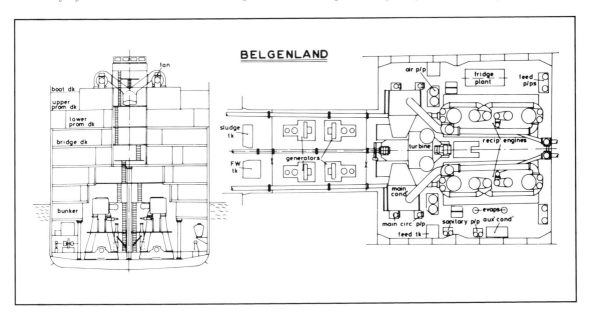

Cleaning the tubes of Belgenland's *No 8 boiler. The twisted strips are 'retarders' fitted in the tubes to promote better efficiency.*

could be extinguished by means of water, which aboard ship was in plentiful supply, but such action with an oil fire would be disastrous as burning oil would simply float on the water. Foam, with its smothering effect, provided an ideal solution.

The 27,150 gross ton *Belgenland* had been designed for a service speed of about 18 knots and so her machinery could be moderately powered compared with that of *Olympic*. Each reciprocating engine of cylinder dimensions 35.5 in, 56 in, 64 in and 64 in by 60 in stroke could develop some 5,600 ihp with the low pressure turbine producing a further 6,000 shp. In effect the plant was but a scaled down version of that fitted in the White Star ships, the turbine rotor being but 11 ft diameter and weighing only 56 tons. The same applied to auxiliary machinery such as electrical generators, where four Allen generating sets could meet a total demand of 1,200 kW at the 100 volts which Harlands seemed to prefer for its passenger vessels.

An interesting, though less attractive, item of auxiliary equipment was the sewage unit. Dis-

charge overboard of solid waste from lavatories had been by means of gravity since they had first been installed in ships and the system worked effectively, until pollution controls came into force more recently. Large passenger ships presented problems in terms of discharge quantity but no real difficulties until cabins were placed low down near the water level.

In order to avoid any problems the waste from all lavatories discharged into sludge tanks positioned in various places throughout the machinery spaces. Periodically a valve at the bottom of the tank would be opened to discharge sludge into an ejector chamber positioned below the tank. With the chamber full and further inlet of sludge shut off, a float in the chamber opened a valve connected to an air reservoir. High pressure air then forced the entire contents of the ejector overboard. Repeated operation completely emptied the sludge tanks. The system not only allowed for effective operation of lavatories placed low down in the ship, but it also reduced the number of overboard discharge connections.[10]

National aspirations of France and Germany for eminence on the Atlantic also found an outlet in development of turbine propulsion, but it was the French who embraced that technology first. Size had become synonymous with prestige and big ships became the order of the day during those years preceding the First World War. But large ships also illustrated economy of scale as increased numbers of passengers could be carried and the mass emigration market had to be satisfied as well as the general traffic.

In 1909 the French Line ordered a 23,650 gross ton ship from Chantiers de l'Atlantique of St Nazaire. *France* was the largest ship that concern had ever owned and, with a service speed of 23.5 knots, the fastest vessel on the Atlantic with the exception of *Lusitania* and *Mauretania*. As was the case for the Cunard pair, direct drive turbines provided the only realistic method of propulsion, but the installation differed somewhat. Instead of just high and low pressure tur-

Sectional views of the French Line turbine ship France *(1912).*

bines triple expansion was employed, for the first time in an Atlantic steamer. Both inboard shafts connected with low pressure Parsons turbines, but in separate compartments high and intermediate pressure turbines powered the port and starboard wing shafts respectively. These wing shafts also had HP astern turbines whilst the inner shafts employed LP turbines for going astern. All shafts rotated at 250 rpm driving four bladed propellers of 12 ft 6 in diameter and 11 ft 10 in pitch. During a 24 hour continuous trial the ship maintained a speed of 25 knots from an output of 47,000 shp, but for normal service only 45,000 shp was required.

Despite the triple expansion, steam pressure of only 200 psi had been provided, supply coming from 11 double ended and eight single ended scotch type boilers employing Howden forced draught. These boilers occupied four boiler rooms, each of which was provided with a funnel for exhaust. Coal consumption tests carried out during trials indicated that the service consumption should be below the expected 1.3 lb/shp/hr, a very acceptable figure for the time and better than that of Cunard's express ships.

There were 14 transverse watertight bulkheads, and the watertight doors could be operated from the bridge as well as locally. Should any

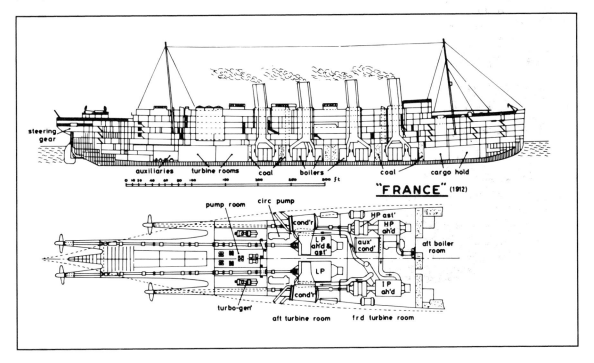

No 1 stokehold of the coal fired France. (Harry Weston Collection.)

compartment become flooded seven pumps, having a total capacity of 2,500 tons per hour, were provided for water removal.

An interesting feature of the ship related to its electrical installation, where separate systems applied to the engine room and passenger spaces. Turbo-generators for engine room electrical supply were located in a watertight compartment just aft of the turbine rooms, but those for accommodation lighting and passenger services occupied a compartment on F deck above the forward turbine room.[11] Positioning of some generators above the waterline had advantages

should flooding of machinery spaces occur, but there would need to be some connecting circuits allowing emergency engine room lighting, at least, to be powered by the passenger system.

Germany's challenge came by way of Hamburg American Line's managing director Albert Ballin. He reasoned that if big ships could carry large numbers of passengers more economically than smaller ships, then giant vessels would show even better results. Doubling the size more than doubled passenger capacity but for the same speed the power, and hence fuel consumption, increased by less than 60 per cent. Some 70 years earlier Brunel had provided similar arguments regarding his paddle steamer *Great Western*, but Ballin's ships would be giants of around 50,000 gross tons.

Ballin professed to be disinterested in the 'Blue Riband' but his ships had to be reasonably fast in order to achieve satisfactory crossing times. They needed to be capable of crossing in under six days in order to attract passengers and so a speed of 22.5 knots appeared to be the most suitable. That order of speed with such large ships required massive power, some 62,000 shp in the case of the first vessel, *Imperator*. Much to the annoyance of Blohm & Voss of Hamburg, HAPAG placed the order with the Vulcan shipyard but that was tempered by the fact that Vulcan had to suffer the early problems associated with such large construction. In addition Blohm & Voss owned the only floating dock capable of lifting ships of 50,000 tons and so Vulcan had to make use of its rival's facilities. Hermann Voss was keen to secure contracts for subsequent ships, as prestige of large ships lay not only with the owner but also the builder, but Ballin was a shrewd businessman. He only sanctioned construction of the second giant, *Vaterland*, by Blohm & Voss if that yard dropped a legal suit concerning reconstruction of a smaller ship, *Patagonia*.[12]

In terms of construction *Imperator* provided the best in safety features. A double watertight skin ran around the ship from double bottom level to a point above the waterline. In addition wing coal bunkers protected the boiler rooms as in *Lusitania*. Transverse bulkheads formed 13 transverse watertight compartments, whilst further longitudinal bulkheads split up the engine compartments. Access between compartments was provided by 36 watertight doors hydraulically actuated and electrically controlled from the bridge employing a system developed by Stone-Lloyd. Doors could be closed or opened, together or separately, from the bridge but local control by means of a lever enabled individual doors to be operated whenever necessary. Gongs at each door signalled that it was closing. The hydraulic force was sufficient to crush any lumps of coal, which was essential for bunker doors.

With the *Titanic* disaster still firmly in mind, Ballin insisted upon sufficient lifeboats for all

on board, 5,227 souls at full capacity. When *Imperator* commenced service during 1913 she carried 83 lifeboats, two of which were motor driven, with a capacity for 5,500 people.[13]

Direct drive turbines provided the only feasible means of propelling the ship, but they differed somewhat from the conventional passenger ship form of the time. Triple expansion Parsons turbines were employed, there being two LP turbines connected to outboard shafts, an IP to the starboard centre shaft and an HP to the port centre. For astern running, HP turbines turned the centre shafts and LP units the wings; astern output amounted to 35,000 shp. In total the turbines contained some 760,000 bronze blades. For normal operation steam was admitted to the HP stage which exhausted to the IP, that in turn exhausting to both LP turbines. Should maximum power have been required it was possible to supply high pressure steam to both HP and IP stages directly, thus treating the IP as another HP stage, allowing each turbine to exhaust to an LP unit on its side of the ship. In that way the machinery on each side could be worked independently.

Boiler plant also proved to be innovative in that water tube boilers had been specified, no less than 46 in number. Arranged in four separate rooms, each 75 ft long, these Yarrow type boilers had been provided with Howden forced draught and could generate steam from a total grate area of 3,760 sq ft and water heating area amounting to 203,000 sq ft. Steam pressure for normal working was 235 psi.[14]

The use of water tube boilers provided a larger heating surface and so allowed for more rapid steam generation, but coal firing remained a limiting factor. If coal could not be brought to the boilers quickly enough and firemen could not shovel coal fast enough, then steam generation rate reduced and maximum power could not be achieved.

Imperator, 909 ft long overall by 98 ft beam and 52,117 gross tons, and her sister from Blohm & Voss *Vaterland*, 950 ft by 100 ft beam and 54,300 gross tons, were practically identical as far as machinery was concerned. The larger ship had a slightly higher speed of 23 knots which her designer, Dr Foerster, attributed to improved lines below water at the stern. In fact the turbines were more powerful, being capable of developing 65,000 shp. Five turbo-generators,

Above *'Imperator' class ship, White Star's* Majestic. (G. Charles Collection.)

Below Majestic*'s main turbine control platform.* (Harry Weston Collection.)

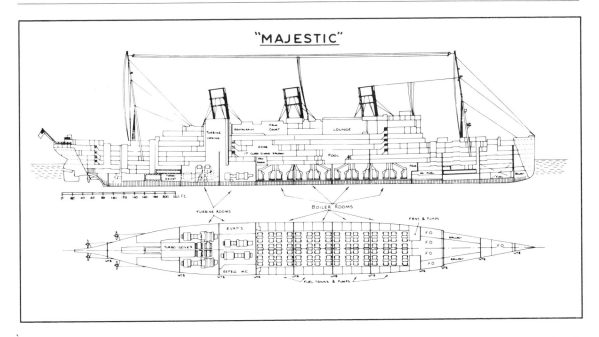

Majestic's machinery layout diagram.

occupying their own room aft of the turbines, supplied power to the 110 volt electrical system whilst an emergency dynamo, powered by a petrol engine, occupied a position on the boat deck.[15] Both forward funnels provided uptakes for the boilers whilst the after funnel merely acted as an engine room ventilator, three steam engine driven fans drawing air from an intake at the funnel base.

Blohm & Voss were fortunate in not constructing the first of Ballin's trio, for *Imperator* actually made a loss for the Vulcan shipyard. The ship was also uncomfortable in that she rolled excessively in all but the calmest of seas. It is certain that such propensity to roll resulted from too much weight being located in her superstructure and early action was required to reduce the conditions. Her funnels had 9 ft removed from them and most upper deck panels were replaced by lighter sections. In addition a considerable weight of cement had to be poured into the bottom of the ship. The order for *Vaterland* went to Blohm & Voss who made several changes in the basic design. These included installation of Frahm anti-rolling tanks, but that was not in response to *Imperator's* problems as the design had been finalized before they became apparent.

A further significant change in design related to boiler exhaust trunking. Instead of passing straight up the centre of the superstructure to the funnel, Blohm & Voss adopted a split uptake formation. That arrangement, it was claimed, improved boiler room ventilation as well as freeing the central section of the ship from obstructions. In order to avoid high accommodation temperatures due to the uptakes, air shafts for boiler room supply surrounded the uptakes, that practice being common on many single uptake ships.

The final part of Ballin's trilogy was *Bismarck*, largest and fastest of the three, but the First World War destroyed his dream. *Imperator* became Cunard's *Berengaria*, *Vaterland* the American *Leviathan* and the then unnamed *Bismarck* eventually saw service under the White Star house flag as *Majestic*. Although launched in 1914 the ship did not enter service until 1922, for even after hostilities ceased shortage of materials and uncertainties regarding her future prevented completion. Eventually White Star purchased the unfinished *Bismarck* from the War Reparations Commission and work commenced on her completion at the Blohm & Voss yard with local workers under the supervision of a special staff from Harland & Wolff.

At 56,550 gross tons, 915 ft (bp) and 100 ft beam, *Majestic* was the largest ship in the world and remained so for many years. The split uptake arrangement had been incorporated but the original design called for more powerful turbines. The HP unit was of combined impulse and reaction type with impulse Curtis wheels being fitted before the Parsons reaction blading. That high pressure turbine powered the port inner shaft with an intermediate pressure unit on the starboard inner shaft and low pressure turbines on both outer shafts, just as in the other ships. Output power for normal running amounted to 66,000 shp going ahead and 35,000 shp astern. During delivery from Cuxhaven to Southampton *Majestic*'s turbines developed 70,000 shp, producing a speed of 25 knots.

That higher power required more steam and an additional two Yarrow water tube boilers had to be provided. Although coal firing had originally been part of the design, delayed completion meant that oil firing could be employed from

Left *The business end of a German giant. An 'Imperator' class ship in drydock.* (Harry Weston Collection.)

Right *Divided uptake arrangements.*

Right *Position of cracking aboard* Majestic *and* Leviathan.

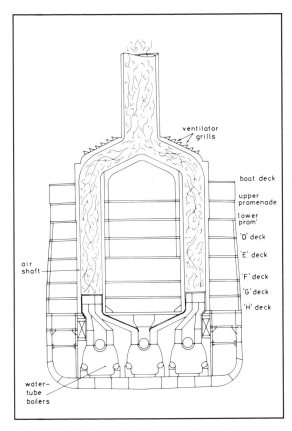

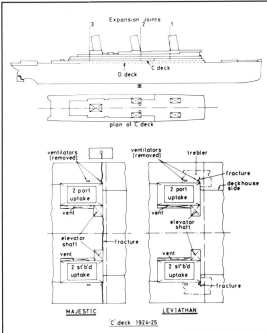

'C' deck 1924-25

new thus avoiding costly conversion. Like her Blohm & Voss sister, *Majestic* had been provided with Frahm anti-rolling tanks and these were retained, unlike those aboard *Aquitania* which became part of the fuel oil storage system.[16]

Although the idea of split uptakes presented attractive possibilities as far as accommodation layout was concerned it did cause major structural problems for both ships. At the end of her 1924 season an inspection of *Majestic* indicated severe cracking of C deck in way of No 2 uptake. A crack extended completely across the deck and down the port hull plating to the first portlight. An immediate inspection of *Leviathan* indicated cracking in the same region, though it was not nearly so extensive.

Strengthening by means of doubling and trebler plates was authorized in both ships, together with elimination of some ventilators in the vicinity. At the time it was considered that fracture had resulted from defective and insufficient material in the region but subsequent events gave reason for re-examination. Five years later much more severe cracking was discovered on *Leviathan*'s C deck, this time in way of No 1 and No 2 uptakes.

Each pair of uptakes was positioned close to an expansion joint in the superstructure, No 2 uptake also having elevator shafts and stairwells nearby. Whenever a ship hogs or sags, bending stresses are transmitted to the superstructure built above the main strength deck and those stresses will be higher than that in the strength deck due to the superstructure height. Compressive stress is relieved by buckling, but that results in creaking of the superstructure. Tensile stress causes cracking and that led to the introduction of expansion joints. In effect deck and casing sides were cut through above the strength deck, sliding covers being provided at the gap. Bending of the ship in a seaway would, therefore, be accommodated by that gap in the superstructure, resulting in an absence of bending stress. That, at least, was the theory but sometimes the designer's calculations proved to be inexact and cracking still occurred.

Cracks in C deck of *Majestic* and *Leviathan* were basically due to fatigue resulting from high tensile stress which the expansion joints should have prevented. Holes in the deck, for uptakes, elevator shafts and so on, served to weaken the deck plating and act as stress raisers, thus

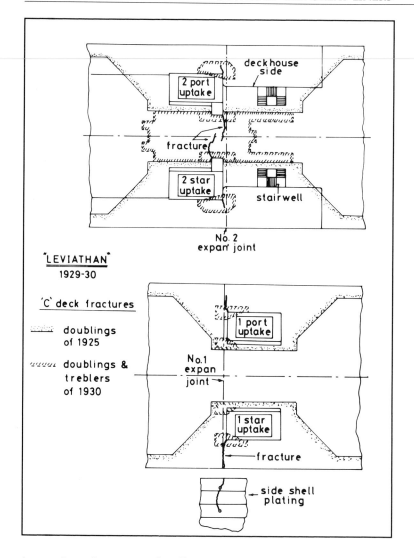

Diagram of Leviathan's *C deck fractures of 1929.*

deck house side

2 port uptake

fracture

2 star uptake

stairwell

No. 2 expan' joint

'LEVIATHAN'
1929-30

'C' deck fractures

doublings
of 1925

doublings &
treblers
of 1930

1 port uptake

No.1
expan
joint

1 star uptake

fracture

side shell plating

increasing the stress locally. Fatigue cracks started at the corners of these holes and gradually spread across the deck. Those cracks near *Leviathan*'s forward uptakes were also due to fatigue, that on the port side also extending down two strakes of shell plating.

Analysis in 1930 concluded that there was no real deficiency in steel quality, the fundamental defect lay in design of the ships. In effect the hull and superstructure had been designed incorrectly, resulting in much higher stresses being induced during hogging and sagging than the weakened deck could withstand.[17] *Berengaria* (*Imperator*) did not suffer the same problem as her decks had not been weakened by the twin

uptakes. It would appear that similar strengths had been assumed for the two later ships as had been determined for *Imperator*. That should not have been the case and it was not repeated when similar split uptakes were employed for *Bremen* and *Europa*.

Although *Majestic* did not enter service until 1922 and the other two Ballin giants performed most of their service under post-war ownership, they were all effectively of 1910 design. Magnificent ships on a grand scale which did not suit post-war conditions, they became something of an anachronism. Human conflict had deprived Ballin of glory and his ships of their true place in maritime history. Employment of such an array of water tube boilers and split uptakes was novel as far as contemporary marine engineering was concerned.

Although the big ships dominated those immediate pre-war years other liners were also under construction for less glamorous duties. Canadian Pacific Railways commenced Atlantic steamship operations during the early years of the century and offered a rival service to that of the long established Allan Line. Introduction of the Fairfield built *Empress of Britain* and *Empress of Ireland* in 1906 marked a move into large and fast tonnage. These 18.5 knot ships were the last high speed Atlantic vessels ordered by a British owner to be fitted solely with reciprocating engines. They were not, however, the last British owned Atlantic liners to be fitted with such engines, that honour falling to Furness Warren's 6,800 gross ton *Newfoundland* and *Nova Scotia* of 1925 and 1926 respectively.

Canadian Pacific did build two of the last large reciprocating engined ships for Atlantic service, *Metagama* and *Missanabie* being ordered from Barclay, Curle for delivery in 1915. These ships marked the major change from reciprocating to turbine machinery and they are worthy of consideration as being last of a long line.

The Canadian run did not demand vessels of such high speed as that to New York, competition being less severe. In addition a smaller number of passengers could be expected resulting in the need for ships of lower tonnage. Allan Line had fostered the Canadian trade and its ships gradually increased in size over the years, but there was little necessity for anything above 15,000 gross tons until the immediate pre-war years. *Metagama* and *Missanabie* were designed to cater for the lower end of the market, with accommodation for 520 cabin and 1,200 third class passengers. Design speed was a modest 16 knots. Although aimed at a poorer class of passenger, these 12,469 gross ton ships had accommodation of high standard and amenities matched those of the best Atlantic liners.

In order that they might negotiate ice, which abounded in Canadian waters for periods of the operating season, the hulls were strengthened. Unlike most other ships of the period they had cruiser sterns, a feature which applied to later Canadian Pacific ships. A system of portable passenger berths was installed in third class accommodation, allowing the number of berths

provided to suit bookings, any spare capacity then being made over to cargo. Other third class features such as dining rooms, smoking room, lounge and hospital had more permanent installation.

Three systems of heating and ventilation were used throughout passenger and crew spaces, with the main supply of heated air coming from the Thermotank system which could maintain 65°F even in the coldest of conditions. Radiators, through which live or exhaust steam at 5 psi circulated, provided local heating in public rooms and were individually adjustable. An additional air circulation and extraction system also extended throughout the ship, with a capacity to ensure eight changes of air per hour in the dining saloons, six changes in the galley spaces and 1,000 cubic ft per hour in the living spaces. The arrangements appear to have exhibited something of an 'overkill' but the provision of suitable heating and ventilation in cold Canadian waters during winter months was a necessity for passenger comfort.

Both ships entered service shortly after the *Titanic* disaster and barely a year after Canadian Pacific's own *Empress of Ireland* sank within minutes following collision with the Norwegian collier *Storstad*. That incident in thick fog during a St Lawrence passage claimed the lives of 840 passengers, 80 per cent of those on board, and 172 of the 420 crew. Again the incident was one of neglect. *Storstad* was held responsible for the incident, but the *Empress*'s master did not order watertight doors to be closed whilst in the fog and that contributed to the rapidity with which the vessel sank. As a consequence of these incidents *Metagama* and her sister were provided with 32 lifeboats, one driven by a motor, providing space for everybody likely to be on board. All boats were of wood, no collapsible type being fitted.

Electric current for lighting, employing some 1,500 lamps, was supplied by three Siemens' dynamos each capable of generating 100 kW at 100 volts. De Laval turbines geared down from 15,000 rpm to 1,050 rpm provided the power for the dynamos. Electricity also operated various items of galley equipment as well as ventilation and Howden forced draught boiler fans.

Each of the twin screws was driven by a four cylinder, four crank, quadruple expansion engine balanced on the Yarrow–Schlick–Tweedy system.

Above *Canadian Pacific steamship* Metagama. (CP Rail Archives.)

Cylinders of 26 in, 37.5 in, 53.5 in and 77 in diameter worked with a stroke of 51 in, the engine employing steam at 215 psi. There was nothing of significance about the engines apart from the fact that they represented the end of an era as far as Atlantic liner propulsion was concerned. The same could also be said for the boiler plant which employed eight single ended scotch boilers of 15 ft 9 in diameter and 11 ft 9 in long. That diameter was almost standard for boilers of this type during the final years of their general use in passenger ships. Howden hot air forced draught using four fans applied, two in each boiler room. In each of these rooms boilers were placed two abreast with furnaces facing to give a single stokehold. Bunkers occupied space at the ship sides as well as between the forward boiler room and No 4 hold.[18]

In comparison with the express liners boiler and engine plant occupied relatively little space aboard these ships, illustrating most effectively the price paid for speed in terms of portion of the ship employed. With a crew of 300 officers and ratings, the vessels carried over 2,000 people but also had space for 400,000 cubic ft of cargo. An effective and efficient ship operating policy had to consider passenger and cargo capacity in order to maximize return on investment. Speed dictated not only an ability to attract certain classes of passenger but also the length of voyage and hence the number of voyages in any year. In turn time to load and discharge cargo had to be taken into account, passenger movement being much faster than cargo. For large express liners one factor which dictated duration of time in port was the loading of bunkers. Passengers, mail, cargo and stores could all be dealt with in less time than it took for bunkering. *Lusitania* and *Mauretania* stowed over 6,000 tons of coal and whilst the whole amount would not need to be taken aboard after each crossing, the figure would be close.[19]

It is not surprising, therefore, that oil became an attractive alternative to coal. Fewer people were required to operate the ship and it could be loaded much faster. Other advantages of oil compared with coal almost paled into insignificance compared with this all important factor.

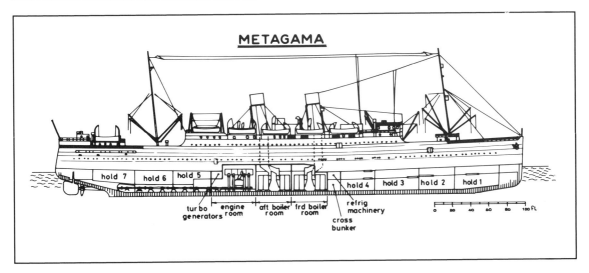

METAGAMA

turbo generators · engine room · aft boiler room · frd boiler room · refrig machinery · cross bunker

hold 7 · hold 6 · hold 5 · hold 4 · hold 3 · hold 2 · hold 1

0 20 40 60 80 100 FL

Above *Sectional views of Metagama.*

Below *One of Metagama's quadruple expansion engines.*

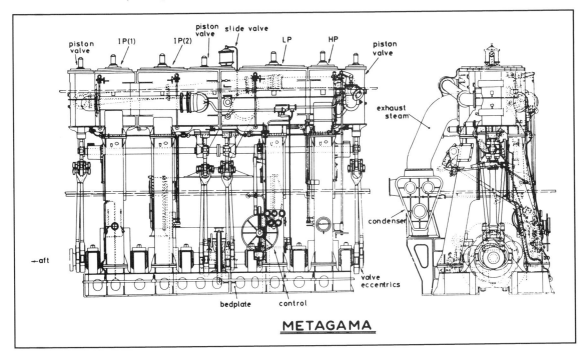

piston valve · 1P(1) · piston valve · 1P(2) · slide valve · LP · HP · piston valve

exhaust steam

condenser

aft

valve eccentrics

bedplate · control

METAGAMA

CHAPTER 8

Oil Firing and Gear Wheels

The use of oil as a fuel for boilers had been proposed during the middle years of the nineteenth century, but the easy availability of coal and relative lack of oil prevented any ready acceptance. During the latter years of that century a number of petroleum companies adopted oil firing, but it still failed to attract major support. Tests carried out by the Royal Navy and its United States counterpart during 1905 illustrated the distinct advantages of oil compared with coal, but it was only when Winston Churchill became First Lord of the Admiralty that positive action could be seen. Admiral Lord Fisher, a noted advocate of oil burning, was appointed to head a Royal Commission to examine oil supply for the RN. The report of 1913 firmly favoured use of oil for fighting ships and conversion of naval ships commenced.

Adoption by commercial shipping lagged behind but wartime operational experience showed the potential and, perhaps more importantly, the sources of oil employed for supplying the fleet became available for merchant ship use when the conflict ceased. Owners became aware of oil's advantages compared with coal, but world-wide availability deterred many from converting tonnage. Such a situation did not exist on the north Atlantic as ports on the eastern and western shores quickly geared themselves to supplying oil bunkers.

The reasons for changing to oil were essentially economic in nature, oil had a higher calorific value than coal and so more heat could be obtained from the same weight. Being a liquid oil would occupy a storage space fully and any odd shaped or even inaccessible space could be employed for storage. Additionally there was no ash to dispose of, less labour was required in firing and bunkering was a much cleaner and faster task. The claim that combustion of oil resulted in less soot falling on decks was not borne out by experience, as most oil burning liners received complaints from passengers about soot ruining clothing.

Crewing costs showed a marked reduction when ships were converted to oil firing. Fewer firemen could tend the same number of boilers as there was no need to rake furnaces and remove ashes. Coal trimmers became completely redundant as pumps moved oil about the ship. As a coal burner *Mauretania* had an engine room staff of 366 men, including 192 firemen and 120 coal trimmers, and consumed over 1,000 tons of coal per day. Following conversion to oil in 1921–22 only 79 people were employed in the engine department and daily fuel consumption fell to about 620 tons.[1] Oil could be pumped aboard rapidly reducing bunkering time and as less was needed there was an increase in cargo capacity.

To avoid coal dust in the accommodation ships had to be practically sealed whilst bunkering, but with oil burning such a time consuming and wasteful task was avoided. Another disadvantage of coal was that bunker fires were fairly common. Heat generated within a bunker space could cause ignition, but this was more inconvenient than dangerous if dealt with promptly. Judicious use of the hose and raking of burning coals readily extinguished the fire, but it took time and labour. The engine room crew of White Star's unfortunate *Atlantic* were actually

Mauretania's No 4 stokehold after conversion to oil firing.
(Harry Weston Collection.)

engaged in fighting a bunker fire when the fateful decision was made to head for Halifax in order to secure more coal.[2] The main disadvantage of oil was that it burned readily and spills could be catastrophic. Stokehold fire fighting arrangements had to be such that any outbreak could be quickly extinguished. Water was not acceptable and foam installations became standard, many being fully or semi-automatic.

One disadvantage of coal firing compared with oil only became evident with water tube boilers and that related to maintaining a fire in good condition. Experience with *Imperator* and *Vaterland* showed that large grates were difficult to service, the breaking up of clinker was slow and cumbersome, maintaining an even fire over the entire grate became almost impossible and fly ash would build up between tubes, leading to overheating. It was only with oil firing that water tube boilers really came into their own and the high forcing rates for which they were ideal could be utilized.[3]

As the great liners were released from wartime duties their owners sent them off for reconditioning in order to fit them for commercial service once more. Such refits could not be undertaken immediately hostilities ceased as many ships were still engaged in trooping duties and it was the early 1920s before many returned to civilian service. Accommodation came in for major attention, but conversion to oil firing became a priority in most cases.

Olympic went back to Belfast and did not resume her Atlantic duties until June 1920 when she became the first large passenger vessel to cross that water burning oil in her boilers. Storage facilities for the oil presented no problem as the double hull arrangement, fitted following the loss of *Titanic*, could be used to advantage. As a result only certain of the former coal bunkers needed to be employed for fuel and that allowed cargo capacity to be increased. Fuel oil capacity amounted to 5,500 tons, sufficient for a complete round trip, and that quantity took only six hours to pump aboard. The saving in time compared with coal bunkering was evident, whilst the saving in weight and space might be appreciated from the fact that only 6 tons of oil were required for the same duty as 10 tons of coal.

Within the ship pipework allowed each of the daily service settling tanks to be replenished from any of the bunker tanks, and any of the 29 boilers could be supplied from each of the settling tanks. That system required about 3.5 miles of fuel pipework, but it did ensure that no boiler could ever be starved of an oil supply. In order to ensure that the oil could be pumped and would burn properly heating was essential. About 4 miles of steam pipes circulated around the bunker tanks and settling tanks.[4]

Oil burning systems differed, but they all depended upon the production of very fine droplets of oil which would burn easily when forced into a boiler furnace. For *Olympic* the Whitelaw mechanical pressure system was chosen. In this heated oil was pressurized by means of steam driven pumps and then sprayed into the furnace through small holes in burner nozzles. As a result very fine droplets of oil were produced and they would mix with air entering through holes surrounding the burner. By means of a regulating valve oil supply quantity to each burner, and hence the firing rate, could be controlled.

Olympic only just beat her rival *Aquitania* back into service, the latter sailing on her initial oil powered trip from Liverpool in July 1920. Armstrong, Whitworth & Co of Newcastle carried out conversion work on the Cunarder, but no widespread use was made of the double bottom spaces for oil storage. Original coal bunkers and the Frahm tanks were converted to carry oil, but

they had insufficient capacity to hold fuel for a complete round trip and so six double bottom tanks also had to be converted. Because of the plentiful supply and relatively low cost of fuel there, bunkering for most major passenger liners was scheduled to take place at New York rather than European ports.

Conversion of coal bunkers was not simply a case of fitting pipework and valves, major structural work was required to strengthen tank sides and make them oiltight. For this purpose electric arc welding was employed in addition to riveting. Bunker tanks were arranged in groups to serve each of the four boiler rooms, but connecting valves allowed for transfer between tanks should that be necessary. For each group of tanks there was also an overflow tank to which any oil would automatically flow in the event of any storage tank being overfilled. At the bunkering station on E deck a supply line connection branched to four 8 in diameter tank filling lines which supplied each group of tanks. As with *Olympic*, the arrangements allowed full bunkers to be taken in six hours.

Four settling tanks were provided in each boiler room, two for a group of three boilers. The tanks had sufficient capacity for 16 hours' steaming, thus a tank could be filled and the oil allowed to settle for about 15 hours before being put on-line. During that settling time water and sludge in the oil settled to the tank bottom from where it might be drained off, thus only relatively pure oil would be pumped to the

Cunard's Scythia *at Liverpool in 1957.*

Diagram showing comparison between oil fired turbine Laconia *of 1922 and the 1912 coal fired reciprocating engined* Laconia.

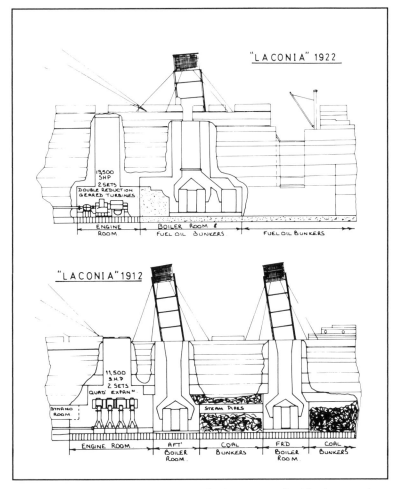

boiler. Any sludge or water in the oil could damage burners and impair combustion. *Aquitania* employed a pressurized oil burner system similar to that of *Olympic*.[5]

A further development enhanced the efficiency of marine propulsion systems during those immediate post-war years, and that was the introduction of geared turbines. A major failing of direct drive turbines lay in the large diameters required to keep shaft rotational speeds fairly low in order that propeller efficiency might be reasonable. Even with large diameter drums the blade speed remained much lower than steam velocity and considerable losses resulted. Charles Parsons realized the problems from the start of his propulsion turbine experiments but it was not until 1910, when he re-engined the cargo ship *Vespasian*, that a practical geared installation put to sea. The system showed a 13.5 per

cent saving in fuel compared with the previous steam reciprocating plant.[6]

The use of gearing allowed turbines to be designed for any available steam condition and that in turn allowed steam pressure and temperature to be increased, thus producing further improvement in operating efficiency. Superheating with high pressure steam became possible, but only after the First World War came to its conclusion as during that period shipbuilding concentrated on the war effort.

Cunard was one of the first Atlantic companies to commence building replacements for its wartime losses. Apart from *Lusitania*, ship losses were concentrated amongst the smaller and slower intermediate liners, thus restocking with ships of that type became the priority. In 1919 the company ordered five 19,700 gross ton ships of the 'Scythia' class, the final two ships,

Franconia and *Carinthia*, appeared later than the original three due to changes in accommodation layout. These 601 ft long by 73 ft beam ships had a service speed of 16 knots and were designed to carry 347 first, 350 second and 1,600 third class passengers.

Notably, the ships employed twin screw geared turbine sets with oil fired scotch boilers. In publicity of the time Cunard emphasized the saving in space of geared turbines and oil firing by comparing *Laconia*, third of the new sisters, with the 1912 vessel of the same name. When running ahead the twin turbine sets developed 12,500 shp whilst for astern operation 70 per cent of that power was available. Propeller speed remained a modest 92 rpm.

Each set consisted of one HP and one IP Parsons turbine in tandem driving the same gear pinion, with an LP turbine driving a separate pinion. Both pinions engaged with the first reduction gear wheel which in turn rotated a pinion driving the second reduction wheel mounted on the main propeller shaft. Flexible couplings connected each turbine with the relevant pinion, these being essential to compensate for slight variations in shaft alignment.[7] *Franconia* and *Carinthia* only had HP and LP turbines, but double reduction helical gearing still applied. Thrust blocks were positioned on the drive shafts after the gear boxes.

Suitable gear ratios reduce the 2,660 rpm HP pinion and 1,783 rpm LP pinion to 92 rpm at the output shaft. Reaction blading applied to all ahead stages but astern turbines, incorporated in the LP casings, made use of a two row impulse wheel followed by 12 rows of reaction blading.[8]

Three single ended and three double ended scotch boilers provided saturated steam at 220 psi. Howden forced draught applied to all boilers, as did oil firing. The relatively low pressure and avoidance of superheating certainly limited the power output and efficiency of the plant.

Below *Central stokehold aboard the 'Scythia' class steamer* Franconia.

Right *Turbine steamer* Franconia. (Glasgow University Archives with permission of Mr W. Lind.)

Below right Franconia's *control platform and watch desk.*

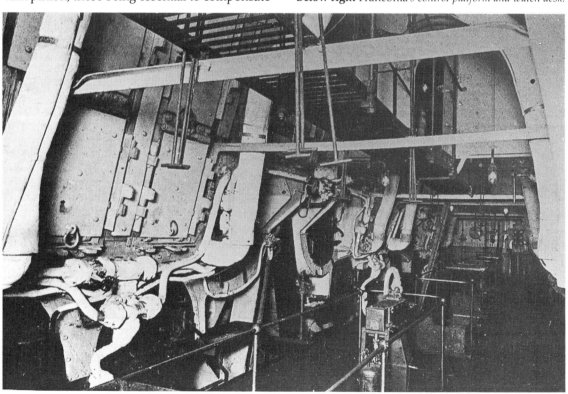

Very similar, but less powerful, installations applied to the six 14,000 gross ton 'Antonia' class vessels constructed at the same time. The two sets of HP and LP double reduction geared turbines provided an output of 8,500 shp from steam at 220 psi. Unlike ships of the 'Scythia' class Antonia and her sisters employed superheated steam, the temperature of steam entering each HP turbine being about 200°F greater than the saturation temperature corresponding to the pressure, ie 200°F of superheat. The Robinson superheaters consisted of small diameter steam tubes fitted inside some main flue tubes of the scotch type boilers. Superheating resulted in more energy being held in each unit mass of steam, thus a greater degree of expansion could be allowed in the turbine before some steam condensed to water. With LP turbines rotating at over 1,500 rpm impact between blades and water droplets could result in severe blade damage.[9]

European owners also set about reconstructing their Atlantic fleets, HAPAG being more intent upon making its presence felt than restoring past glories. Four 21,000 gross ton ships of the 'Albert Ballin' class were very much poor relations compared with the 'Imperators' but they served their purpose. Albert Ballin, first of the class, came from the Blohm & Voss yard at Hamburg in 1923 and was quickly followed by

One set of geared turbines and a gear set for the 'Antonia' class Cunard steamers. (Harry Weston Collection.)

the identical Deutschland. In terms of propulsion plant there was nothing special about the ships, geared turbines employing superheated steam being specified. Four single ended and four double ended oil fired scotch boilers supplied steam at 210 psi to turbine sets arranged with ahead and astern HP and LP stages on each of the twin shafts.[10]

An unusual feature of the ships and the two later sisters lay in the fitting of Frahm anti-rolling tanks. Instead of the usual arrangement the anti-rolling tanks were contained within bulges in the sides of the ships. Openings in the plating allowed sea water to enter and leave the tanks rather than remain contained. Tanks only had connection in the air passage at the top, the lower water connection being dispensed within this modified Frahm system. How effective the tanks were is unknown, but only Blohm & Voss appear to have persisted with the arrangement.[11]

As built the ships had a speed of about 14.5 knots, but by 1929 increased traffic suggested that there was an economic advantage in operating them more intensely. A seven day passage between Cherbourg and New York required a 19 knot speed and so re-engining was put in hand. Four water tube boilers replaced the original scotch type, these new boilers operating at 400 psi. The new geared turbines had an output of 26,000 shp compared with the 13,500 shp of the original plant, but the new installation took up no more room than the old. In addition to

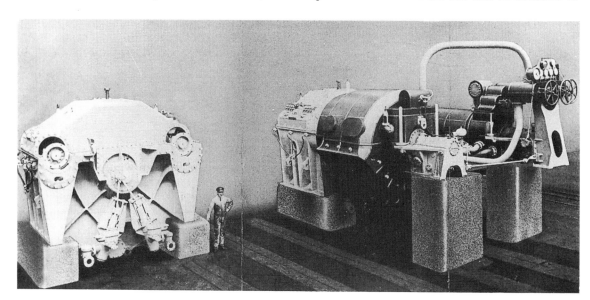

the Howden forced draught system a turbo-driven gas extractor fan also operated in the uptakes to provide a positive removal of waste gases.[12]

Italian companies also set about reconstructing their fleets, with Lloyd Sabaudo taking a leading role. *Conte Rosso* and *Conte Verde* came from Beardmore's yard on the Clyde during 1922 and 1923 respectively. They were identical ships of 18,200 gross tons, 570 ft long by 74 ft beam, with a service speed of 18.5 knots, and were fitted throughout with British built equipment. Double reduction geared turbines powered both shafts, the output of each set being 11,000 shp at 92 rpm propeller speed. The main dimensions of gear wheels were:

	No of teeth	Diameter (in)	Speed (rpm)
HP pinion	48	10.7	2,950
LP pinion	84	18.4	1,686
First reduction wheel	359	77.3	394
Second reduction pinion	80	29.9	394
Main gear wheel	343	126.3	92

As with most ships of the period scotch type boilers were fitted, there being six double ended and two single ended arranged in two boiler rooms. Steam at 200 psi was passed through Robinson smoke tube superheaters to provide a 220°F superheat temperature. Howden forced draught and oil firing systems were fitted, but provision was made for easy conversion to coal firing should that ever prove necessary. During the early and mid-1920s some concern still existed regarding security of oil supplies. To allow for such conversion cross bunker tanks between the boiler rooms and forward tanks could carry coal or oil and four ash ejectors were fitted in each boiler room. Boiler conversion required furnace fronts to be changed and ash bars fitted.[13]

The electrical installation aboard these ships attracted some interest as it was the first time in an Atlantic liner, and possibly any merchant ship, that the Admiralty practice of using ring mains had been employed. Insulated copper cable with a core of 2 sq in formed the ring main, the cable being the largest in section then installed in a merchant ship. Three 110 volt 150 kW turbo-generators supplied the main electrical power, a paraffin engine driven generator of 33 kW capacity being provided for emergency purposes.[14]

Lloyd Sabaudo went back to Beardmore for a similar but slightly larger ship, *Conte Biancamano*, in 1925. Again the builder employed a ring main for electrical supply, automatic remote controlled circuit breakers feeding each of 16 branch circuits. Push buttons allowed these breakers to be opened or closed from the switchboard positioned in the main engine room, but local control was also provided in each case. The slightly higher speed, 19 knots, and large size, 626 ft long by 76 ft beam and 24,400 gross tons, required greater power than for *Conte Rosso* and her sister. Twin compound geared turbines producing a total 21,000 shp at 95 rpm were sufficient to drive the ship at 19 knots. Again steam supply came from scotch boilers operating at 200 psi and 220°F superheat, these boilers also being capable of conversion to coal firing.[15]

Conte Biancamano proved to be the last major Italian liner built outside that country. A very similar ship, *Conte Grande*, was actually constructed in Trieste three years later, the design probably being based upon that developed by Beardmore.

It was not until near the end of the decade that a liner company made use of water tube boilers, apart from the 'Imperator' class ships the practice was limited to naval vessels. Reluctance to adopt that new technology related to the overall propulsion plant, as scotch boilers could readily deal with pressures and superheat temperatures then required for turbines. Additionally higher temperatures and pressures needed stronger and more expensive materials. Development of water tube boilers progressed over the years, but installations were confined to naval ships even though manufacturers tried to interest commercial operators.

There is evidence to suggest that White Star investigated possible re-engining of *Majestic* with high pressure superheated plant. Although that ship only entered service in 1922 she was effectively of 1912 design with plant to match. Yarrow & Co, developers of the famous Yarrow water tube boiler, informed the company that it would be possible to replace the original 48 boilers with 18 similar sized units of new design operating at about 400 psi, a further five boilers being fitted for port use. In addition to an increased power output of 86,000 shp the new machinery would only have occupied two-thirds the space taken by the original plant.[16] That nothing came of the plan is to be regretted.

Only Canadian Pacific, under the direction of its dynamic chief superintendent engineer John Johnson, made any headway with regard to high pressure water tube boilers. Introduction of the 'Duchess' class with *Duchess of Bedford* in 1928 marked a radical change in marine propulsion and others soon followed when the advantages could be observed. In terms of size, 21,500 gross tons, and speed, 18 knots, these ships fell into the common category but the opposite was true of the propulsion plant. Two sets of Parsons single reduction geared turbines produced a total ahead power of 20,000 shp with about 65 per cent of that being available from the astern turbines. HP, IP and LP stages had separate pinions which engaged with the 14 ft diameter main gear wheel on the propeller shaft.

Of standard impulse-reaction form, the turbines alone were nothing exceptional save for the fact that they had been constructed to deal with high steam pressures and temperatures. It was the boiler installation which marked the turning point in marine steam systems. For main propulsion purposes six Yarrow three drum boilers supplied steam at 370 psi and 686°F, whilst for

auxiliary purposes two single ended scotch boilers were employed. The scotch boilers operated at 200 psi and as well as providing steam for heating and driving some auxiliary engines, also supplied make-up feed for the water tube boilers. That came by way of a connection into the IP turbines and so avoided any risk of contaminated feed water entering the high pressure system from storage tanks.

In making use of high pressure steam improved efficiency was possible, but only if the steam could be used to maximum effect. That meant employment of steam in turbines, not in reciprocating engines which had been traditionally employed for driving pumps, fans and other auxiliary equipment. 'Duchess' class ships had most items of such plant powered electrically, the current being supplied by two 500 kW British Thomson-Houston geared turbine generating sets. Two B & W diesel driven generators of 450 kW were also provided with a further 75 kW diesel driven generator being available for emergency purposes.[17]

Johnson had designed his engine rooms as

Canadian Pacific's Duchess of Richmond. (Canadian Pacific.)

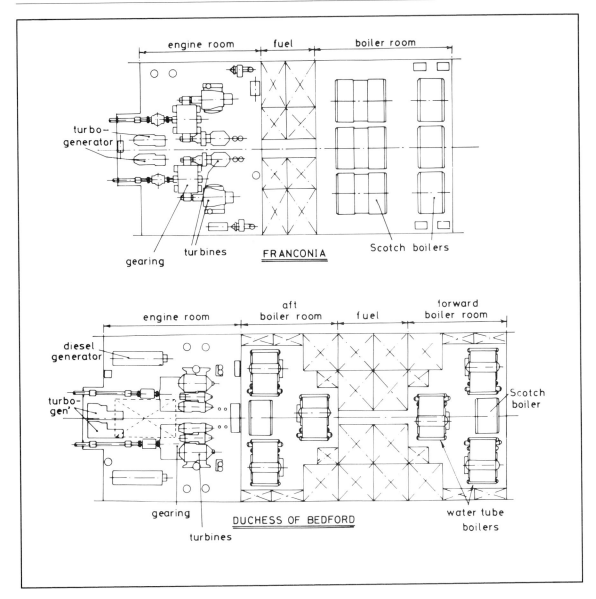

Comparison between engine room layouts of 'Scythia' and 'Duchess' class ships.

complete units for maximum efficiency rather than considering propulsion plant alone and then adding other equipment for specific purposes. The builder's guaranteed fuel consumption for all purposes of 0.7 lb/shp/hr was bettered by 0.075 lb after running-in, whilst that for propulsion only fell to 0.57 lb/shp/hr. For the time the figures were remarkable.[18]

It might be presumed that the use of high pressure, high superheat water tube boilers provided an easy and economical solution to the problem of liner propulsion. Such boilers were more economical to operate than scotch boilers, whilst for an equivalent evaporation rate per square foot of heating surface the water tube boiler was also less costly to construct. The size of boiler and turbine plant for a particular output power would also be lower because less steam was required. That also reduced the size of condensers required, plus that of the servicing auxiliaries.

Duchess of Bedford *as the post-war* Empress of France. (Canadian Pacific.)

Johnson, in his 1929 Institution of Naval Architects paper 'Propulsion of Ships by Modern Steam Machinery', gave predicted costs for plants of different powers and in all cases the high pressure system proved to be less expensive. A high pressure installation for 18,000 shp would cost £256,000 whilst a similarly powered low pressure system would be £10,000 more expensive. For 60,000 shp the high pressure system, at £690,000, was £45,000 cheaper than the low pressure. Such figures mean little in a practical sense, unless it was the intention to construct ships of such powers, but they do serve to illustrate an additional advantage in progressing to high pressure plant.

However, as in all things, a price had to be paid for the advantages of high pressure and development of such boilers did not simply come about, it was earned the hard way. Better material had to be developed in order to withstand higher pressures and temperature, both in boilers and turbines. In the operation of that type of boiler absolute purity of feed water, by excluding oil and scale forming matter, was an essential prerequisite. In the 'Duchess' class oil contamination was avoided by only using high pressure steam in the turbo machinery, which had no internal lubrication. Leakage of sea water into boiler feed due to condenser tube failure had been a constant worry to operators, but the introduction of cupro-nickel tubes almost eliminated the risk. *Duchess of Bedford* and her sisters had such tubes. Oxygen dissolved in boiler feed water was known to cause corrosion and the use of closed feed systems greatly eased the problem by isolating feed water from the atmosphere. For some reason Canadian Pacific's 'Duchesses' had open feed systems.[19]

Duchess of Bedford and *Duchess of Richmond* both survived the Second World War, becoming *Empress of France* and *Empress of Canada* respectively. Although the latter ship became a total loss following a disastrous fire at her berth in Gladstone Dock, Liverpool during January 1953, *Empress of France* remained in service until 1960 having been given tapered funnels the previous year.

Empress of Japan, later to become *Empress of Scotland*, originally served on Pacific routes after some Atlantic trips but returned to Atlantic service following war duties. Larger and faster than the 'Duchesses' (at 22.25 knots her 1931 time remains a Pacific record), she extended Johnson's design philosophy. Twin sets of three stage, single reduction geared turbines, which were of similar form to the 'Duchess' type, developed 30,000 shp during normal running. Boiler installation was also similar, comprising six Yarrow water tube and two scotch boilers, but the Yarrow boilers generated steam at 425 psi and 725°F. A closed feed system had been adopted for *Empress of Japan* which entered service in 1930, only two years after *Duchess of Bedford*. Two 600 kW turbo-generators and four 300 kW diesel generators provided electrical power.[20]

Although Johnson's engine installations were highly efficient it was the Holland America Line's 28,300 gross ton *Statendam* which claimed the title 'Most Economical Steamship in the World'. The ship had actually been laid down at Harland & Wolff in 1921, but slow construction for various reasons delayed launch until 1924. Restrictions on American immigration and depressed Atlantic trade produced little need for further tonnage and the unfinished *Statendam* remained a basic hull structure. In 1927 Holland America had the ship towed to Holland for completion, turbines manufactured in Belfast and other British built machinery going with the ship for installation by Wilton's Slipway and Engineering Co of Rotterdam. At the restart of construction new more powerful machinery was decided upon, but it had to fit between the original engine room bulkheads. Harlands supplied the new turbines and diesel generators.[21]

Two sets of Parsons single reduction geared turbines of the, by then common, three stage form provided a maximum output of 22,000 shp. Six Babcock & Wilcox water tube boilers,

with solid forged steel drums, supplied steam at 430 psi and 650°F; for normal service only five boilers were needed, the sixth being available if necessary. For port use a small oil fired Cochran fire tube boiler provide saturated steam at 100 psi. Instead of employing separate boilers for low pressure steam applications, *Statendam*'s designers employed steam from the main range, that steam being desuperheated and reduced in pressure. Such an arrangement had advantages, including that of reduced engine room space. The desuperheater basically consisted of a steel shell into which superheated steam and water were sprayed, a float operated valve maintaining a water level in the shell. In cooling down superheated steam some water was evaporated resulting in a higher steam quantity, but at lower temperature and pressure suitable for heating and other purposes.

As with the 'Duchesses' considerable use was made of electricity for driving pumps, fans and deck machinery in order to limit HP steam applications to main turbines. Electrical supply came from four generators of 400 kW capacity, each being driven by a diesel engine of B & W design.[22]

In order to obtain maximum economy full use

Empress of Scotland (formerly Empress of Japan) illustrating the mass of ventilators carried by ships of the period. (Canadian Pacific.)

French Lines' outdated Paris, *of 1913 design but which only entered service in 1921.* (Harry Weston Collection.)

had to be made of waste heat. That included feed heating by means of exhaust steam and combustion air preheating to optimum effect by means of exhaust gases. Combustion air temperature rose to 345°F whilst the flue gas temperature fell to 320°F. In order to obtain make-up feed water of the highest purity two evaporators were fitted. They utilized steam from the LP range to evaporate sea water which was then condensed, forming high quality distilled water. Energy saving by these means and efficient lagging resulted in a fuel consumption for all purposes of 0.61 lb/shp/hr, slightly better than that achieved by *Duchess of Bedford*.[23]

Relatively small ships seemed to dominate construction during the 1920s, but a couple of larger ships were introduced by the French Line. *Paris* appeared in 1921 although she had been laid down in 1913. Delayed by the war this 34,550 gross ton, 21.5 knot ship was rather outdated in terms of machinery, apart from the oil firing installation. Direct drive turbines had been superseded by geared systems but post-war restrictions on materials and lack of time for redesign probably dictated the style. The same

cannot, however, be said for *Ile de France* which entered service in 1927.

This fine and elegant 43,150 gross ton liner was the pride of the French merchant fleet, but at 23 knots just failed to be a record breaker. To drive this 758 ft (bp) giant at that speed powerful engines developing some 52,000 shp had to be installed on quadruple screws. Surprisingly direct drive Parsons turbines were the choice despite the fact that geared installations had proved to be more economic. That retrograde step may have been produced by a reluctance to try gearing on such a powerful ship, the only other geared turbine ship in the fleet being the Birkenhead built *De Grasse* of 1924. At the time problems were being experienced with some double reduction gearing systems, resulting in a widespread adoption of single reduction, but that would have been no reason for completely rejecting gearing altogether.

French yards had no real experience of geared turbine construction for merchant ships and, in view of those problems being experienced elsewhere, there may have been a reluctance to gain that experience with such a large plant. Subsidized by the French government, *Ile de France* was to be the 'Pride of France', construction of her machinery in a foreign yard

Ile de France, *a 1927 built ship with inefficient direct drive turbines.* (French Line.)

would have been out of the question. Obsolete and inefficient direct drive turbines offered the only solution.

Without gearing, compound turbines had to be arranged in the most convenient form on the four propeller shafts. Pure reaction Parsons turbines designed for at least 13,000 shp at 230 rpm drove each shaft, the centre shafts being powered by LP units whilst the outer port and starboard shafts were driven by HP and IP turbines respectively. Astern turbines also powered each shaft, the outer being HP and centre LP. Astern LP turbines occupied the same casing as the ahead units, but astern HP turbines had their own separate casings.

Because of the direct drive turbine arrangement high pressure superheated steam could not be employed effectively, there being a limit on shaft speed and turbine diameter. The relatively low pressure of 230 psi certainly restricted fuel economy, but so did the use of direct drive turbines. Instead of scotch boilers or water tube boilers, French Line adopted Prudhon-Capus boilers which combined both fire and water tubes. Basic structure was similar to that of the

scotch boiler but each of the four furnaces connected with a common back chamber. Water tubes, connected to drums at top and bottom of the boiler shell, occupied that space and were heated by flue gases before they passed through the fire tubes. A sand and firebrick lining insulated that chamber.

Twenty boilers, 12 double and eight single ended, each having a Howden forced draught system, supplied steam for all purposes. Claims had been made that Prudhon-Capus boilers were 10 per cent more efficient than scotch boilers of similar size and that it was also possible to reach maximum steam pressure much faster after flashing-up. Certainly the increased heating surface of the boiler compared with a plain scotch type would support such arguments, but increased complication must have presented problems. The geared turbine liner *Champlain* of 1931 employed water tube boilers, as did the turbo-electric *Normandie* of 1935. In the case of *Normandie* and the motorship *Lafayette* of 1930 auxiliary boilers were of the scotch type.

Only '*Ile*'s' two forward funnels exhausted main boiler gases, the aftermost being primarily used for engine room ventilation. An extensive Foamite system protected boiler and engine rooms against fire, each compartment having a

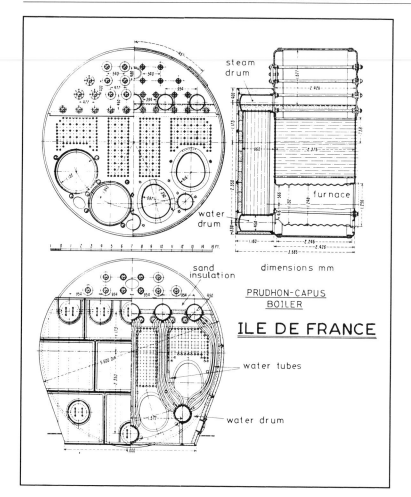

34 gallon steam operated Foamite unit as well as a number of portable 2 gallon units. Three 650 kW turbo-generating sets supplied the main electrical power at 220 volts with a 55 kW diesel driven unit being provided for emergency purposes. Although the turbines had a design output of 52,000 shp they could develop almost 60,000 shp should circumstances have directed, thus giving the ship a valuable reserve of power.[24]

One advantage of direct coupled turbines which must have been appreciated by passengers was that of quietness, but they were a rather retrograde step. The ship was, however, afflicted by the problem of vibration, almost certainly induced by the propellers as the turbines themselves were perfectly balanced. After five years in service a major overhaul was required with stiffening being employed within sections of the hull to minimize the problem.

Overall *Ile de France* may have been exceptional in terms of her accommodation and interior decorations, but her engine designers seem to have been less adventurous. The same charge could not be levelled at those responsible for North German Lloyd's *Bremen* and *Europa*. Although constructed by different yards, A.G. Weser of Bremen building the former and Blohm & Voss of Hamburg the latter, these ships were considered to be sisters, but major differences existed as far as machinery was concerned. Ordered simultaneously and launched within 24 hours of each other, the intention had been that both ships should enter service together but strikes at Blohm & Voss and a severe fire in March 1929 delayed completion of *Europa*.

Frahm anti-rolling tanks were common to both ships, as were divided flue uptakes and expansion joints on the boat deck. Shell plating of *Bremen* had been arranged with butts facing forward, the idea being to reduce drag by forming a low friction layer between hull and water. In both vessels a bulbous form of bow was incorporated in order to reduce wave making resistance, that of *Europa* being fuller and with a flatter nose than her sister. Because of the Frahm tanks neither ship had bilge keels, a step also taken to minimize drag. Rudders also differed, *Bremen*'s being of Oertz form whilst *Europa*'s was an ordinary balanced spade type.

Above water level the funnels provided the most noticeable difference, the 'falling raindrop' cross section of *Bremen*'s funnels contrasting with the elliptical form of *Europa*'s. How effective these features were in promoting speed is difficult to assess as both ships produced record Atlantic crossings. Overall, however, *Bremen* proved to be marginally the faster, but that

possibly resulted from her machinery. The squat funnels had been intended to reduce drag and that they may have done, but they also caused soot to fall on deck. Passenger convenience dictated that they be raised by some 10 ft, although even that failed to prevent the problem. In 1954 *Europa*, by then the French Line's *Liberté*, had her funnels topped with domes producing two of the largest funnels ever seen on a passenger ship.

The principal dimensions for both ships were:

	Bremen	*Europa*
Length (overall)	932 ft 8 in	936 ft 9 in
Length (bp)	888 ft 1.75 in	888 ft 1.75
Breadth	101 ft 9 in	102 ft 1 in
Gross tonnage	51,656	49,746
Machinery	Single reduction geared turbines	Single reduction geared turbines
Boilers (water tube)	21	24
Propellers	4	4
Service speed	27.5 knots	27.5 knots
Decks	11	11

The design of *Europa*'s machinery installation lay in the hands of Dr Frahm, whilst Professor

Bremen's machinery layout and split uptakes.

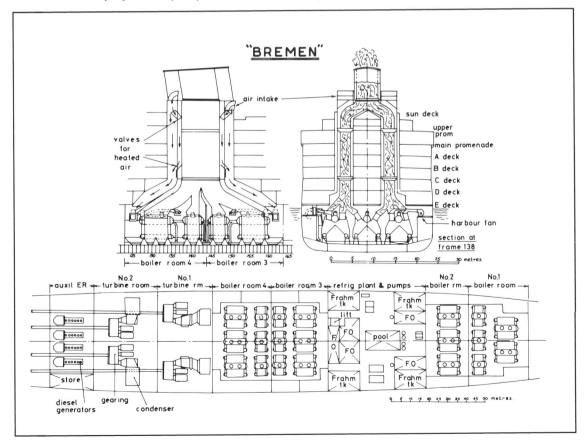

Gustav Bauer designed that for *Bremen*. Machinery layout for both ships was very similar with the four boiler rooms, placed forward of the turbine rooms, being separated into groups of two, one group forward and another aft of a space containing auxiliaries, settling tanks and anti-roll tanks. All of *Europa's* boilers were double ended, whilst her sister had nine single ended but they were of the same basic triple drum form. Owing to narrowing of the hull from amidships to forward, *Europa's* boilers became progressively smaller with fewer burners. For constructional reasons boilers had to be built into the ships as soon as the double bottom tank top plating was finished, rather than being lowered in place whilst fitting out.

Steam pressure of 330 psi and temperature of 700°F applied to both ships. For main engine and auxiliary purposes a steam generation rate of 550 tons per hour had to be maintained. In both ships divided flue uptakes allowed for a clear central accommodation section as it had done aboard *Vaterland* and *Bismarck*. Howden forced draught applied to *Europa's* boilers, with induced draught being employed to assist.

Bremen's boiler rooms operated on the closed stokehold system, only the single ended boilers, used in port, having forced draught. Steam turbine driven fans supplied the air, one to each boiler room. Air heaters at boiler top level provided the main form of air heating, but in cold weather pre-heating could be arranged by operating valves which directed air from deck ventilators down the sides of the exhaust trunking. The arrangement was intended to benefit personnel by avoiding cold Atlantic air being circulated around the boiler rooms. Marine engineers frequently discussed the relative merits of forced draught by means of the Howden system and that due to a pressurized stokehold. Overall there was no definite advantage either way, it usually depended upon personal preference and type of boiler installation. The Howden system with its separate air flow to each furnace required a considerable amount of ducting. In addition there could be different air flows to each furnace, causing problems with firing rates. A pressurized stokehold suffered no such problem and needed a minimum of ducting, but it

Left *One of* Bremen's *geared turbine sets.*

Below left *With covers removed, the turbines and gearing are visible.*

Below *Water tube boilers as fitted in* Bremen *and* Europa.

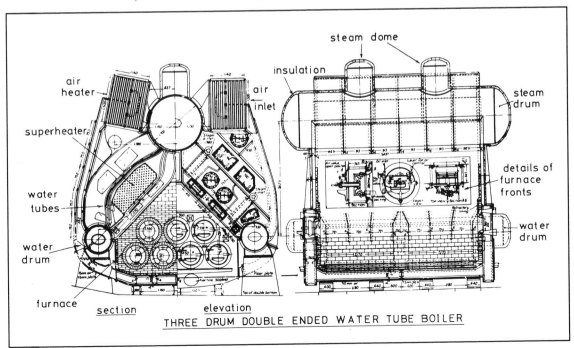

THREE DRUM DOUBLE ENDED WATER TUBE BOILER

only allowed access to boiler rooms by means of air locks. Professor Bauer made his choice of the latter system for *Bremen* on the basis of favourable reports coming from *Berengaria* and *Majestic* whose original Howden arrangements had been replaced by closed stokeholds.[25]

Whilst all four of *Bremen*'s propellers turned outwards, only the two inside, or aftermost, of *Europa*'s screws operated in that way, the two outboard propellers turning inwards. Frahm considered that the forward screws turning inwards would have an advantageous effect on the two aftermost propellers. Both ships had triple expansion turbine sets geared to each output shaft, *Bremen* employing three separate turbine shafts and gear pinions. *Europa* had HP and IP turbines mounted on a common shaft with a single pinion driving the gear wheel, the LP turbine being positioned on the opposite side of the gear wheel, giving a lower more compact arrangement.

Bremen entered service without problems and on her maiden westbound voyage in July 1929 wrested the 'Blue Riband' from the ageing *Mauretania* with an average speed of 27.83 knots. For her return crossing the average speed increased to 27.91 knots. The unfortunate *Europa* enjoyed a less auspicious start when, at the end of her 24 hour full power trial, failure of the HP turbine second stage impulse blading occurred. On return to Bremerhaven all four HP turbines were removed for new blades to be fitted. Subsequent trials produced a continuous 125,000 shp with a two hour maximum of 135,000 shp, design contract power being 92,500 shp. *Europa* captured the 'Blue Riband' on her maiden voyage, but later lost it back to her

sister. In terms of power and performance both ships were exceptional, a fact more remarkable because of their different designers and builders.[26]

Fuel consumption for all purposes during trials at 114,000 shp amounted to a hefty 0.735 lb/shp/hr, about 900 tons per day. That compared very favourably with older ships of similar size, *Aquitania* having an oil consumption of 1.12 lb/shp/hr for all purposes, but it compared unfavourably with contemporary smaller classes such as Canadian Pacific's 'Duchesses'. For normal running only some 90,000 shp would be developed, producing lower overall fuel consumption figures, thus illustrating the price to be paid for speed.[27]

As with many ships of the period *Bremen* and *Europa* utilized electrical energy for many auxiliary purposes including deck winches and engine room pumps, as well as the extensive hotel services needed to keep 2,000 passengers comfortable and happy. Four 520 kW diesel driven generators provided the main direct current supply at 220 volts, with two 100 kW emergency generators being positioned on the sun deck. Although most equipment operated on 220 volts, a 110 volt sub-circuit was provided for cabin purposes and supplied by three 150 kW electric motor driven generators.[28]

Both ships were a triumph for their respective builders and designers. Each was an individual with its own identity, but they became a well matched pair when it came to operational performance. Not only did they attract the attention of marine engineers and naval architects from both sides of the Atlantic, but they restored German maritime pride and prompted other national challenges.

CHAPTER 9

National Pride

Ever since the time of *Great Western* and *Sirius* individual Atlantic steamers had their champions amongst the general public, whilst some became symbols of chauvinism on a national scale. That nationalistic fervour reached its peak during the 1930s when, although the world was gripped by a depression, many countries subsidized symbols of nautical pride. Such financial incentives may have been employed to promote an idea of superiority, but not all vessels were designed to compete for the notorious 'Blue Riband'. In many cases the money invested was a means of achieving some degree of employment in depressed shipyards and marine

Canadian Pacific's giant liner Empress of Britain. (Glasgow University Archives with permission of Mr W. Lind.)

engineering areas and so might be considered as political. The fact remained, however, that the 1930s produced some of the most attractive and powerful ships ever to cross the Atlantic. Without that depression and patriotic fervour, which was to bring the world once more to conflict, many of these ships might never have been constructed.

Canadian Pacific's *Empress of Britain*, although an outstanding vessel of the period, cannot be considered as belonging to a single country for she was registered and built in Britain but owned by a concern with its base on the western side of the ocean. A massive ship of 42,000 gross tons she was larger than any vessel ever owned by the company and intended for cruising during the winter months when Atlantic trade dimin-

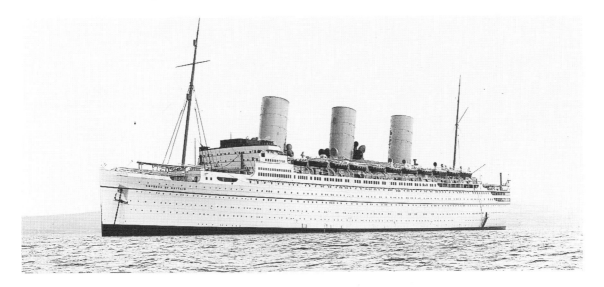

Empress of Britain's main control platform. (CP Rail Corporate Archives.)

ished. In order to capture continental trade her owners decided upon a Southampton base with calls at Cherbourg, whilst size dictated a Canadian terminal of Quebec rather than Montreal. Dimensions of length (bp) 730 ft, breadth 97 ft 6 in and load draught 32 ft had been determined by expected ports of call on any cruising itinerary. That condition dictated size of many liners during later years.

For Atlantic service a normal speed of 24 knots had been desired and that required a quadruple screw arrangement with steam turbine drive. Each turbine set consisted of HP, IP and LP units working in series with separate pinions driving a single reduction gear wheel. Ahead power came from impulse-reaction turbines whilst impulse HP and LP stages provided astern power amounting to about 60 per cent of that developed whilst running ahead. At 24 knots some 60,000 shp was required, but an additional 4,000 shp could be developed for indefinite periods should that have been required. Steam at 425 psi and 725°F came from eight Yarrow water tube boilers and a single boiler to the design of John Johnson, chief superintendent engineer of Canadian Pacific. Because of the high steam temperature cast steel had to be employed for HP and IP turbine casings whilst HP blades were of monel metal.

Turbines on the inboard shafts developed

two thirds of the total power with the outboard units developing one third. For winter cruising a desired slower speed could be maintained by the inner turbines and so the ship had been designed such that propellers on the outer shafts would be replaced by dummy bosses making *Empress of Britain* into a twin screw ship. That arrangement dictated dry docking before and after each cruising season, but was more economical than operating four turbine sets at reduced power conditions or allowing one pair of screws to idle in the water. The arrangement was repeated over 40 years later when the Atlantic liner *France* became the cruise ship *Norway*. Such a novel solution to the operation of a dual purpose ship is likely to have come from the inventive John Johnson.

Johnson's pursuit of efficiency developed from the plan first introduced aboard the 'Duchesses'. A closed feed system replaced the open arrangement and more effective regenerative condensers were employed. In addition to the nine water tube boilers, space was found for two scotch boilers. The purpose of these was the same as in the 'Duchess' class, namely to evaporate raw feed water so that only pure distilled feed ever entered the main steam system. Compared with other installations it may have seemed an elaborate affair, but at such temperatures and pressures, higher than contemporary

Right *Forward turbine room aboard* Empress of Britain. (CP Rail Corporate Archives.)

Below *Generator room,* Empress of Britain. (CP Rail Corporate Archives.)

liners, boiler water had to be absolutely pure. Attention to detail paid off as, during normal service conditions, *Empress of Britain* returned fuel consumption figures, for propulsion only, of 0.543 lb/shp/hr at 60,000 shp. That bettered the 'Duchess' class and even *Queen Mary*.[1]

Johnson's own design of boiler, constructed by John Brown who built the ship, appears to have been installed in order to give a full scale test of its capabilities. Two large drums, one above the other, were connected by curved water tubes thus forming a combustion chamber, which was further divided in two by vertical water tubes. That arrangement provided a considerable amount of heating surface area for the three burners in each part of the combustion chamber. As with the Yarrow boilers installed, it operated on Howden forced draught thus providing reasonable conditions for comparison. Trials showed that the Johnson boiler could generate nearly double the amount of steam per square foot of heating surface compared with most mercantile installed water tube boilers. Its

Tube arrangements of the Johnson designed boiler fitted in Empress of Britain.

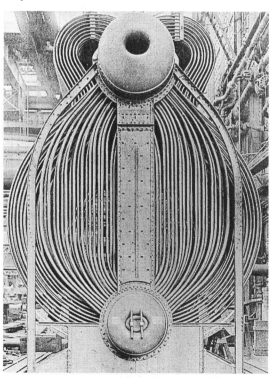

166 ton operating weight was less than the 244 ton Yarrow boilers which had a smaller output. Development of the boiler was limited as Canadian Pacific built no more liners for many years and large boiler manufacturers had a stranglehold on the industry.

Most auxiliaries were electrically powered using four 450 kW diesel generators and two 800 kW turbo-generators.[2]

Italy's interest in Atlantic operations had blossomed during the 1920s and at the end of that decade two of the three major companies on that route decided to supplement their fleets with larger tonnage. Navigazione Generale Italiana ordered 51,075 gross ton *Rex* from Ansaldo Shipyards of Genoa, whilst the competing Lloyd Sabaudo went to Cantieri Riuniti dell' Adriatic at Trieste for the slightly smaller *Conte di Savoia*. Although frequently classed as sisters because of their similarity in appearance, the ships were different in speed and power. Fusion of the two companies with Cosulich Line during 1932 to form the Italia Line brought both ships under a single house flag.

Rex was designed for speed with four sets of three stage Parsons single reduction geared turbines providing ahead power on four screws. At 27 knots these turbines developed 100,000 shp, but in service that could be surpassed should demand dictate. In capturing the westward 'Blue Riband' during August 1933, with an average speed of 28.92 knots, her engines must have produced considerably more power. Astern turbines on the two outermost pinions provided the usual 60 per cent power for operating astern. Normal operating steam conditions of 355 psi and 660°F fell short of those applicable to *Empress of Britain*, but the turbines had been designed for a maximum of 385 psi and 716°F. Massive size compared with the Canadian Pacific ship gave that extra power.

Main steam plant consisted of 12 water tube boilers, eight double and four single ended, arranged in two boiler rooms. These three drum units followed the arrangement employed for the German liner *Bremen*. A similar closed stokehold form of air supply also applied, six geared turbine fans being employed for the purpose. Two scotch type boilers positioned in the electrical generator compartment maintained steam at 230 psi for auxiliary purposes. Howden forced draught applied to both of these boilers.

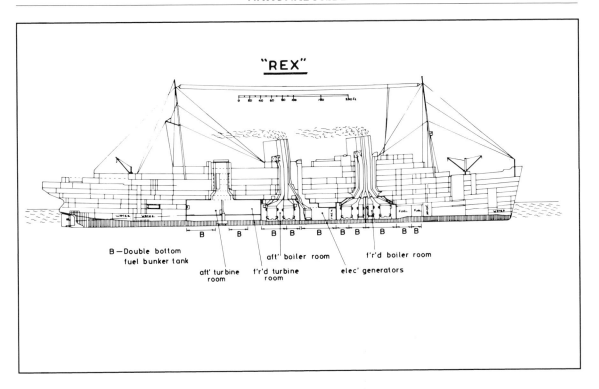

"REX"

B—Double bottom
fuel bunker tank

aft' turbine   f'r'd turbine
room   room

aft' boiler room   f'r'd boiler room

elec' generators

Above *Sectional view of the Italian liner Rex.*   **Below** *Geared turbine set.*

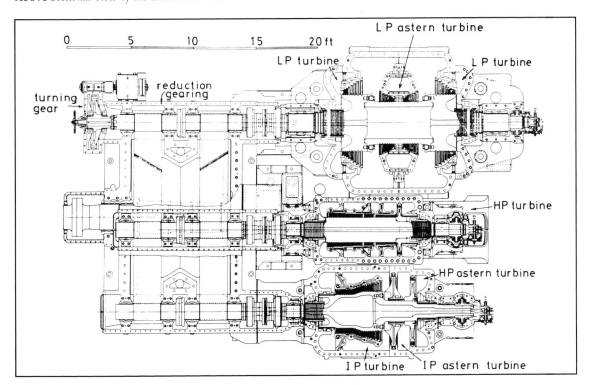

LP astern turbine

LP turbine   LP turbine

turning
gear

reduction
gearing

HP turbine

HP astern turbine

IP turbine   IP astern turbine

As might be expected on such large ships carrying 2,042 passengers, electrical demand was considerable. Three turbo-generators of 1,250 kW normal output and three 280 kW diesel generators maintained electrical power with a diesel driven 30 kW unit available for emergencies. These generators could, at maximum rating, supply some 5,640 kW in total, but normal service requirements only amounted to about 2,200 kW.

Rex was similar in appearance to *Bremen* and made use of several features found in the German ship including the bulbous bow and Oertz rudder. In addition her underwater butts in the shell plating also faced forward. It is easy to draw the conclusion that the Italian ship was a copy of her German contemporary, but such would be rather simplistic. There may well have been collaboration between the yards, some items such as the four propeller shaft brackets actually being sub-contracted to German manufacturers, but *Rex* remained an Italian designed and built ship. All good shipbuilders kept themselves abreast of the most promising ideas, and Italian yards were as keen as any others to produce quality products. Oertz rudders and the other ideas were common knowledge and appeared to have been successful aboard *Bremen*, so their incorporation in other ships might be expected.

In a number of ways *Rex* was superior to *Bremen*. Although she carried some 160 passengers fewer, her total crew amounted to 756 whereas the NGL liner required a complement of 960. Fuel consumption during sea trials at 28.5 knots amounted to 0.59 lb/shp/hr for propulsion alone, a figure better than that for other express ships of the period.[3]

Conte di Savoia differed from her Italian sister in a number of engineering respects, although the main propulsion plant remained the province of geared steam turbines. Each of the four propeller shafts was driven, through single reduction gearing, by series HP, IP and LP Parsons reaction turbines having their own pinions. An astern unit, contained within the LP casing, comprised three impulse stages followed by several reaction stages. In total these four sets could produce 100,000 shp for normal operation and more when required.

Boiler plant consisted of ten three drum Yarrow boilers operating on forced draught, but with induced draught fans also being incorporated in the uptakes should their use be considered necessary. These boilers had been designed to operate at 450 psi and 725°F. Three forced draught scotch boilers provided 180 psi for auxiliary purposes and hotel services. All forced draught fans and many pumps were electrically driven, requiring an extensive power supply capability. Six turbo-generators and two diesel generators, all with a capacity of 850 kW, maintained electrical supply, being used in groups to meet any demand. That demand varied with passenger requirements, but one feature incorporated in the vessel, and for which she was most famous, took a considerable amount of energy whenever it was in operation. *Conte di Savoia* was the first large liner, and the first ship on the Atlantic, to make use of gyroscopic stabilizers.[4]

Gyroscope theory indicates that when the axis of a rotating mass is changed there will be a force exerted which opposes that change. That theory was used to develop a gyro-stabilizer which applied a force to the hull opposing the force coming from a wave which was trying to cause the ship to roll. Obviously the force needed to be applied before large angles of heel were achieved in order to restrict the degree of rolling or pitching. In effect a stabilizer of this form would act as an anti-rolling brake and prevent large angles of roll building up. In order to allow the gyroscope to react, a sensing system had to be developed and that operated by means of a control gyro which noticed any alteration in the vessel's trim.

Conte di Savoia had three such gyroscopic stabilizers housed in a compartment forward of the boiler rooms. Each unit contained a 13 ft diameter flywheel weighing 108 tons, that flywheel being rotated by a directly connected 420 kW induction motor. In order to change the axis of flywheel rotation a separate 75 kW precession motor was fitted, acting through a gear wheel which engaged with a stabilizer rack. A steel housing surrounded the flywheel and was held by bearings in a cradle. Alternating current allowed more effective control of motor speeds and as the ship's electrical system was direct current it was necessary to provide rotary converters for each stabilizer. A brake on the precession motor shaft provided for exact control of the flywheel's rotational axis.

At its highest rotational speed of 910 rpm the

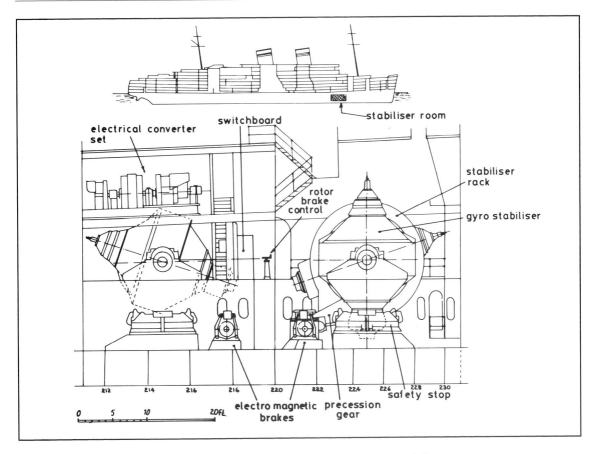

Above Conte di Savoia's *system of gyroscopic stabilizers.*   **Below** *Gyroscopic stabilizer system.*

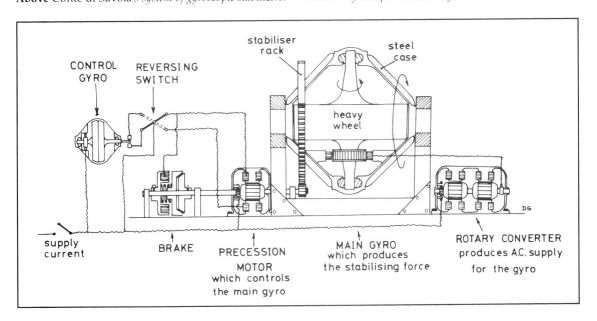

flywheel had a peripheral velocity of over 420
mph and at such speed wind resistance generated considerable heat. Each casing, therefore,
had to be ventilated. Maximum angle of axis tilting either side of the vertical amounted to 63°,
buffer stops preventing further movement. Any
restoring moment exerted by the gyro-stabilizers
depended upon the rotational speed of the
flywheel, variable between 800 and 910 rpm,
and the speed at which its axis of rotation
changed, speed of precession. Maximum restoring force came when the axis of rotation was
vertical, but with the axis tilted fore or aft a horizontal force would also be applied to the hull
causing yawing. The control system, therefore,
had to be arranged so that it regulated rolling
but did not induce uncomfortable and dangerous
yawing of the ship. Because of difficulties at the
time in analysing all wave conditions, an arbi-
trary rate of precession was chosen which
meant that complete stabilizing under all conditions could not be expected.[5]

In operation the system proved to be effective, but only to a limited extent and it had to be
shut down under certain conditions to prevent
danger due to yawing. No other Atlantic liner
ever made use of the same form of roll stabilization. Its total weight of 600 tons amounted to
1.34 per cent of the ship's nominal displacement.

The Italian government subsidized construction and operation of both ships because of their
publicity value, Rex's 'Blue Riband' record being
beyond price. The amount was not officially dis-
closed, but must have fallen well short of the
staggering £15 million given by the French
government for construction of Normandie. From
the start this ship was intended to be the biggest,
fastest and most luxurious on the Atlantic. That
she was all three is undeniable and her turbo-
electric propulsion plant was powerful and different.

Although Normandie's size had been chosen
for passenger capacity and comfort the ship's
length was governed by other factors, not least
her intended speed. In order to account for
wave peak positioning in relation to the stern,
so that maximum immersion for propellers
could be achieved, changes in dimensions had
to be made following tank tests. Originally the
length was set at 905 ft and breadth 105 ft, but
initial investigations and subsequent tank tests
produced dimensions of greater size. Eventually
the designers settled upon a length (bp) of 961
ft 11 in and shell breadth of 117 ft 9 in, the maximum draught of 36 ft having always been determined by available water at ports of call. Gross
tonnage varied depending upon measurement

The giant and graceful Normandie. (French Line.)

and spaces enclosed but amounted to about 80,000 making the ship, at the time, the largest in the world. Her designed speed of 29 knots also made her the fastest. Maiden voyage crossings in 1935 at average speeds of 29.94 knots westbound and 30.35 knots eastwards gave her the 'Blue Riband'. Over the years races with Cunard's *Queen Mary* produced even higher speeds, 30.58 knots and 31.2 knots westbound and eastbound respectively during 1937, but the 'Queen' eventually won.

For such speeds massive power was essential and that could only be provided by turbines, but direct drive units were not economically practical and the French Line appears to have had a dislike for gearing. Electric drives were not new but nothing of the power, 160,000 shp maximum, had been attempted before. Such drives offered a number of advantages over gearing, including the avoidance of gear noise, full power being available astern and astern turbines not being required. French lack of experience at cutting gearing may also have contributed to the final choice. In effect the turbo-electric plant was much like a miniature power station, with large motors driving the screws. Four sets of identical turbo-alternator units provided the power, each one consisting of a compound turbine directly coupled to the alternator. These three phase alternators, with a normal operating voltage of 5,500, produced current at different frequency depending upon turbine speed, the maximum being 81 hertz at 2,430 rpm.

Each screw shaft had its own sychronous propulsion motor capable of operating between 5,500 volts and 6,000 volts at frequencies up to the maximum produced by the alternators. At 81 hertz a 10 to 1 speed reduction between turbine and propeller shaft could be maintained. Both in power and size, 21 ft tall, 19 ft wide and 26 ft long, these motors were impressive. During normal operation each alternator supplied its own designated motor, but the control system allowed for alternative arrangements should the situation demand. Both motors on one side of the ship could be supplied by either alternator on that side allowing for emergency operation or slow running whilst cruising, the owner having indicated that *Normandie* would be employed in cruising if the situation demanded. It was possible to run alternator sets at reduced power but they would then be less efficient, full power on fewer

alternators being more economic and less demanding on the machinery.

Main steam at 400 psi and 660°F was supplied by 29 Penhoet three drum water tube boilers, whilst four single ended scotch boilers generated saturated steam for auxiliary purposes at 140 psi. Main boilers operated on Howden forced draught with two air intakes for the fans. One took air from the hottest parts of the boiler rooms in order to keep temperatures reasonable, whilst the other drew air from a space surrounding the furnace uptakes. Those uptakes were split, as on *Vaterland*, allowing for larger public rooms in the middle of the ship. Forced draught also applied to the scotch boilers which were employed mainly for heating purposes.

As might be expected on such a massive vessel, the amount of auxiliary equipment was enormous, much of it being electrically driven. Six turbo-generators, each with a 2,200 kW capacity at 220 volts, supplied lighting and power outlets with direct current at 110 volts. Two of the generators could be made available for ship propulsion purposes in an emergency whilst another two were only employed in supplying power to engine room auxiliaries. Two 150 kW diesel emergency generators occupied a room on the starboard side of the promenade deck.

Apart from its extensive nature very little of the auxiliary plant was unusual, the ship being described most completely in a special edition of *The Shipbuilder* in 1935, reprinted by Patrick Stephens Ltd in the 'Ocean Liners of the Past' series.

During *Normandie*'s maiden voyage it became evident that vibration was likely to be a problem, and subsequent trips emphasized the fact. Vibration was most severe at the stern near the forward propellers and in parts of the deck structures. Initial action was to introduce stiffening members in the affected areas, more extensive action having to wait until the end of the first season. Alterations included widening and stiffening the thrust blocks as well as modifying the propeller shaft brackets with a view to reducing water turbulence near the propellers. New four bladed screws to a special design were also fitted. *Normandie* lost one of those screws at Le Havre in April 1936 and made the following round trip with only three. On 6 September the following year she lost the inner port propeller of a new set and also completed a round trip on only three.

Measures taken cured much of the vibration, although it was never completely eliminated. When Cunard's *Queen Mary* took the Atlantic record, French Line decided to go for increased speed and commissioned a further set of screws which were fitted during the winter of 1936–37. In addition to these new four bladed screws the main generating sets and motors were completely overhauled and supplementary steam nozzles on the turbines opened to increase steam flow. That measure increased power output to 180,000 shp which, at a propeller speed of 231 rpm, produced a ship speed of 32 knots.[6] Record crossings east and west during 1937 could be attributed to those modifications and the new screws, but the ship was just about pressed to the limit and her Cunard rival showed that she had something to spare. Had the war not intervened it is possible that Gallic pride would have forced that little bit more out of *Normandie*'s machinery, but that is just speculation.

The unmistakable Queen Mary *with large air inlet cowls.*

Cunard had not constructed an express Atlantic liner since *Mauretania* and by the end of the 1920s she was beginning to show her age in terms of the new competition. The company investigated proposals to replace one of the existing three express ships, *Mauretania*, *Aquitania* and *Berengaria*, but thoughts quickly turned to the idea of maintaining a two weekly service with only two ships. For such a service a five day passage had to be obtained. Machinery to produce an average speed of 28.5 knots had to be reliable, with a capability of operating for a season of 11 months without major repairs. Commercial considerations dictated a large ship of some 80,000 gross tons and in 1929 Cunard invited a number of leading engineers to form a committee for the purpose of recommending the type of propulsion machinery.

Consideration was given to single reduction geared turbines as well as turbo-electric drives, both with scotch and water tube boilers, and to diesel electric propulsion. Unanimously the committee decided upon single reduction geared turbines with water tube boilers on the grounds of reliability, simplicity of operation, weight, initial and operating cost, efficiency, and

freedom from noise and vibration. They also recommended the use of high pressure water tube boilers with superheaters and air pre-heaters.[7]

The story of Queen Mary's construction with its suspension of work and subsequent government help following Cunard's merger with White Star is well known and need not be repeated. The delay did, however, put the ship behind Normandie on the Atlantic, whereas she should have been in service before the French giant. John Brown & Co carried out many tank tests with models in order to obtain the most effective hull form and determine the necessary machinery power, that being in the region of 158,000 shp for normal purposes but an ample margin was allowed for reserve.

Quadruple expansion Parsons impulse-reaction turbines connected through gearing to each of four screws, steam inlet conditions to the HP being designed at 350 psi and 675°F. HP and first IP stages were positioned forward of the gearing with second IP and LP stages aft of the gear casing, all stages having separate pinions engaging with the gear wheel. The HP stage had an impulse wheel at the inlet section in order to shorten the reaction part. All other stages were of reaction form with the LP steam being divided into two flow paths, entry being at the centre of the turbine. For astern operation a single HP impulse stage was incorporated in the second IP casing with a low pressure impulse stage in the ahead LP casing. Impulse blading was machined from solid stainless steel bars whilst reaction blades were made from low carbon stainless iron rolled to form the required section.

Boiler plant consisted of 24 Yarrow five drum water tube boilers, located in four boiler rooms, and three double ended scotch boilers, working at 250 psi and 200°F superheat, for supplying auxiliary steam. These boilers operated on Howden forced draught but the main boiler plant employed a pressurized closed stokehold system of draught. Tubular air heaters, flue gases passing through the tubes, took combustion air from the stokehold and directed it to the furnaces through a space contained between furnace brickwork and an outer steel casing. That arrangement not only increased the air temperature but helped keep firebrick temperature reasonable, thereby prolonging its life. Main boiler safety valves were set to life at 425

psi, normal pressure being 400 psi, and maximum steam temperature was 700°F. The difference between those figures and turbine inlet conditions was accounted for by pipelines and valve losses.

Most auxiliary plant aboard Queen Mary operated with electric drives and the engine room electrical system was kept separate from the hotel system. Seven turbo-generators of 1,300 kW at 225 rpm provided the power. These machines had a 25 per cent overload capacity for two hours, but could withstand 50 per cent overload for five minutes without difficulty. Engine room generators took steam from the main system, but the hotel sets were supplied by the scotch boilers. That allowed hotel services to be maintained in port without the need to keep the water tube boiler flashed up. The major use of electrically powered auxiliary machinery followed on from the ideas put forward by Canadian Pacific's John Johnson and it proved to be of considerable advantage in a ship the size of Queen Mary.

In addition to the normal Thermotank ventilation arranged throughout the accommodation, a limited system of air conditioning also applied to certain public rooms. As with all statistics applying to the ships those for the ventilation system were amazing: with the system fully operational electric motors consumed some 1,050 kW and fans delivered in excess of 118 million cubic feet of air per hour through 40 miles of trunking. Five independent air conditioning plants throughout the ship regulated temperature and humidity in selected areas. Heating and cooling systems attempted to maintain a temperature of 70°F at all times. When the outside temperature rose to 100°F the air conditioning system could maintain a temperature in selected rooms at a reasonable 82°F. Control of humidity fell within very comfortable ranges, even with 100 per cent relative humidity outside that inside was a modest 55 per cent.[8]

The performance of Queen Mary in capturing the Atlantic record is well known, average speeds of 30.99 knots westbound and 31.69 eastbound being achieved during August 1938. Speed is related to power which in turn is related to fuel consumption, but the 'Mary' was economical in respect to contemporary ships. In excess of the nominal 158,000 shp was needed to achieve the record crossings, but for normal operational voyages it was sufficient and her fuel consumption for propulsion purposes amounted to 0.586 lb/shp/hr during the first year. Later that figure fell to 0.56 lb/shp/hr or 948 tons per day. Hotel service fuel consumption was about 2 tons per hour.[9]

Queen Elizabeth, Cunard's second ship for the weekly schedule, was different from the 'Mary' in appearance but in terms of machinery they were very alike. The new ship was slightly larger in terms of dimensions and gross tonnage, but nominal turbine power remained the same at 158,000 shp. In fact the geared turbines were practically identical in form and layout. Boiler plant differed to take account of advances made in boiler design during the intervening years. The 'Lizzie' had only 12 Yarrow double flow water tube boilers for main and auxiliary purposes. Reduction in the number of boilers allowed two funnels instead of three to be employed. Steam conditions remained the same as aboard *Queen Mary*. Air for the closed stokehold fans was admitted through slats at the base of the funnels, thus eliminating the need for the large ventilators as fitted to the earlier ship. That air passed down ducting surrounding

each funnel, thus preventing adjoining accommodation from becoming overheated.

Four geared turbo-generators supplied electrical power for engine room and hotel services and these occupied a single room between the two sets of boiler rooms. These were certainly the largest turbo-generators fitted in any ship up to that time and for many years afterwards, each having a capacity of 2,200 kW. Compared with her intended running mate, *Queen Elizabeth* frequently made use of fewer items of plant but these were of higher power or output. Forced draught fans fell into that category, only 24 being fitted instead of 32, and these could each deliver 110,000 cubic ft of air per minute.

Passengers fared just as well aboard the 'Lizzie', when she eventually entered commercial service, as they did aboard her older consort. Her air conditioning plant was more extensive, conditioned air at the rate of 10 million cubic ft per hour circulating compared with 7 million for *Queen Mary*. The three stacker seemed to remain the more popular, however,

Queen Elizabeth *had boiler room air inlets at the base of each funnel.*

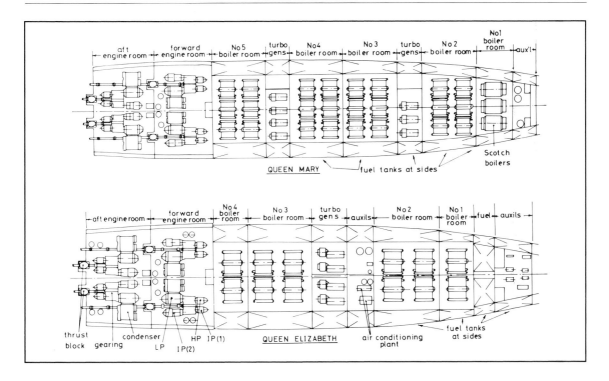

Above *Comparisons between the machinery space layouts of both 'Queens'.*

Below Queen Elizabeth *lays a smoke screen across Southampton as her boilers are flashed-up.*

probably on account of her pre-war image and attraction as a 'Blue Riband' holder. From an engineering viewpoint *Queen Elizabeth* was the superior ship, being more efficient and, therefore, more economical to operate. For the same 158,000 shp output her propulsion only specific fuel consumption amounted to 0.553 lb/shp/hr, giving 936 tons per day, a saving of 12 tons compared with *Queen Mary*.[10]

Queen Elizabeth's career was restricted by the Second World War, and by the time she entered commercial service the glorious days of the 1930s had gone. With *Queen Mary* in possession of the Atlantic record there was no need for any chasing just to raise the speed, but it is interesting to speculate as to whether 'Lizzie' could have made a record crossing had there been the desire. She had the power and more modern plant but Cunard had no, official, interest in records. The appearance of *United States* in 1952 removed any possibility.

The 1930s were dominated by gigantic liners, few other major Atlantic passenger ships actually being constructed during that period. Economic factors dictated construction and the recession had curtailed American facility for travel. Over capacity resulted in many of the fine old liners going for scrap as the post First World War

ships could easily meet demand. In general only symbols of national prestige were constructed, taxpayers footing the bill.

Ships did not have to be in the 1,000 ft range to qualify for government subsidy if a particular state considered the investment to be worthwhile. The value placed upon having a 'ship of state' cannot be quantified, but construction of a large ship in a home shipyard put people to work and was of considerable political benefit during times of hardship. A factor common to all Atlantic liners built during the 1930s was that they were constructed in national shipyards rather than overseas.

The Dutch government subsidized its heavy engineering industries by granting loans to the Holland America Line for construction of a 36,300 gross ton vessel, *Nieuw Amsterdam*. Built by the Rotterdam Dry Dock Company, this 713 ft long ship was not only built and outfitted by Dutch craftsmen but most of her engineering plant originated from factories in Holland. Where no suitable Dutch design was available items would be manufactured locally under licence. That situation applied to the six Yarrow design water tube boilers which were constructed by the N.V. Koninklijke Maatschappij of Flushing, Yarrow supplying all necessary drawings.

Those side fired, five drum boilers produced

Pride of the Dutch fleet, Nieuw Amsterdam.

steam at 630 psi and 750°F, only five being needed for normal full steaming conditions. Forced draught on the open stokehold system was provided by six screw type fans, one for each boiler, which drew warm air from the boiler tops and forced it to the furnaces via heaters and a casing which surrounded the furnace brickwork. A scotch donkey boiler, working at 150 psi, provided steam for hotel use in port, at sea reduced pressure steam could be bled from between turbine stages or obtained from the main range via reducing valves. At the HP turbine 20,000 lb of steam per hour could be bled at 140 psi for the high pressure feed heaters and the laundry, whilst a further 35,000 lb per hour could be taken at 85 psi for hotel services and fuel tank heating. After the HP stage some 26,500 lb was available at 60 psi for intermediate pressure feed heating. Such an arrangement illustrated careful design of the plant and avoided the need for widespread pressure reduction systems.

The boilers occupied a room forward of the turbine compartment and all flue uptakes connected with a single funnel, the forward one. The after funnel was a dummy, serving as ventilator for machinery spaces.

Two sets of Parsons triple expansion geared turbines provided propulsion on twin screws. Because of the very high pressure, which allowed for ample use of bled steam, a super high pressure turbine preceded the HP stage. That super high pressure turbine transmitted its power to the IP turbine shaft through single reduction gearing, the IP turbine then connecting to the main gear wheel by means of its shaft pinion. HP and LP turbines each had their own pinions. The gearing was, therefore, a mixture of single and double reduction. Each turbine set could develop 17,000 shp, this being apportioned, super HP 3,450 shp, HP 5,350 shp, IP 2,150 shp and LP 6,050 shp. Turbines and gearing were constructed by the same concern which manufactured the boilers.

The turbine system marked a departure from the more traditional arrangement, but it also required careful attention in terms of materials and manufacture. As well as stainless steel or iron for blading and rotors, attention had to be paid to insulation in order to prevent excessive heat loss resulting in a lower efficiency and higher engine room temperatures.

Three turbo-generators, 850 kW normal capacity at 220 volts, supplied electrical power whilst at sea, two 425 kW diesel driven generators being available for use in port. The diesel engines were designed and manufactured by the Dutch company Werkspoor. All power circuits, for electric motors and similar high energy consumers, worked at 220 volts but lighting circuits operated at 110 volts through five 110 kW convertors.[11]

During speed trials in March 1938 *Nieuw Amsterdam*'s engines developed 34,000 shp giving the ship a speed of 21.8 knots, fuel consumption for all purposes being 0.61 lb/shp/hr, a very respectable figure indeed considering the amount of steam used for non-propulsion purposes. Whilst the ship could not match *Normandie* or *Queen Mary* in terms of size or speed she was a triumph of Dutch shipbuilding and design, pushing forward marine technology just that little bit further through the extensive use of bled steam.

Considering that most Atlantic traffic terminated at an American port, mainly New York, relatively few American owned ships competed for passengers. During the 1920s United States Lines offered the only real challenge to European ships, and then with a rather mixed bag of older tonnage, mainly of German origin and including *Leviathan*, the former *Vaterland*. In 1930 two 24,289 gross ton steam turbine vessels were ordered from the New York Shipbuilding Corporation of Camden, New Jersey to replace three vessels of the former fleet. *Manhattan* and *Washington*, the largest American built merchant ships when delivered in 1932 and 1933 respectively, were the first north Atlantic trade ships constructed by an American yard for 35 years. Government money to the tune of three-quarters of the construction costs subsidized the ships which were built with a view to conversion for use as naval auxiliaries.[12]

Steam turbine propulsion plant followed the single reduction geared form with HP, IP and LP Parsons turbines connecting to the main output gear wheel by means of separate pinions. Both turbine sets were designed for a total normal output of 30,000 shp in order to give the ships a service speed of 20 knots. Additional power could be obtained up to 34,500 shp by utilizing a steam by-pass and extra nozzles on the HP turbines. Six Babcock & Wilcox water tube boilers supplied steam at 400 psi and 670°F, the boilers being placed in two rooms separated by auxiliary machinery and fuel oil tanks.[13]

Originally the two funnels were rather low affairs, but problems with soot falling on deck soon necessitated an increase in height. These ships were not really special in terms of construction and marine engineering, but they did represent renewed American interest in ship construction for Atlantic operations. It was not, however, until the end of the decade that another major Atlantic passenger liner left an American yard. Her introduction into commercial service was delayed by the war raging in Europe, but her design illustrated well the views of William Francis Gibbs and served notice on others of things likely to come.

America in turn became the largest merchant ship constructed in the United States, but she did not operate her intended Atlantic route

Machinery layout of United States Line's America *showing the original squat funnel form.*

until the coming of peace, her war years being spent as the troopship *West Point*. By the time she entered commercial service in November 1946 Gibbs was well advanced upon plans for an even larger and more spectacular vessel. At some 33,500 gross tons and 22 knots *America* was larger and faster than *Manhattan* and her sister, but she also had a more modern streamlined appearance. Despite the problems experienced with soot aboard the earlier ships *America*'s funnels were rather squat; only the after funnel served as a boiler uptake, the forward one containing an emergency generator and related equipment. Again the funnels had to be raised in order to reduce the risk of smoke blowing over the decks.

Two sets of geared turbines produced 34,000 shp for normal service operations, there being three separate turbines in each set. High pressure turbines of pure impulse type turned at 3,300 rpm and connected to the output shaft by means of double reduction gearing. Intermediate and low pressure turbines of reaction

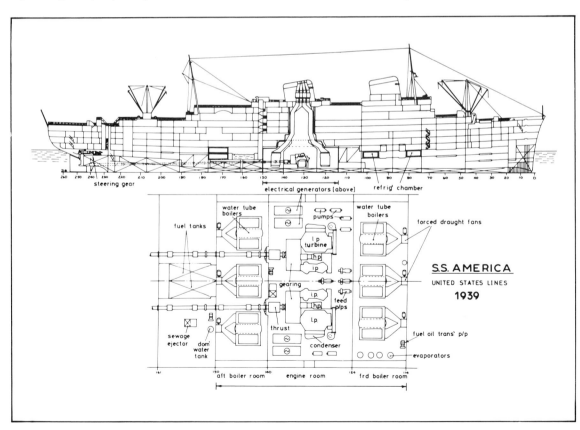

America in the 1960s with taller funnels.

form connected to output through single reduction gearing. Astern turbines were located in the IP and LP casings.

Six Babcock & Wilcox water tube boilers supplied steam, the pressure and temperature being slightly higher than employed aboard *Manhattan*, 425 psi and 725°F respectively. The closed stokehold form of forced draught as fitted in the earlier ships was not favoured for *America* and individual forced draught fans were provided for each boiler. Two boiler rooms, each containing three boilers, were arranged one either side of the turbine room, a rather unusual formation which kept the boiler rooms apart to safeguard steam supply, but maintained a compact machinery space. On trials during June 1940 the ship's machinery was pushed to its maximum 42,850 shp giving a speed of 25.3 knots. Fuel consumption at normal output was 0.5845 lb/shp/hr.[14]

America marked the end of an Atlantic era, an era she failed to serve, and also heralded a new age, but that age changed dramatically before she could prove her worth. In effect she was constructed too late to serve one Atlantic age and too soon to meet the changed situation of the post-war era and, apart from her valuable wartime contribution, need never have been built.

CHAPTER 10

Enter the Diesel

It was in 1892 that Dr Rudolf Diesel obtained a patent for an internal combustion engine cycle in which the fuel would be ignited due to heat generated by compression of air in the cylinder. That patent spawned many different variations of an engine which became universally known by the name of its inventor, the diesel engine. Before any practical engine had been constructed many engineering firms took out licences for the manufacture of engines based upon the operating cycle and soon other concerns were caught up in the enthusiasm for this new power unit. Each manufacturer developed his own engines and so, although operating on the same principle, they were all different in terms of detailed construction.

Engines for factory installations and road vehicles were soon developed, but marine application had to wait. River and coastal craft were fitted with diesel engines during the first decade of the twentieth century, but early in the second decade the East Asiatic Company of Copenhagen took the bold step of ordering three 4,964 gross ton ocean going diesel engined vessels. Two were constructed by the Danish shipbuilders Burmeister & Wain, with the third being built on the Clyde by Barclay, Curle & Co. Each vessel was propelled by two Burmeister & Wain (B&W) four-stroke reversible engines which developed a total of 2,500 ihp. The Danish built ships had engines constructed in Copenhagen, but the Scottish yard built the engines for its vessel, *Jutlandia*, under licence from B&W. *Selandia*, the first ship delivered, attracted world-wide attention and Winston Churchill, then First Lord of the Admiralty,

visited her in London at the commencement of the maiden voyage to Bangkok. The visit prompted him to comment, 'It is my welcome duty to congratulate Denmark, the ancient seafaring nation which has pointed the way and taken the lead in an advance which will be epochal in the development of shipping. This new type of ship is the most perfect maritime masterpiece of the century.'[1]

These ships were not passenger liners, nor did they sail on the Atlantic, but they are worthy of mention here because they pointed the way towards the future and prompted a widespread adoption of the diesel engine for marine propulsion purposes. The third vessel of the trio, *Fionia*, was actually sold to the Hamburg America Line during its maiden voyage in 1912. Lord Pirrie inspected the ship at Kiel with HAPAG's Albert Ballin and had nothing but praise for the new form of motive power. His single phrase, 'The future' summed up the situation perfectly.[2] It was, however, to be another 13 years before a motor driven passenger liner took to the waters of the Atlantic, and even then Scandinavian influence predominated.

The young Swedish American Line had operated its Gothenburg–New York service with second-hand steam powered tonnage, but the surge of Swedish emigration to the USA in 1923 encouraged the planning of a new ship. The line was part of the Brostrom shipping combine which already operated a number of motor vessels, but it was a bold decision to power the new ship with diesel engines. The Tyneside yard of Armstrong, Whitworth & Co was chosen to build the ship, but the engines would be constructed in Copenhagen by Burmeister & Wain. Any innovation in a commercial world takes courage but to install the most powerful diesel engines ever fitted in a ship intended to serve on the notoriously unpredictable north Atlantic was something of a step in the dark. Vibration could kill a passenger liner's reputation in a single voyage, and diesel engines were known to induce vibration.

At her delivery in 1925 *Gripsholm* was rated at

Burmeister & Wain four-stroke double-acting engine.

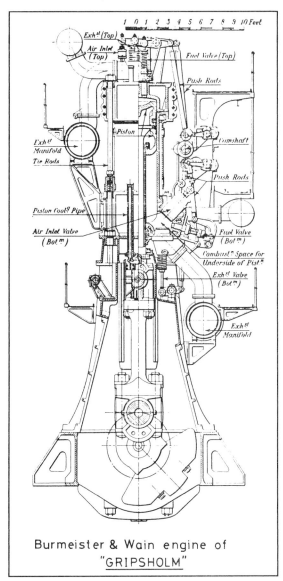

Burmeister & Wain engine of
"GRIPSHOLM"

18,815 gross tons and could accommodate some 1,643 passengers in three classes.[3] Main propulsion machinery consisted of twin six cylinder B&W reversible, four-stroke, double-acting diesels each driving its own shaft. The total output from both engines was small compared with large Atlantic liners of the day, but at 13,500 bhp the plant was in a class by itself as far as internal combustion machinery was concerned and gave the ship a service speed of 17 knots with the propellers turning at 125 rpm. Pistons 840 mm diameter had a stroke of 1,500 mm but it was their double-acting operation which allowed the development of such high power.[4] (See Appendix 3.)

Like other marine engines of the period these were true diesels, operating upon the principle devised by Dr Rudolf Diesel whereby combustion in the cylinder took place at constant pressure. This required the fuel to be blasted into the cylinder through a valve by means of compressed air with a pressure up to 1,000 psi. Such a requirement necessitated air compressors which would run constantly whilst the main engines operated and supply the air via large pressure vessels known as reservoirs. Naturally the compressors, of which there were three, also had diesel engines to drive them, these being 700 bhp four cylinder B&W engines turning at 170 rpm. Compressed air was also used to start the main and auxiliary diesel engines and so it was essential that a full charge of air was maintained in the reservoirs in order that starting could be achieved.

Two of the three air compressors operated whilst the main engines were running and so one always remained on stand-by as spare or underwent routine maintenance. Auxiliary equipment, such as pumps, steering gear and winches, was electrically driven with that power being provided by three diesel dynamos. Only one or two were normally needed at sea depending upon circumstances. Each three cylinder, 500 bhp diesel turned its dynamo at 200 rpm to produce a maximum power of 330 kW at 220 volts. Total auxiliary diesel engine power was, therefore, 3,600 bhp and amounted to more than the main propulsive power of most motorships then afloat.

Main engines and support electrically driven pumps for cooling water and lubricating oil were located in the after engine room whilst the

Left *Middle platform of* Gripsholm's *engine room.* (Paul Nielsen–B&W.)

Right *Top platform level in* Gripsholm's *engine room.* (Paul Nielsen–B&W.)

Below right *Layout arrangement of* Gripsholm's *machinery spaces.* (Paul Nielsen–B&W.)

compressors, electrical generators, air reservoirs and other service pumps occupied a separate compartment immediately forward. Efficient silencing of the exhaust from the diesels was essential for passenger comfort and so sets of silencers had to be found room on the boat deck at the base of each funnel. Both main engines had two silencers, one for the exhaust from above the double-acting pistons and the other to quieten the exhaust from the combustion space below. Two silencers served the forward funnel, one each for the sets of diesel generators and compressors.[5] They all performed well and no complaints appear to have been made concerning noise from the exhaust or even about vibration. The ship did not suffer from the habitual passenger annoyance endemic on Atlantic steamships, that of smuts from the funnel exhaust. More complete combustion in diesel engine cylinders also avoided the hazard which existed whenever boilers were flashed-up or the firing rate was changed.

Gripsholm did, however, have a boiler plant in order to provide steam for accommodation heating units and operating the 30 ton per day fresh water evaporator. Two oil fired boilers of the multi-tubular scotch type occupied a small closed stokehold immediately forward of the auxiliary engine room. At the time nobody seems to have considered the possibility of

making use of the waste energy in the ample diesel exhaust gas. The era of exhaust gas boilers was to come later.

Gripsholm's maiden voyage to New York gave the first opportunity for time trials of the most powerful diesel installation afloat and the engines performed faultlessly. During the eight day run across the Atlantic the main engines developed some 16,300 bhp with a daily average fuel consumption of 54 tons.[6] Throughout the first year of operations the average daily fuel consumption was 55.15 tons for main and auxiliary engines with another 5.85 tons for galley and boiler. No steamship of comparable size and speed could match that and there was also a saving on engine room crew which comprised chief engineer, nine assistant engineers, one deck engineer, three electricians, eight oilers and wipers, three firemen and one storekeeper.[7] Owner and passengers were well satisfied and *Gripsholm* became a popular ship. Following wartime service under the banner of the Red Cross, a major reconstruction during 1949 resulted in modernized passenger accommodation and increased tonnage. The opportunity was taken to fit a raked bow and swept-back funnels but *Gripsholm's* original machinery remained; it was obviously functioning to the satisfaction of all concerned.

Service between Gothenburg and New York

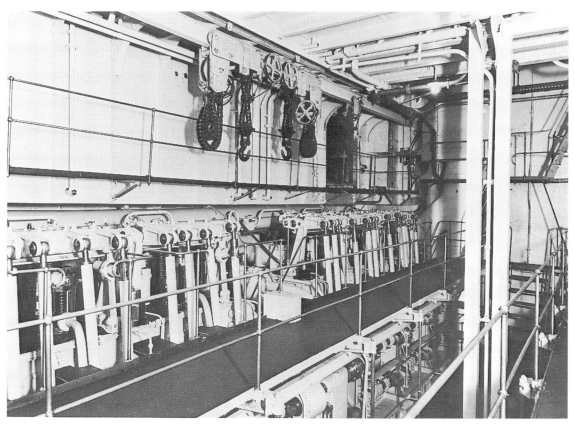

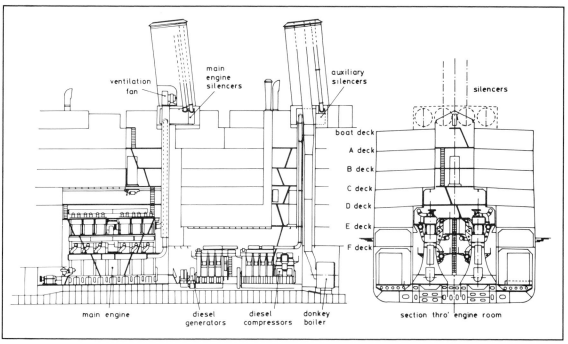

ventilation fan

main engine silencers

auxiliary silencers

silencers

boat deck

A deck

B deck

C deck

D deck

E deck

F deck

main engine   diesel generators   diesel compressors   donkey boiler

section thro' engine room

continued until 1954 when the ship was placed on a joint Swedish American/North German Lloyd service from Bremerhaven. The Germans were so impressed with the elderly motorship that they purchased her outright the following year and she became NGL's *Berlin* under the West German flag. Diminishing traffic eventually defeated her and at the end of 1966 Italian interests took her for scrap. Considering that the large marine diesel engine was still in its development stage when Swedish American took the bold step to install that form of propulsion, it is ample testimony to the skill of those engine designers, builders and operators that the original machinery lasted in an Atlantic liner for 41 years.

Such good early results with *Gripsholm* prompted her owners to construct a running mate with the same form of propulsion. *Kungsholm* was larger at 21,532 gross tons and had accommodation for 1,575 passengers, some 42 fewer than her older sister. The ships could be classed as sisters, but passenger apartments in the later vessel were decorated in a more Swedish style. Blohm & Voss of Hamburg built the ship although the two main engines were again provided by the Copenhagen works of Burmeister & Wain. These engines were practically identical to those fitted in *Gripsholm* except that they had eight cylinders and when turning at 100 rpm could produce 15,000 bhp to give the ship a speed of 17 knots. The engine bedplate had been stiffened and some other minor changes made in order to produce steadier run-

ning but they were essentially of the same design as the earlier engines.[8]

Engine room layout was much the same as for *Gripsholm*, but the two boilers were placed at the sides of the auxiliary engine room rather than take up space in their own forward compartment. To account for the increased amount of blast air required, each of the three compressors was driven by a 850 bhp four cylinder B&W diesel engine. A larger potential electrical demand was met by three 450 kW rated dynamos driven by three cylinder B&W engines capable of producing 700 bhp. Similarity between the machinery spaces of both liners can have been no accident, for the success and economy of *Gripsholm* dictated that *Kungsholm* should follow the same pattern.

During sea trials in the North Sea a serious explosion occurred resulting in the loss of life. Ever since the introduction of enclosed crankcases to diesel engines the possibility of a crankcase explosion had been appreciated and feared. Operation of the engine causes lubricating oil to break up into small droplets, but these are normally too large to ignite. If a high temperature exists at a bearing or other point where there is friction then the oil is vapourized. This vapour condenses to form very fine mist-like droplets which will be ignited by the high temperature 'hot spot'. An explosion results with likely disastrous consequences and that is what happened in the case of *Kungsholm*.

The B&W engine made use of a chain drive from the crankshaft to rotate the camshaft,

Left Gripsholm *as reconstructed in 1949.* (Paul Nielsen–B&W.)

Right Kungsholm *of 1928.* (Paul Nielsen–B&W.)

which in turn operated the valves. A bearing bush on the starboard engine chain drive overheated and caused the crankcase explosion. The severity was such that steel access doors were blown from the crankcase sides and several sections of floor plating were lifted. Small fires broke out within the engine room but prompt action by the engineers prevented their spread. Five people died and 19 were injured, whilst the engine room sustained considerable damage.[9] A resultant inquiry did not attribute blame to anybody but it emphasized the potential dangers inherent with diesel engine operation. Even today the possibility of a crankcase explosion is feared and very strict regulations exist to minimize the risk.

The damage was rectified and *Kungsholm* commenced her maiden voyage from Gothenburg to New York on 24 November 1928. With her elder sister she maintained a scheduled summer service across the Atlantic, but the accommodation design had been specifically aimed at the cruise market and an increasingly larger proportion of time was spent in warm Caribbean waters. Requisitioned and bought by the American government in 1942 *Kungsholm* became the troop transport *John Ericsson* and served the remainder of the Second World War in that capacity. A fire caused damage whilst at a New York berth in March 1947 and the ship was then resold to her original owners who intended restoration for cruising. For Swedish American Line the sight was depressing. One Scandinavian commentator considers

the ship to have been 'plundered bare',[10] but the demands of war make no concessions to beauty. Sold to Home Lines, in which Swedish American had a large stake, the former *Kungsholm* was rebuilt and became *Italia* under the Panamanian flag. Her original machinery remained in operational condition and served the ship well on south and north Atlantic routes until 1960 when a four year spell in familiar Caribbean waters brought a long and eventful career to an end.

Kungsholm did not last quite so long as *Gripsholm*, but they both kept their original machinery until the end. Considering that they were pioneer Atlantic motor liners that is a proud boast and indicates the soundness of the B&W design and the skill of the Danish engine builders.

It was not only Sweden which had an interest in diesel propulsion for passenger liners, the Italians also held views in that direction. For its service to South America the Cosulich Line of Trieste decided to lay down two 23,900 gross ton vessels with twin screws turned by B&W engines similar to those used for the Swedish pair. At the time Burmeister & Wain seemed to have cornered the market for large direct drive diesel engines.

Both ships were built by Cantieri Navale Triestino, Monfalcone and *Saturnia* commenced her maiden voyage to Buenos Aires towards the end of 1927. *Vulcania* was still in the course of construction when her owners decided that both ships should operate on the Mediterranean

Right Saturnia's *1927 engine room layout.*

to New York service. The newer ship was adapted whilst fitting out, but *Saturnia* was transferred immediately and modification to the passenger apartments had to wait. In terms of the engine room arrangements the ships were identical.

Stabilimento Tecnico Triestino built the B&W designed engines which were of identical cylinder bore and stroke to those fitted in *Gripsholm,* but there were eight cylinders instead of six. An interesting addition to the design, however, was that of an electrically driven supercharger. This device served in much the same way as forced draught did for a boiler in that it supplied air to the engine at an increased pressure (2 psi above the atmospheric pressure) and so more fuel could be burnt, thus increasing the power output. By means of this device each engine was able to deliver 10,000 bhp, an increase of 1,000 bhp on the normally aspirated version. The supercharger fan was rated at 150 bhp and, being electrically driven, additional generating capacity was required. A 220 volt dc electrical system was installed in the ships, with power coming from two 900 kW generators situated in the auxiliary engine room and a single 450 kW

generator in the main engine room. In each case the generators were driven by B&W trunk piston engines rated at 1,350 bhp and 675 bhp respectively. Three air compressors for starting and fuel injection were also provided. Two oil fired Cochran vertical boilers working at 100 psi supplied steam to meet all heating requirements.[11]

It was the use of supercharging which distinguished these Italian ships from other motor driven liners of the period and the increased power it made available gave the ships a designed service speed of 19–19.5 knots. Not only were they the largest, but they were also the most powerful and fastest motorships in the world. The honour did not last long and quickly went to another Italian vessel.

The rival Navigazione Generale Italiana operated ships on the New York and Buenos Aires routes with vessel interchangeability to suit the seasons. In 1926 its 32,600 gross ton turbine steamship *Roma* became the largest vessel in Italy's merchant fleet, but plans were already in hand to construct a consort with motor propulsion.[12] Apart from the propulsion plant *Augustus* was virtually a sister of *Roma* but with a slightly

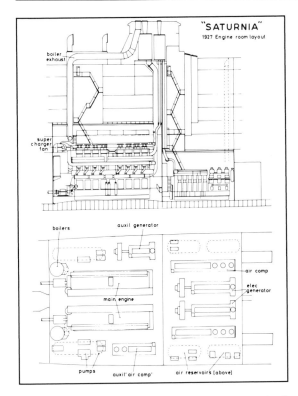

"SATURNIA"
1927 Engine room layout

larger gross tonnage. B&W engines did not find favour with the owner who preferred MAN (Maschinenfabrik Augsburg-Nurnberg) designed two-stroke double-acting engines constructed in Italy under licence by the Cantieri Officine Savoia. The two-stroke engine could produce more power from the same size compared with its four-stroke counterpart, but it required an air supply under pressure to remove exhaust gas from the cylinder and replenish the combustion air charge. Although the four-stroke engine remained popular with some owners it was, in fact, the beginning of the end and two-stroke engines soon became the norm for direct drive propulsive purposes.

Augustus was by far the largest motor liner then constructed and in order to move her 33,650 gross ton bulk through the water at a design speed of 18.5 knots a very powerful propulsive plant was required. At the time engine power was restricted by the strength of the crankshaft and it was not simply a case of increasing the number, or size, of cylinders in order to increase output. Factors such as torsional vibration and bending needed to be considered. To provide sufficient power to

drive *Augustus* a quadruple screw arrangement was needed with each six cylinder MAN–Savoia engine being capable of continuously developing 6,250 bhp at 120 rpm from cylinders 700 mm diameter and 1,200 mm stroke. Three electrically driven fans supplied scavenge air to the engines, although only two were required for normal service conditions, and each had its own diesel driven generator. As with the other motor liners a 220 volt supply of electricity powered all auxiliary machinery, the current being provided by three 600 kW generators. No attempt was made to make use of the exhaust gas waste heat, and two oil fired boilers had to be provided in order to supply steam for laundries, galley and accommodation heating purposes.[13]

Main engine driven compressors provided air at 1,050 psi for blast injection and at 420 psi for starting, the storage being in large reservoirs. *Augustus* proved that large liners could be propelled by diesel engines economically. Fuel consumption proved to be moderate at 0.305 lb/ihp/hr and compared very favourably with that of *Roma*. Although the normal output power amounted to 25,000 bhp, effective two stage silencing reduced exhaust noise to levels of a steamship and the freedom from vibration attracted particular praise.[14] In order to provide increased power a decision was made to replace the diesels with geared turbines and *Augustus* was withdrawn from service in 1939. That in no way detracts from the advances shown by the original machinery, but illustrates the demand for speed on the Atlantic in the immediate prewar years. An air raid on Genoa destroyed the ship whilst she was being converted to the aircraft carrier *Sparviero* in 1945.

With the German designed MAN engine to the forefront of diesel development it was not long before a German shipowner decided to test the Atlantic waters with a motor driven passenger liner. Two combination passenger/cargo liners were delivered to the Hamburg America Line during 1929 and they represented the first geared diesel systems to be installed in any large passenger ship. *Milwaukee* and *St Louis* had similar arrangements, but they differed in certain respects. Both made use of four high speed double-acting two-stroke engines driving two propeller shafts through gearing, but in *Milwaukee* the engines were directly coupled to the gearing whilst *St Louis* had fluid clutches between engines and gearing. That refinement probably resulted from a preference of the builders, Bremer Vulkan; *Milwaukee* was built by Blohm & Voss who had previously constructed a number of single screw ships with geared installations for the same owners.[15]

Blohm & Voss had, in fact, developed the geared diesel drive in order to make use of submarine engines in merchant vessels where a slowly rotating propeller was essential for operating efficiency. It was not, however, simply a case of connecting an engine or two to a gearbox for, unlike with a turbine drive, the diesel engine drive consisted of a series of pulses due to the firing of individual cylinders. That pulsating drive could cause damage to the gear wheel teeth because of chattering. Blohm & Voss carried out extensive research into the problem of gear drives before the system was released for commercial use.[16] It is possible that Bremer Vulkan were unhappy with the arrangement and interposed a fluid clutch between engines and gearbox in order to dampen out any possible vibration effects. The clutch also allowed an engine to be disconnected from the drive should that prove necessary.

Use of indirect drives allowed smaller faster rotating engines to be used compared with direct drive systems. Such engines required less headroom and so the engine space could be made lower. A saving of at least one deck over the engine room length could, therefore, be made giving increased passenger or cargo capacity. Hamburg America Line took full advantage of that fact thus allowing these relatively small ships, 16,700 gross tons, to carry some 1,000 passengers and a fair amount of cargo. A further advantage derived from the use of higher speed engines was that their normal operating speed was far above the natural frequency of the hull and so avoided vibration which caused irritation to passengers.

The MAN engines were the first high speed double-acting two-stroke diesels to be constructed for marine work. Although similar to those installed in *Augustus* they were smaller, only 485 mm bore and 660 mm stroke. At 225 rpm each pair of six cylinder engines could generate 6,300 bhp which was similar to the power output of a single *Augustus* engine, but the high speed engines were some 10 ft shorter and even

when the length of the gearbox was taken into account there was little difference in overall length. In terms of width the geared installation occupied more space, but the saving in at least one deck due to the lower height was of paramount importance. Although the system did not find immediate widespread favour amongst passenger ship operators, the seeds were sown for future development.

Scavenge air came from electrically driven fans, but blast and starting air was provided by main engine driven compressors. Four main diesel generators were of the MAN four-stroke type but they made use of solid fuel injection rather than blast injection, thus saving on the requirement for compressed air. A further innovative feature as far as diesel driven Atlantic liners was concerned could be observed in the use of waste heat for steam production. *Milwaukee* had two boilers placed in the auxiliary engine room but *St Louis*'s two boilers were positioned on a raised platform aft of the main engines. The result was that only the forward funnel of *Milwaukee* expelled exhaust, the after one being a dummy with air suction vents. The boilers could also be oil fired for steam generation in port or when running at slow speed. If steam demand was low then the excess engine exhaust could be made to by-pass the boilers and go direct to a silencer.[17]

Use of waste heat for generating steam improved an already high efficiency for the diesel installation. By the late 1920s it was a recognized fact that the diesel engine was more economical to operate than a steam plant despite the fact that internal combustion engines burnt more expensive diesel oil rather than the heavier bunker grade residual fuel upon which boilers could operate. Lubricating oil consumption was higher than for steam reciprocating engines or turbines, whilst initial capital costs and maintenance costs were also greater. The real benefits of the motorship lay in its more efficient use of fuel and its reduced engine room manning levels.[18] More efficient combustion of light diesel oil in an engine's cylinder resulted in cleaner exhaust and reduced risk of smuts which plagued the steamship, coal or oil fired. Motor liners did not need high funnels to ensure that exhaust cleared the decks and so the characteristic squat smoke stack became standard.

With high powered passenger ships other

Milwaukee *of 1929 with a geared diesel engine installation.*

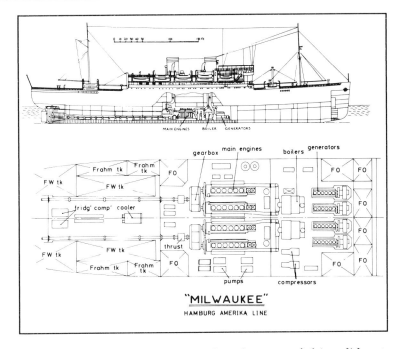

factors had to be considered, not least the suspected problem of vibration and the natural prejudice of the owner. More rapid adoption of the diesel engine for Atlantic liner propulsion was restrained by the limited power available from internal combustion engines. A steam turbine plant could produce considerably higher power than was obtainable from an internal combustion piston engine.

The adoption of quadruple screws, as with *Augustus*, was one way around the problem and it was also tried with the Furness Withy liner *Bermuda*. Not strictly a trans-Atlantic liner, this vessel was built by Workman, Clark & Co in 1928 for the luxury New York to Bermuda service. Each propeller was independently driven by a four cylinder Doxford opposed piston engine normally producing 2,800 bhp at 110 rpm. The total power was low compared with other installations, but they gave the 19,000 gross ton ship a service speed of 17 knots. The main reason for choosing the opposed piston Doxford engine lay in its very good balance which minimized the possibility of vibration.[19] For a luxury liner that was of paramount importance.

The French Line took a similar view when it decided upon quadruple screws for its foray into the diesel propulsion field. *Lafayette* entered service in 1930 but the type of drive did not appear to find favour as a slightly larger sister, *Champlain* of 1931, had steam turbines and no other diesel passenger liner was ever built for the company's trans-Atlantic services. *Lafayette*'s four main engines were of two-stroke double-acting MAN design and similar, but of reduced cylinder bore and stroke, to those installed in *Augustus*. Each engine developed 4,500 bhp at 150 rpm, allowing the 21,500 gross ton liner to realize a service speed of 18.25 knots. Although the use of diesel exhaust gas for generating steam in a waste heat boiler was firmly established practice at the time, steam plant consisted simply of two oil fired scotch boilers. Being a smaller ship than *Augustus*, the electrical requirement of *Lafayette* was lower and served by MAN driven generators, three of 700 kW and two of 500 kW. A considerable amount of electrical energy was required to drive any two, of the three, turbo-blowers which operated constantly in order to keep the main engines supplied with scavenge air.[20]

Britain was not to be left out of the race and had its own motor liner champion in the form of Lord Kylsant, the rather autocratic 'ruler' of Harland & Wolff's shipbuilding empire and Royal Mail Lines' shipping combine, which included White Star. Lord Pirrie, the former commander at Harlands had been very enthusiastic about diesel propulsion ever since his visit to *Fionia* at Kiel and had encouraged close links with Burmeister & Wain. His enthusiasm infected Kylsant with the result that companies within the Royal Mail Group developed a tendency to make use of diesel propulsion, even for passenger ships.

In 1925 the White Star Line, then still under IMM control, decided to spend its way out of the 1920s depression. During summer of that year an order was placed with Harland & Wolff for a 60,000 gross ton liner to be called *Oceanic*.[21] Although work was suspended the following year the project remained alive and design work resumed in 1927 following Royal Mail's acquisition of White Star. Finance of some £9,000,000 was required to construct the ship and that amount could not be readily obtained. However, the ever resourceful Kylsant did organize the building of a 27,000 ton motor vessel for the Atlantic service. *Britannic* was laid down in 1927 and delivered to White Star in 1930. With the order for *Oceanic* being confirmed in 1928 design work continued, but slowly.[22] There was much discussion as to the form of propulsion to be adopted but in May 1929 Kylsant stated publicly that the drive would be electric. Whether the prime movers were to be steam turbines or diesel engines had not been decided.[23] It never was. In September of that year *Oceanic*, Harland & Wolff ship No. 844, was finally abandoned and work concentrated on a sister for *Britannic*.

The diesel electric version of *Oceanic* called

for no less than 47 six cylinder, exhaust gas turbo-charged, four-stroke engines of B&W design. A total output in the region of 275,000 horse power was expected from the plant which would weigh 17,000 tons. Large electric motors connected to each of four screws were expected to drive the ship at 30 knots.[24] Three squat funnels, typical for motor vessels of the period, gave *Oceanic* a pleasant appearance, but the ship was not to be and the concept of diesel electric propulsion for a large Atlantic liner had to wait almost 50 years for the re-engining of *Queen Elizabeth 2*.

Compared with *Oceanic*, *Britannic* might be considered as something of a let-down but she was nothing of the sort and marked Britain's entry into the trans-Atlantic motor liner field. Her external appearance typified the motor liner of the period, especially those built by Harland & Wolff. Only one of the two low raked funnels actually carried exhaust, the forward being a dummy and used for radio communications equipment.

Britannic was a 26,500 gross ton, twin screw ship with a designed service speed of 17 knots. As only two direct drive engines were employed they had to be amongst the most powerful constructed to that date. Harlands' close links with Burmeister & Wain dictated that the 10,000 bhp engines would be of standard B&W four-stroke, double-acting design. Airless fuel injection systems had by that time shown themselves to be simpler and more efficient

White Star motorship Britannic. (H. Weston.)

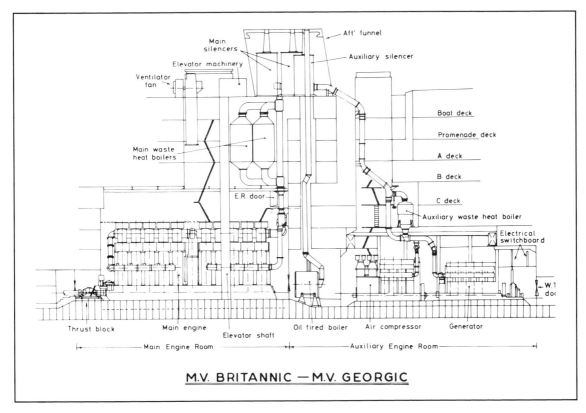

Main silencers

Aft' funnel

Auxiliary silencer

Elevator machinery

Ventilator fan

Boat deck

Promenade deck

A deck

Main waste heat boilers

B deck

E.R. door

C deck

Auxiliary waste heat boiler

Electrical switchboard

W.T. door

Thrust block   Main engine   Oil fired boiler   Air compressor   Generator

Elevator shaft

Main Engine Room   Auxiliary Engine Room

M.V. BRITANNIC — M.V. GEORGIC

Engine room layout for Britannic *and* Georgic.

than blast injection, due to elimination of blast air compressors, but the engines of *Britannic* retained the older arrangement. In fact the engines for *Britannic* and *Georgic* were the last Harland built engines to be fitted with blast injection,[25] the system remaining with each ship until it was scrapped.

With ten cylinders 840 mm bore by 1,500 mm stroke the engines were giants, but could have developed even greater power had pressure charging been utilized. Being of the four-stroke form it was not necessary to provide scavenge air under pressure as with the two-stroke and so an opportunity for higher power potential was not taken. In many respects the installation was merely an enlarged version of the plant installed in *Gripsholm*, few of the improvements embodied in the Italian and German ships being obvious. Four diesel engine driven blast air compressors were provided, whereas a change to solid injection or the use of main engine driven compressors would have reduced

initial costs and saved space. Waste heat boilers were, however, installed, four connected to the main engines and one to the generator engines. Two single ended, oil fired, cylindrical boilers provided steam in port for heating and cooking purposes.

With a capacity for 1,550 passengers in three classes there was a considerable need for electrical power and four diesel driven generators of 500 kW capacity were installed in the auxiliary engine room forward of the compressors. As with other motor liners of the period all pumps and auxiliary machines were electrically driven including the refrigerating plant. The carbon dioxide plant cooled the cargo and provision rooms by means of circulating brine and each CO_2 compressor consumed 55 kW at full power. Throughout the ship over 7,000 30 watt lamps were fitted and in the cabin class galley there were three large ovens each with a rating of 145 kW whilst the tourist and third class galley ovens consumed 208 kW. Hot presses and game roasters were also electrically powered.[26] The use of all electric galley equipment could place considerable strain on the generating capacity. In order to avoid unnecessary operation of generators close co-operation between catering and engine departments was required. During preparation periods for meals additional electrical generating capacity would be provided.

Georgic was identical to Britannic in appearance and machinery installation, save for some minor differences. Instead of a flat superstructure front as applied to her elder sister, Georgic had a gracefully curved section. The difference was essentially cosmetic, although it increased the size of some public rooms. That and some other dimensional changes increased the size to about 27,750 gross tons making Georgic Britain's largest motor vessel. In the engine room the only difference of any note was in the waste heat boiler system. Each main engine had but one exhaust gas boiler whilst two auxiliary exhaust gas boilers were fitted, one each for the generator and compressor engines.[27]

In service both ships performed economically and reliably. Throughout 1935 comparative data was gathered and this showed that Britannic averaged 17.5 knots westbound and 18.5 knots eastward. Georgic managed to improve on those figures by 0.25 knots in each case, but with engine revolutions 1 rpm higher at 95 rpm and 97 rpm respectively. That increased speed was obtained at the cost of additional fuel consumption. The older ship's daily consumption for all purposes, main engine and auxiliaries, was 80 tons westward and 82 tons east. Georgic's consumption was 1 ton higher in each case.[28] Considering the high electrical load and the speed of the ships the fuel consumption figures were considered to be very good, comparing favourably with the Cunard White Star steamships then in service.

Both vessels proved themselves to be popular with passengers, vibration never appearing to be a problem. For the engineers life was never so easy. Blast injection of fuel necessitated large compressors which ran continuously whilst the main engines operated. Such compressors relied upon the effective functioning of suction and discharge valves and to ensure that effectiveness almost constant attention was needed. Junior engineer officers would find that the task of grinding and replacing valves occupied most of their time on board; a mundane but essential task which, like most of that type, was generally considered to be 'good training'. Blast injection systems also caused cylinder relief valves to lift when the engines were started due to the high pressure which would build up in the cylinder as fuel ignited. During manoeuvring the engine rooms of Britannic and Georgic were always shrouded in a fog of engine smoke, which irritated the duty engineers but went unnoticed by the passengers.[29]

National pride has frequently been satisfied

Polish motorship Batory.

by the owning of a large fleet of merchant vessels especially if impressive passenger liners were amongst the number. Following the First World War Poland became an independent state once more and acquired the port of Gdynia from which such liners might sail to New York. The economic wisdom of building passenger liners might have been questioned, but such ships were seen as symbols of nationhood and worth the risk. Two liners were ordered from the Monfalcone yard of the Italian shipbuilders Cantieri Riuniti dell' Adriatico and were designed to allow for pleasure cruising should trade not be sufficient on the Atlantic.

Gdynia America Line's *Pilsudski*, named in honour of Marshal Joseph Pilsudski who became temporary head of the new Polish state, was delivered during 1935 and the second vessel, *Batory*, during 1936. Identical ships of 14,400 gross tons they resembled an earlier motor vessel the yard had produced for the Mediterranean to India service and so it is unlikely that the owners had much say in the design apart from laying down basic specifications. These twin screw ships could carry over 1,000 passengers in three classes and they were constructed to the highest safety standards with ten watertight compartments. Main engines, constructed by the shipbuilder, were of Sulzer two-stroke, single-acting type with airless fuel injection. Each engine could produce 6,250 bhp at 130 rpm from its nine 720 mm bore by 1,250 mm stroke cylinders. Instead of employing electrically driven scavenge blowers the engines employed double-acting air pumps driven from the crankshaft and so they were self-contained units and did not rely upon other machines for their operation.

Two Cochran composite boilers, installed at the forward end of the engine room, provided all steam requirements when at sea or in port. Four electrical generators, also powered by Sulzer engines, each with a rating of 210 kW could supply current to the 220 volt dc system. Two of the diesels were also coupled by mechanical clutches to compressors for the supply of starting air.[30] For the 19 knot service speed main engine fuel consumption during the first full year of service averaged at 39 tons per day for *Pilsudski*. Electrical generators, of which two were always running, consumed 1.3 tons per day whilst the boilers burnt 2.5 tons per day in port. Consumption was, therefore, about half

that of *Britannic* for a ship of about half the tonnage travelling slightly faster.[31] On the basis of the figure the Polish ships would appear to have the more economical installation. Compared with other Atlantic motor liners it showed a saving in space with no requirement for blast air compressors or scavenge fans with their extra electrical load. Lessons were being gradually learned.

It had been the Cosulich Line's intention to put *Saturnia* and *Vulcania* on the South American services and construct large powerful vessels for the New York run. Results of service trials with the two motor vessels were awaited before a decision could be made as to the type of machinery for the new ships, but expectations were that diesel propulsion would be chosen.[32] The slump in Atlantic passenger traffic changed matters and orders for new ships never materialized. An amalgamation of three Atlantic lines forced by the Italian government brought the Italia Line into being in 1932, although the Cosulich concern retained a measure of independence until 1937. With the *Rex* and *Conte di Savoia* operating the express service from Italy there was a need for fast secondary liners, but no money for construction.

Re-engining of *Saturnia* and *Vulcania* offered the ideal solution. They were relatively new and comfortable ships which just lacked sufficient power for the increased speed demanded. Strangely, different main engines were chosen for each ship and there appears to have been no logical reason for that decision, which would have caused problems relating to crew familiarization and spares. *Vulcania* received two ten cylinder, two-stroke, double-acting Fiat engines each with a designed output of 13,000 bhp at 128 rpm. *Saturnia*'s two ten cylinder two-stroke, double-acting Sulzer engines were each required to develop 14,000 bhp at 130 rpm during normal service. Maximum output in each case was considered to be 18,000 bhp for the Fiats and 20,820 bhp for the Sulzers. Both types of engines employed airless fuel injection.

A restriction imposed upon re-engining was that there should be no increase in the engine room space occupied by main and auxiliary machinery. Changes in the auxiliary machinery differed between the ships but included the fitting of composite boilers to make use of the waste heat in the exhaust gas. Aboard *Vulcania* a

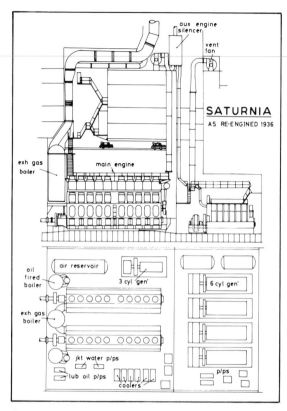

Saturnia's engine room layout following re-engining in 1936.

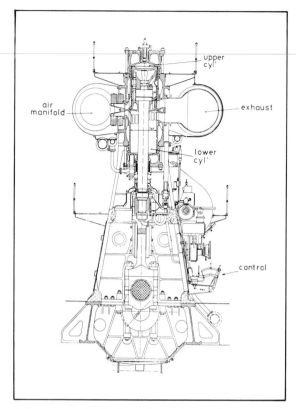

Sulzer two-stroke, double-acting engine fitted in Saturnia.

steam driven turbo-dynamo, capable of generating 400 kW, was installed as well as a 700 horsepower steam driven turbo-blower which was available to supply scavenge air to the main engines should the two diesel driven reciprocating scavenge air pumps fail. *Saturnia* used electrically driven scavenge air fans similar to, but more powerful than, the earlier arrangement.[33]

Re-engining increased the service speed of both ships from 17 knots to 20 knots with an average increase in daily main engine fuel consumption from 85 tons to 102 tons.[34] Speed had to be paid for not only in capital charges, but also in fuel costs. It is, however, interesting to compare the fuel consumption with a steamship of the period. Canadian Pacific's 'Duchess' class liners of 1928 were considered to be very efficient for that time. Being smaller, 20,100 gross tons, and slower, 18 knots, the advantage should have been with them, but on a lower output of 18,000 shp they consumed about 110 tons of fuel each day for propulsion purposes alone.[35]

The diesel had arrived, especially for the medium sized passenger ship, but some people refused to recognize the fact.

Scandinavian shipowners were less reluctant than most to embrace the internal combustion technology and many of them did so with enthusiasm. Prior to the outbreak of the Second World War only one other motor liner commenced service on the north Atlantic and she belonged to Norwegian American Line. *Oslofjord* was built in Germany by Deutsche Schiff-und Maschinenbau AG, Weft AG Weser and, following the earlier German preferences, was fitted with geared main engines. MAN double-acting two-stroke engines were coupled in pairs to gearboxes using Vulcan fluid clutches and each gearbox connected directly to a propeller shaft. Each engine had a designed output of 4,400 bhp at 215 rpm but the gearing reduced the propeller speed to a maximum 120 rpm giving the 18,650 gross ton ship a normal service speed of 19 knots.

Typically for a motorship, most auxiliaries were electrically driven and four MAN single-acting four-stroke diesels were each connected to 400 kW generators. Some auxiliaries, including an air compressor, were steam driven, that steam being provided by exhaust gas boilers at sea or oil fired boilers in port. A fairly extensive CO_2 fridge system was fitted to meet the usual perishable stores duty and the increasing demand from trans-Atlantic passengers for ice and iced water.[36] *Oslofjord* had a very pleasing appearance with the forward dummy funnel enhancing the profile. Unfortunately she became a casualty of war after only two years of service.

Another Atlantic motor liner also failed to survive the war, in fact even a second attempt failed to enter commercial service. Happy with the performance and commercial success of *Gripsholm* and *Kungsholm* the Swedish American Line decided to construct a larger vessel with the specific intention that she would be used for cruising during the Atlantic winter off-peak season. In 1936 the contract was placed with Cantieri Riuniti dell' Adriatico and construction commenced in March of the following year at the Monfalcone yard. Of some 28,000 gross tons the new ship was to be called *Stockholm* and would carry 1,350 passengers on trans-Atlantic service and 640 when cruising. The Atlantic

service speed of 19 knots called for engines with an output in the region of 22,000 bhp.

The engines were of Sulzer SD type for simplicity. That simplicity lay in the fact that the engines were single-acting rather than double-acting and the reduced power from each of the ten cylinder engines necessitated the use of three in order to obtain the desired speed. The owner had preferred the direct coupled engine system, rather than the geared arrangement, because crew experience lay in that direction. The contract stipulated electrically driven auxiliaries and five 870 kW diesel generators were to provide the power.[37] The practically completed *Stockholm* was destroyed by fire in December 1938, but an immediate decision was made to construct an almost identical replacement using the original engines, or as much as could be salvaged. That replacement *Stockholm* was slightly larger at about 30,000 gross tons although the propulsive power remained the same. The war had, however, intervened and neutral Sweden could not take delivery of its flagship. Sold to the Italians and renamed *Sabaudia*, the ship was set aside for trooping but never converted. Allied bombing finally destroyed her, but at the end of the war she was raised and salvaged. One of the engines was then fitted in a new cargo ship *Trieste*.[38]

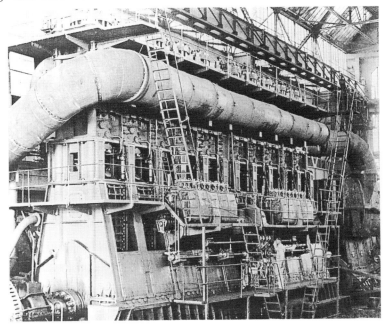

One of Vulcania's *ten cylinder Fiat engines during shop trials.*

CHAPTER 11

Post-War Resurgence

The aftermath of the Second World War saw many traditional Atlantic liner companies in a depressed state as far as tonnage was concerned. Germany's fleet was non-existent, any ships left afloat were distributed amongst the victors as reparations. It was neutral Sweden which took the first steps to rebuild, plans being drawn up before the conflict ended. Post-war conditions were unknown, but the Swedish American board was not going to be left without ample berths to meet any demand. However, nobody knew what that demand might be and how it would be influenced by air transport or shortage of money. In the end the solution was a compromise, a ship of moderate passenger capacity but fairly large cargo space. It was a far cry from the magnificent liners ordered from Italy, but the war had changed more than the map of Europe.

Circumstances dictated that the ship be constructed in Sweden and the order went to the Gotaverken yard in Gothenburg, that concern also building the two main diesel engines. These were eight cylinder single-acting two-stroke engines to Gotaverken's own design and they developed 15,600 bhp at 110 rpm, giving the 11,650 gross ton ship a service speed of 19 knots.[1] In honour of the two failed Italian attempts the new vessel was given the name *Stockholm*, but there all similarity ceased. Known throughout the company as the compromise nobody wanted,[2] *Stockholm* did introduce the novel Gotaverken engine to passenger liner service but the ship had no real claim to fame until she collided with *Andrea Doria* off Nantucket in 1956. That notoriety ensured a

place in maritime history, a place the ship never deserved and the owner never sought.

Norwegian American Line opened peacetime Atlantic commercial service with its *Stavangerfjord* in August 1945 and it quickly became evident that replacement tonnage for the war casualty *Oslofjord* was urgently needed. Traffic on the Scandinavia to New York run was very promising but, as with *Stockholm*, design work had commenced long before the conflict came to an end. Technical staff worked on plans for the liner from 1942 until the order for its construction was placed with the Netherlands Dock and Shipbuilding Company of Amsterdam in 1946.[3] It says much for the optimism and determination of the Norwegians that they planned for a future peacetime passenger service whilst their country was still occupied by enemy forces.

Continuing the Scandinavian preference the new vessel, also called *Oslofjord*, was diesel engine driven but these engines were to a Dutch design. Stork double-acting, two-stroke engines were stipulated and a twin screw configuration was adopted in order to obtain the required power for the service speed of 20 knots. Each seven cylinder engine had a designed output of 8,175 bhp at 130 rpm from cylinders of 720 mm bore and 1,100 mm stroke. There was nothing outstandingly different about the engine design nor the installation, in fact the overall system was very much of late 1930s vintage, but the war had stifled all but military development.

A characteristic of all Stork engines was the use of chromium plated liners using the Dutch

Van der Horst system and such an arrangement was employed in the engines for *Oslofjord*. Chromium plating was claimed to reduce wear and hence prolong the cylinder liner's operating life, but it was expensive and never really caught on with other engine builders although the system did find favour with Stork and some Dutch shipowners.

Following the usual practice scavenging air was supplied by electrically driven blowers, the power being supplied by diesel generators. Three such blowers were provided, one being in reserve, although there were four generators. As was usual these generator engines also came from the same manufacturer as the main propulsion units but were of four-stroke design. Surprisingly no attempt was made to recover energy from main engine exhaust gas and all steam came from two oil fired cylindrical boilers. However, two waste heat exchangers utilized

the generator exhaust to heat the main boiler feed water. It was an economy of sorts, but greater improvement could have been obtained by the use of a properly designed exhaust gas boiler installation.[4]

Operating out of Scandinavian waters necessitated adequate heating of the ship and so a considerable steam supply was required; the use of waste heat for that purpose would have reduced the fuel bill. Ventilation arrangements differed from that normally fitted aboard liners, air being admitted to cabins through ceiling light fixtures with regulating handwheels being provided to control the temperature. Careful consideration of the ventilation system allowed most of the trunking to be installed during early stages of construction with the result that it mainly remained hidden from sight. A total air displacement of 385,000 cu ft/min was provided by 54 electrically driven fans, the stale air being

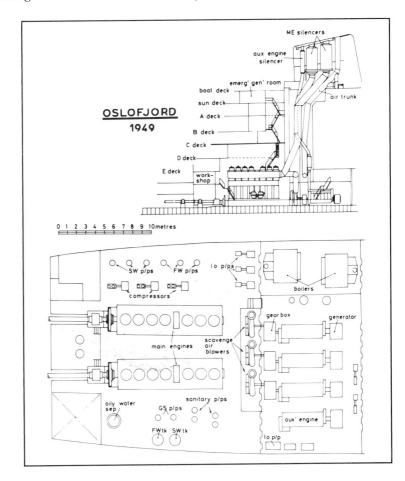

Layout of machinery spaces in the 1949 built Oslofjord.

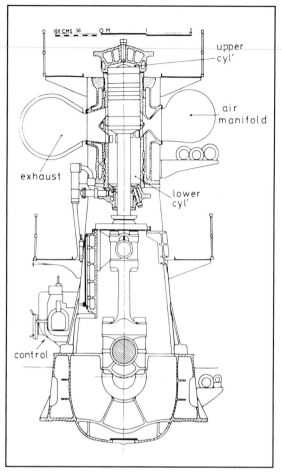

discharged up the single funnel.[5] *Oslofjord*'s profile was very pleasing, her clean lines giving the uncluttered appearance which characterized post-war liner construction. Although primarily designed as a trans-Atlantic vessel *Oslofjord* was also built with a view to the cruise market from American ports, a market her owners had exploited during pre-war years.

A return to peace in 1945 did not completely assuage the fears of the anxious shipowner. His ships, at least those which remained, were no longer at risk from torpedo, mine or bomb, but what would the future hold? Uncertainty concerning passenger traffic gripped all owners and many held back their rebuilding plans until the market could be better assessed. Unlike the situation which prevailed at the end of the previous conflict, there were few captured prizes to be distributed amongst the victors' fleets. New tonnage would have to be constructed and building costs had escalated. Like the Scandinavian owners, Cunard Line managers also had eyes on the luxury cruise market believing that Americans released from the restrictions of war would provide a willing source of revenue.

A decision was quickly reached to build a large ship specifically for that purpose, with the added consideration that she might be used to

Left *Stork design two-stroke engine fitted in* Oslofjord.

Below *Cunard's cruise/Atlantic liner* Caronia.

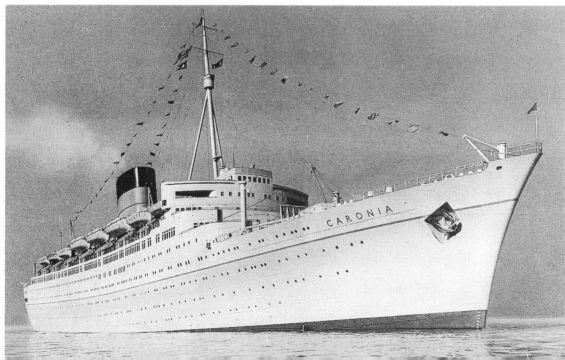

fill in for the large trans-Atlantic 'Queens' whilst they underwent summer overhaul. *Caronia* was ordered from the traditional Cunard builder, John Brown & Co, and was launched in October 1947. A positioning voyage to New York in January 1949 preceded the extensive cruising for which she had been primarily constructed. Public rooms were air conditioned and a departure from the usual Cunard livery, in favour of light green for hull and superstructure, was made to keep the ship cool under tropical conditions. A sprayed coating of asbestos was applied to the hull interior in order to minimize overheating whilst cruising or heat loss on the Atlantic.[6]

Steam turbine propulsion remained the order of the day as far as Cunard was concerned, but there were advances compared with *Queen Elizabeth*. Although the war had restricted development of large diesel engines, improvements in steam plant could be made due to metallurgical progress prompted by that conflict. *Caronia* had two propellers connected to geared turbines, each installation comprising series connected impulse-reaction high, reaction intermediate and reaction low pressure ahead turbines. In the event of any turbine failure cross connections allowed that turbine to be by-passed. Impulse astern turbines were provided in the intermediate and low pressure casings. The high pressure turbine gearing was double reduction whilst the intermediate and low pressure turbines were single reduction. Better quality materials allowed the steam pressure to be increased to 600 psi and the temperature to 800°F, although inlet conditions to the turbines were slightly lower. Such steam conditions not only improved efficiency but also allowed for a smaller high pressure turbine, which operated at a higher speed necessitating that double reduction gearing.

Overall the size of turbine and boiler plants were smaller due to the increased steam condition and that saved on engine room space. Development of fabrication techniques during the war resulted in improvements in quality and a greater confidence in the use of fabrication for parts which had been traditionally cast. Pre-war turbine and gear casings were invariably of cast iron, but fabricated low pressure turbine casings and gear casings found employment aboard *Caronia*. Surprisingly welding was still not con-

sidered suitable for the other stage turbines, although it was employed for constructing pressure vessels. Increasing use of welding could be observed, not only in hull construction, but also for parts such as bearing pedestals thereby saving a considerable amount of weight.

Six Yarrow double flow type water tube boilers supplied steam for main and auxiliary purposes and those boilers employed welded drums. There were four large five drum boilers and two small boilers of the same type specifically for use in port. All boilers operated under a closed trunk, forced draught system with open stokehold, induced draught fans being positioned in the uptakes below the dust collectors. Air heaters of the rotary regenerative Ljungstrom type were provided for each boiler. For normal operations the plant developed 35,000 shp giving the 34,000 gross ton *Caronia* a speed of 22 knots.[7]

Caronia's four 225 volt, 1,100 kW turbo-generators took steam direct from main or auxiliary boilers, but up to 15,000 lb per hour of steam, at 60 psi, could be bled from each for heating and galley purposes. That arrangement avoided the use of desuperheaters and low pressure systems whilst in port and it simplified the steam plant. It was recognized as the first use of 'pass-out' turbines in a British ship although such arrangements were common with land based turbines.[8]

The reduced number of boilers required due to the higher steam conditions allowed a single funnel to be fitted and that had benefits as far as accommodation layout was concerned. Without doubt that single large smoke stack was as impressive as it was unnecessary, a smaller device would have served just as well for discharging the boiler gases but it would not have suited the ship. Aesthetics govern passenger ship design almost as much as practicality.

Although the 'Queens' came through the war unscathed the intermediate fleet suffered considerably, amongst others five of the six 'A' class vessels were lost. Replacement was essential if the company aimed at resuming some form of intermediate service. As the potential market could only be guessed at in 1945 the cautious approach appeared to be the most sensible. Two 13,700 gross ton passenger cargo liners were ordered, *Media* from John Brown & Co and *Parthia* from Harland & Wolff. *Media* was delivered in 1947 and *Parthia* the following year. Both ships had accommodation for 250 passen-

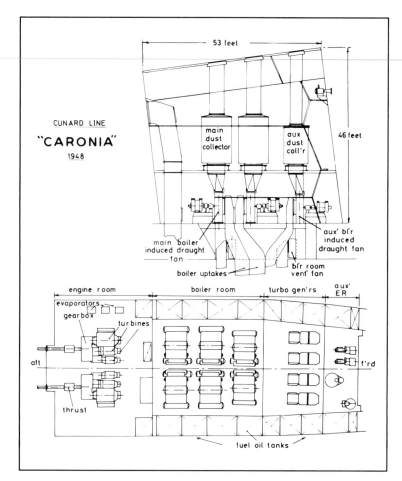

CUNARD LINE
"CARONIA"
1948

53 feet

46 feet

main
dust
collector

aux
dust
coll'r

main boiler
induced draught
fan

aux' bl'r
induced
draught fan

boiler uptakes

bl'r room
vent' fan

engine room

boiler room

turbo gen'rs

aux'
ER

evaporators
gearbox
turbines

aft

f'rd

thrust

fuel oil tanks

Left Caronia's *machinery layout and massive funnel structure.*

Right *Yarrow water tube boiler as fitted in* Caronia.

gers with space for over 370,000 cu ft of general cargo and 60,000 cu ft of refrigerated cargo. The ships fitted the immediate requirements, but at a later stage it became evident that such combination ships were not ideal for the type of service envisaged by Cunard. Time spent in port handling the cargo was excessive and prohibited a quick turn round for the passenger trade; hotel service staff still had to be paid.

The twin screw ships were turbine driven with impulse-reaction high pressure turbines working in series with reaction low pressure units. Through double reduction gearing the normal 13,600 shp from the turbines gave the ships a service speed of 17 knots. Three row impulse astern turbines were fitted in each low pressure casing. Two Yarrow five drum boilers supplied steam to the turbines at 430 psi and 750°F, each boiler having forced and induced draught fans. Low pressure steam at 100 psi for

heating and galley purposes came from two auxiliary Cochran boilers whilst in port, but at sea a steam generator fulfilled that requirement. The generator heating source was normally steam bled from the HP main turbine, but steam could be taken directly from the boiler during low power conditions or to meet a sudden demand for low pressure steam.

Most ancillary equipment was electrically driven and power at 220 volts came from four 375 kW generators driven by Ruston & Hornsby diesel engines. The diesels furnished gas to a Clarkson waste heat boiler, the sole function of which was to operate the fresh water evaporators. Refrigeration equipment was extensive, with five compressors having a total power consumption of 230 kW. Two of the compressors were arranged to cover accommodation air conditioning requirements and the plant could maintain 82°F and 55 per cent relative humidity

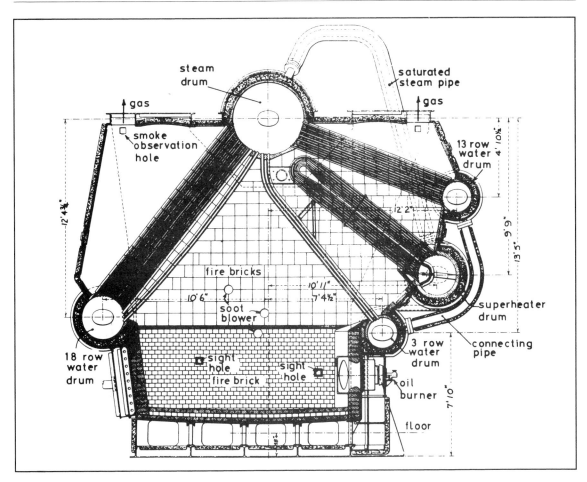

with outside conditions of 90°F and 75 per cent. During cold weather the system arranged for a 70°F accommodation temperature and 45 per cent relative humidity.[9]

These ships were nothing revolutionary in terms of their plant, but *Media* did have one claim to fame. Apart from being the first post-war constructed Atlantic liner to enter service, she was also the first Atlantic liner to be fitted with fin stabilizers.

The concept of an activated fin stabilizer system was not new, a patent having been taken out as early as 1898 by a Mr Smith of Stirling, Scotland. In 1925 Motora's Japanese patent was more practical, with systems being fitted in several ships. The arrangement relied on a geared mechanism for activation of the fins and was too slow in reacting to be of any great benefit. It was only in the 1930s when two British firms, Denny of Dumbarton and Brown Brothers of Edinburgh,

combined forces that an effective hydraulically actuated fin system with gyroscopic control was produced. During the 1930s and 1940s the Denny–Brown fin stabilizer proved itself on small warships and cross-channel ferries, but in 1950 the P&O liner *Chusan* became the first large vessel to be so equipped.[10] Successful performance guaranteed adoption for Atlantic liners.

Cunard installed fin stabilizers aboard *Media* and quickly followed that with a similar arrangement on *Parthia*. *Queen Elizabeth* received a twin set as did *Queen Mary*, but care had to be taken with such systems in order to avoid interference effects on the after set of fins due to the wake from the forward set. Careful positioning was essential. Single set fins were generally sited as near amidships as possible in order to avoid additional forces on the fins as the ship pitched. With these and other ships already in

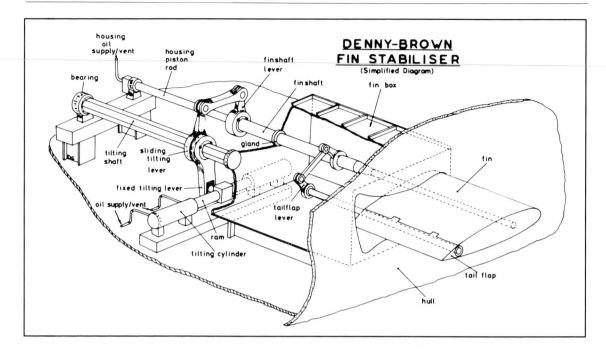

DENNY-BROWN FIN STABILISER
(Simplified Diagram)

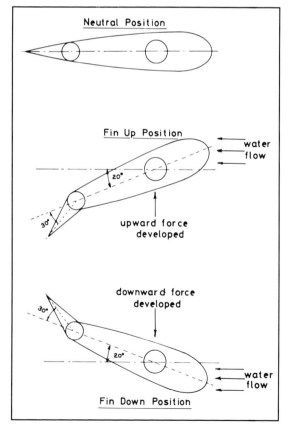

Above *Denny–Brown fin stabilizer arrangement.*

Left *Action of fin stabilizer.*

service, the retrofitting of stabilizers caused problems in that some existing items of machinery usually had to be repositioned and work had to be undertaken over a period of time in order to avoid delay to the ship. In the case of the *Queen Mary*'s plant, preliminary work commenced in 1956 with preparatory fitting taking place during the 1957 annual overhaul and final installation during the 1958 overhaul. Considerable difficulty was encountered in siting the stabilizer compartments which was eventually accomplished by repositioning some items of boiler plant and arranging the stabilizers so that the operating rams were vertical rather than horizontal. As with *Queen Elizabeth*, one set of fins was positioned amidships and the other set some 126 ft forward.[11] New building after the early 1950s always made provision for fin stabilizers in the design.

Fin stabilizers are similar to semi-balanced rudders, but they project horizontally from the hull and are placed low down near the turn of the bilge. Size depended upon the installation concerned but typically a fin would project about 12 ft from the hull and so had to be retractable in order to allow for berthing and to reduce drag in calm weather when the effect of the fin was not required. The stabilizing effect could be produced by rotating the fin through an angle with the ship in motion thereby producing a righting motion to counteract the roll. Stabilizer fins fitted to the *Empress of England* had an outreach of 12 ft and a fore to aft length of 6 ft 6 in, giving a total area of 78 sq ft. The load on a single fin at 20° angle with the ship's speed 22 knots was 70.2 tons, providing a righting moment of 6,434 tons/ft.[12]

Fins were also provided with tails which could be moved relative to the main fin and so increase the restoring force. Tails had an area of about 0.2 to 0.25 of the total fin area. In most cases fins could be rotated some 20° either side of horizontal with tails being rotated about 30° relative to the fin. That rotation of the tail was automatic as the fin twisted and was produced by means of linkages from the fin twisting shaft. During, say, a roll to starboard the fin on that side of the ship would be turned to the nose up attitude, whilst the fin on the other side of the ship would take up a nose down attitude. Such action would produce a righting couple to counter wave induced rolling. In order to obtain the correct restoring action the fins had to be rotated very quickly as the wave caused the ship to roll. Rapid hydraulic actuation together with sensitive gyroscopic control allowed the fins to move through a total angle of 40° in about two seconds. It was only that ability which allowed the fin stabilizer to be effective.

Various factors influenced the righting moment provided by the fins and extremely careful design was essential to suit fins to a particular vessel. Obviously fin area was important, but that had to be matched to fin arm length and ship speed in order that the ship of a particular displacement and metacentric height might be prevented from rolling. The action of stabilizing fins is very much like that of aircraft wings in that a force, up or down, is provided as a fluid acts on the section. Depending upon the angle of the fin to that fluid the force is large or small, up or down. Fins which functioned effectively at normal full speed would not do so if the ship was running at reduced speed. Certain sea conditions also made fins ineffective and they did nothing to counter the uncomfortable effects of pitching.

As already mentioned, the hydraulic fin actuating system had to be very powerful and rapid in action, but the whole effectiveness of fin stabilization depended upon an accurate control system which could react instantaneously to change in ship attitude. The heart of the control system was the gyro unit which contained two gyros, namely a vertical gyro and a velocity gyro. Where twin stabilizer systems were provided each was completely independent apart from the main activation switch on the bridge. The vertical gyro, as the name suggests, reacted to changes in the ship's vertical position but the control unit incorporated a natural list switch. That would be activated in order to prevent the stabilizers attempting to rectify a natural displacement from the vertical which was due to say ballast or fuel transfer rather than rolling.

The velocity gyro, mounted horizontally across the ship, was influenced by angular

Queen Mary, *a large ship with two sets of stabilizers.*

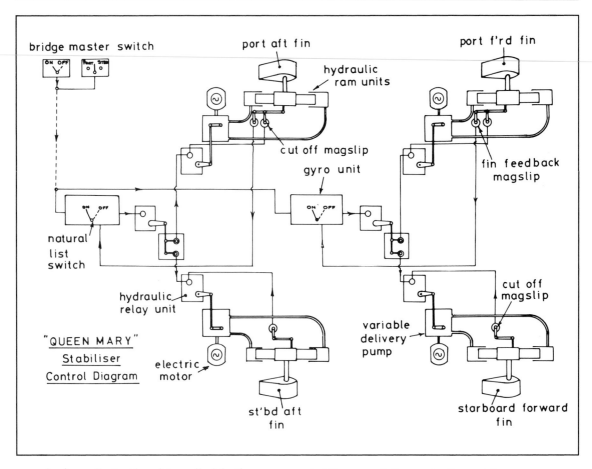

Stabilizer control diagram for Queen Mary.

speed of a roll. As the ship rolled both gyros would react, producing a combined electrical signal with a strength related to the angle of roll and the rate at which that angle was changing. That signal activated hydraulic relays on each side of the ship and these in turn regulated the output from variable delivery hydraulic pumps. Oil from the pumps was supplied to ram units and these, by means of tiller arm devices, rotated the fins in the direction and by the angle directed from the gyro control unit. Electrical feedback to the gyro unit indicating the current fin attitude was provided by magslips; basically electric motor devices which perfectly reproduce positioning at a distance and also allow for amplification. Cut off magslips also allowed the oil supply to the rams to be stopped when the fins had reached maximum angle of rotation.[13]

In the case of twin installations it was possible to test the stabilizer effect in calm weather by having one set of fins force roll the ship and the

other set correct that roll. That was actually carried out aboard *Queen Mary* on 29 March 1958 when forced rolls of plus and minus 10° were induced at 28.5 knots using fore and aft sets alternately and stabilizing with the other set.[14] These tests confirmed operational results with other vessels that fin stabilizers were effective in moderating rolling under most, but not all, sea conditions. Installation of such systems became accepted practice but there was a price to pay. Added weight, including loss of buoyancy, could be high, in the case of the *Queen Elizabeth* it amounted to 456 tons. Cost was more difficult to quantify, but for installations in the early 1950s averaged at about two to three per cent of the price of the ship.[15] Owners felt that the cost was worthwhile. Early fin stabilizers were drawn into the hull directly, but that took up considerable space. From the early 1960s many ships, including *QE2*, were provided with fins which could be stowed sideways by means of a pivot mechanism. Such an arrangement occupied less space within the hull.

The large or fast Atlantic liner has long been looked upon as a symbol of national prestige and that view still prevailed after the end of the Second World War, in fact, it still held good into the 1960s. American liners had always come out second best to their European counterparts, but the flame still burned within some naval architects for an American owned ship to eclipse all others. In nobody did that flame burn more fiercely than William Francis Gibbs. Tirelessly he pursued the cause and eventually won backing for his supership. No shipping company could afford to finance the vessel he envisaged but United States Lines wanted such a ship and the American government was prepared to subsidize its construction and operation. Gibbs convinced those in authority that the ship could act as a fast troop transport should the need arise and in doing so obtained a larger proportion of the construction cost from the US Navy. The total cost amounted to some $78 million, twice the cost of a conventional ship of that size. United States Lines contributed some $35 million, the shipping subsidy board $18 million and the US Navy $25 million.[16]

Much has been written about the interior and operation of Gibbs' supership, *United States*, and it is unnecessary to repeat the details as it is the machinery which is under consideration. Until 1968 the power plant remained a navy secret and only the barest information regarding performance of the ship was released before then. As it turned out there was nothing unusual about the underwater hull form or machinery, it was just that the engines were the most powerful ever installed in a merchant vessel. Naturally, steam turbines were employed and they drove quadruple screws through double reduction gearing. Two stage turbines were used, with steam being bled off between HP and LP stages for auxiliary purposes such as evaporators and heating. Each turbine set could generate in excess of 55,000 shp. Steam entry conditions to the HP turbine were an amazing 920 psi and 960°F. Design limits for the forced draught Babcock & Wilcox boilers were 925 psi with a superheater outlet temperature of 1,000°F.

Machinery was actually arranged in separate

Hinged fin stabilizer of QE2.

rooms, there being two boiler rooms, two turbine rooms and two auxiliary machinery rooms. The forward boiler room contained four boilers, each with ten burners and each capable of producing 269,000 lb of steam per hour. In that room were also situated feed pumps and a 1,500 kW turbo-generator. Positioned immediately aft of that boiler room was the forward turbine room which also contained two further turbo-generators and electrical switchboards. Aft of the turbine room was an auxiliary engine room containing varied equipment including four air conditioning machines and three evaporators, each of which could produce 250 tons of fresh water per day.

That group formed a unit in its own right and drove the forward and outboard propellers. A similar set of three rooms, separated from the forward set by a deep tank, drove the after and

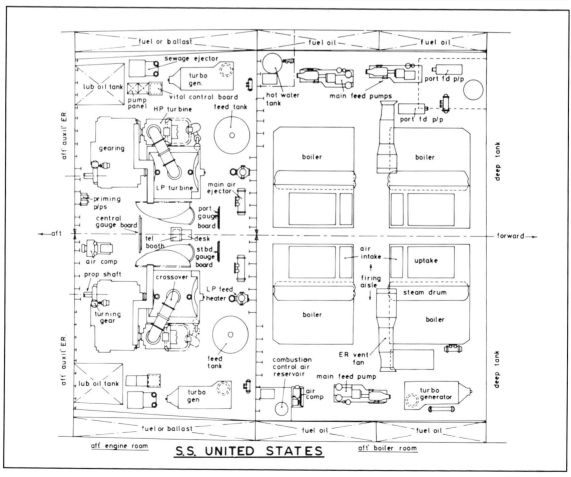

S.S. UNITED STATES

inboard screws. The design allowed each set of rooms to function in isolation, thus in the event of damage disabling either group the ship could proceed on two screws, still capable of 26 knots. A complex system of pipe crossovers allowed any combination of boilers and turbines to be connected should the need have arisen. The entire plant was basically the same as fitted to a 'Midway' class aircraft carrier.

Trials results were also kept secret for many years, but they show that the 53,329 gross ton *United States* averaged 38.32 knots into a 20 knot wind when running at full power; 241,785 shp. A maximum speed in excess of 42 knots was achieved making the 'Blue Riband' taking speeds of 35.59 knots eastbound and 33.92 knots westbound seem like cruising. In normal service the ship maintained 29–30 knots on a daily fuel consumption of about 740 tons and

her fuel capacity gave a steaming range of 10,000 nautical miles. Under such normal conditions only six of the eight boilers were used and then at reduced pressure and temperature, the plant operating at about half capacity. Without a doubt the 'Big U' was in a class by itself as far as machinery was concerned. All of that power required an engineering complement of 47 persons keeping a three watch system.

Propellers were originally to have been four bladed, but vibration analysis studies indicated that two four bladed and two five bladed would give the best results. The forward outboard four bladed screws normally operated at 139 rpm whilst the after inboard screws rotated at 141 rpm, giving the ship a speed of 29.5 knots. The speed difference was also adopted to reduce vibration. No fin stabilizers were installed, the bilge keels being all that was considered neces-

Above left United States *during sea trials.* (United States Lines.)

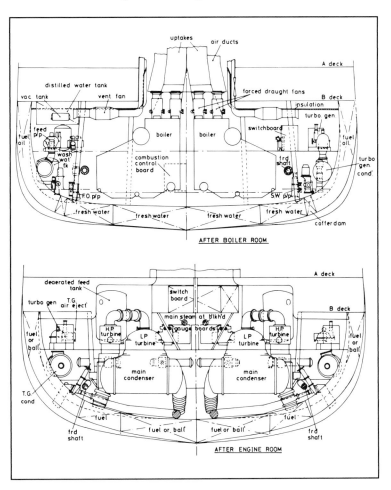

Left *Plan view of the after boiler and turbine rooms of* United States.

Right *Section through after boiler and turbine rooms of* United States.

United States *at Southampton; her massive funnels give an impression of power.*

sary to minimize rolling. In terms of watertight subdivision *United States* was superior to any merchant vessel ever built and could remain afloat in a stable condition with four adjacent compartments flooded. Wing fuel and ballast tanks extended above the waterline at B deck and down to the double bottom tanks, effectively forming a double hull. Fortunately these defences were never tested.

As a commercial proposition the ship could never have been built, nor could it have operated, without the US Government's operating subsidy which amounted to $72 million between 1961 and 1969.[17] The maritime enthusiast should, however, be grateful that she was constructed. Her power, performance and style marked a fitting finale to the Atlantic 'Blue Riband' challenge.

After the *United States* it might be considered that there was nothing left to say regarding Atlantic liners and their machinery, but that was far from the case. The 'Blue Riband' may have been won for the final time, but there was still the routine business of transporting hundreds of thousands of passengers across that 3,000 mile stretch of unpredictable water.

Italy renewed its interest when the Italia Line constructed two elegant 29,000 gross ton liners, *Andrea Doria* and *Christoforo Colombo*, for its Genoa to New York run. They entered service in 1953 and 1954 respectively and were based upon *Giulio Cesare* and *Augustus*, built two years earlier for the South American run. In comparison with the 'Queens' and *United States* they were small and slow, but their performance exceeded that expected of intermediate liners. But then they were not intermediate as far as the Italians were concerned, they were top class Mediterranean liners very much in the tradition of *Rex* and *Conte di Savoia*.

As with other passenger construction of the period a great deal of light weight aluminium was used in construction of the superstructure. Such material enabled a larger ship to be built within any draught restriction and, in some cases, allowed an extra deck to be incorporated without affecting stability. Unlike Atlantic liners on the northern routes, *Andrea Doria* and her sister were fully air conditioned. Higher temperatures encountered on the southern route necessitated such a luxury which 'spoilt' the passengers somewhat. The advantages of full air conditioning were self evident for New York and northern waters became rather warm during summer months and most shipowners saw the light. Future new construction was invariably air conditioned throughout and many owners took steps to extend the air conditioning which only then applied to public rooms. Such a step became essential if the ship was to be sent cruising.

The new Italian ships were propelled by steam turbines despite the success obtained with *Saturnia* and *Vulcania*, but it was considered that turbines provided a simpler machinery layout and allowed an ample margin of power. Each of the twin turbine sets comprised three separate stages with double reduction gearing to the propeller shaft and was designed to develop 25,000 shp for normal service. Under those conditions the shafts turned at 140 rpm driving the ship at 23 knots, but at a maximum 30,000 shp from each engine the ship could achieve 26.4 knots. High pressure turbines had two impulse stages and 19 reaction stages, but the intermediate and low pressure turbines were entirely reaction. Crossover connections allowed any turbine to be isolated in the event of damage, allowing the two other stages to continue functioning.

Four Foster–Wheeler water tube boilers supplied steam, but normal service speed could be maintained with only three on range. In contrast to the boilers aboard *United States* those on the *Andrea Doria* and *Christoford Colombo* operated at 655 psi and 840°F, but then the same power was not required nor was the subsidizing money available. Two 1,000 kW turbo-generators provided electrical power at 220 volts whilst any of the five 750 kW diesel engine driven generators could be employed to supplement or supply all power in port with boilers shut down.[18]

1953 also saw entry into service of the Greek Line's 22,000 gross ton *Olympia*, the only vessel that concern ever ordered from a builder. Built on the Clyde by Alexander Stephen & Sons she was a typical high quality passenger liner in which British yards of the period specialized. The steam turbine plant introduced the latest ideas in turbine design as developed by Pametrada including built-up nozzle plates and diaphragms. The Parsons and Marine Engineering Turbine Research and Development Association, Pametrada, was set up in 1944 by a number of British turbine manufacturers to co-ordinate and develop research into steam and gas turbines.

The twin two stage double reduction geared turbines had a maximum rating of 25,000 shp, but for normal running produced some 24,000 shp to give the ship a service speed of 21 knots. Astern turbines were incorporated in both stages and were of the impulse type, as was the HP stage. The LP turbine was a double flow reaction unit, which meant that steam entered at the middle of the casing and flowed axially in both directions through two separate turbine units in the same casing. Such an arrangement helped to balance the considerable axial thrust which was produced in single flow turbines.

Fabricated steel gear wheels and nickel-steel pinions reduced turbine speed from 4,030 rpm for the HP and 3,700 rpm for the LP to a very sedate 140 rpm at the propeller shaft. As had then become accepted practice, the gear casings were fabricated affairs but first and second stage casings were separate units in order to facilitate machining and erection. Foster–Wheeler boilers provided the steam, two being of the standard 'D' type and two of the controlled superheat type. That superheat temperature was a moderate 800°F and the pressure only 525 psi.

A high electrical load because of the air conditioning, hotel services and engine room auxiliaries was satisfied by five 600 kW, 220 volt direct current diesel generators.[19] Main turbines gave some trouble during the second year of service, but that was soon rectified. She was, however, a good basic liner for which British yards had an unenviable reputation. Unfortunately that reputation did not guarantee survival during the recession of future years.

Before that recession came Cunard and Canadian Pacific indulged in a fervent, even rash, flurry of construction to modernize their Canadian services. Without doubt some form of renewal was essential, but in the light of changing circumstances the designs could have been made more suitable for easy conversion to cruising. Too large a cargo capacity appears to have been provided which, as with *Media* and *Parthia*, kept the ships tied up in port for too

Cunard 'Saxonia' class ship Carinthia.

long a period. Economically they may not have been justified but, like *Olympia*, they did illustrate the high quality of British engineering. Cunard's 22,000 gross ton quartet all came from John Brown on the Clyde, commencing with *Saxonia* in 1954, the other vessels *Ivernia*, *Carinthia* and *Sylvania* following in 1955, 1956 and 1957 respectively. Canadian Pacific took delivery of its Fairfield built 25,500 gross ton *Empress of Britain* in 1956 and *Empress of England* from Vickers on the Tyne a year later.

Although the two classes were different in many respects, in order to comply with particular company requirements and ideas, they did have certain things in common. Dimensions had to suit the locks in Liverpool and be such that the ships could safely reach Montreal without grounding or contacting bridges. Air conditioning applied throughout to passenger and crew accommodation, with individual adjustment of cabin temperature being selectable. Thermotank Ltd supplied the heating and air conditioning units for both groups of ships, temperature and

humidity control being available. The use of cabin air conditioning avoided the need for electrically driven cabin fans which were a source of inconvenience and complaint aboard many ships. Aboard the 'Empress' vessels filtered conditioned air was recirculated from certain public rooms in order to economize on heating and cooling capacity. In neither case did air conditioning apply in the engine room, such a system being thoroughly impractical, but effective ventilation was essential.[20]

The twin screw 'Saxonia' class ships employed two stage double reduction geared turbines of which the HP turbine was all impulse and the double flow LP turbine all reaction. LP astern turbines were fitted in the LP casings but HP astern turbines, fitted on the HP ahead turbine shafts, had their own casings. Four Yarrow three drum water tube boilers provided steam at 530 psi and 800°F, these being fitted with MeLeSco superheaters. This type of

Canadian Pacific's Empress of Britain. *Decks free from ventilators and the 'designer' funnel characterize a ship of the 1950s.* (Canadian Pacific.)

superheater was similar to the sort fitted to locomotives in that it had its own steam headers, rather than a drum as in the Yarrow five drum boiler. An essential feature of all boilers in order to keep heating surfaces clean was the employment of soot blowers. Six manually operated Clyde soot blowers were used to direct high pressure steam over steam generating and superheater tubes in order to remove carbon deposits.

As with all passenger liners of the period a considerable electrical demand had to be met and that was done by provision of four 750 kW turbo-generators of British Thomson–Houston design. Each unit had its own condenser and a gearbox to reduce the 6,000 rpm turbine speed to 750 rpm for the generator drive. As well as engine room auxiliaries, water provision, air conditioning and lighting, the electrical supply

operated eight elevators, three for passengers, three for stores, one for baggage and an engine room lift. An essential item coming under the engineering department's control was that of sewage disposal. Strict regulations governed the discharge of raw sewage into enclosed docks as well as harbours and coastal waters of north America, thus making some form of disposal system essential. Collection tanks placed well below the water line provided storage capacity until discharge could be permitted and also allowed for effective operation of sanitary units in cabins positioned near the water line.

Saxonia and her sisters had space for 300,000 cu ft of cargo, of which 15,000 cu ft could be refrigerated. Three 100 kW electrically driven freon compressors kept the three main insulated compartments at low temperature. Two of those compartments were cooled to 10°F whilst the third could be maintained at 0°F. The refrigeration plant also served passenger and crew provision rooms at temperatures from 40°F to 0°F, as well as the cooled drinking water supply, kit-

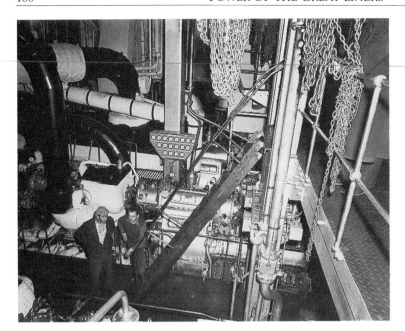

Right *The Dutch liner* Statendam *with Welsh bonnet funnel top.*

chen cold rooms and the air conditioning plant. Throughout the living area a Grinnell automatic sprinkler system provided protection against fire, the ship being divided into 20 separate self contained sections for increased safety. A large pressurized tank could instantly supply water at 120 psi to any of the water sprinklers should there be a temperature rise in its vicinity. Immediately a sprinkler operated an alarm would sound and a fire pump cut-in to maintain water supply to the sprinklers. Cargo spaces had smoke detecting appliances and CO_2 flooding, whilst the machinery spaces were provided with a very comprehensive CO_2 flooding system as well as hand extinguishers.[21]

Propulsion of the twin screw 'Empress' liners was by means of three stage Pametrada double reduction geared turbines developing a total of 27,000 shp in normal service or 30,000 shp as a maximum. Impulse type HP and IP ahead turbines connected in tandem on the same shaft but in different casings, and they turned at 4,195 rpm. Double flow reaction LP ahead turbines rotated at 3,452 rpm. For astern running HP and LP impulse turbines were provided. A novel feature applied to the ahead turbines in that they operated on a reheat cycle. Steam at 600 psi and 850°F was supplied to the HP turbine but the exhaust did not pass directly to the IP stage, instead it was heated back to the initial

temperature before entering the IP. Such an arrangement improved efficiency and minimized the risk of steam condensing within the lower pressure turbines. Any water droplets which might form could cause serious damage at the high rotational speeds.

Main steam came from two Foster–Wheeler controlled superheat boilers and one Foster–Wheeler reheat boiler which, in addition to its normal evaporation of 50,000 lb of steam per hour, could reheat the entire turbine steam flow back to 850°F. Low pressure steam for tank heating and other purposes was provided by a steam-to-steam generator, the generating steam being taken from the controlled superheat boilers. For use in port a Howden–Johnson boiler could supply steam to the low pressure main at 200 psi. The steam plant was, therefore, more complex than that of the Cunard vessels but no comparative data exists to indicate whether that complexity, and extra capital cost, was justified in terms of improved economy. Overall fuel consumption values can be misleading as several factors need to be considered, not least the hotel service load and weather conditions.

Canadian Pacific chose an operating voltage of 225 volts for the electrical supply aboard *Empress of Britain* and her sister rather than the more common 220 volts. More equipment could, however, operate satisfactorily at that

voltage without major modification. Two turbo-generators, each with a capacity of 1,200 kW, formed the main source of electrical power, but in port three 500 kW diesel generators were available.[22]

With both classes of ship considerable efforts were made to avoid the seemingly ever present problem of exhaust smuts falling on deck spaces. Induced draught fans certainly helped the situation as they forced the exhaust from each boiler at high velocity through the funnel outlets. These were essential anyway to the effective functioning of dust collectors. Dry collectors of the vortex type were applied to the 'Empresses' and the *Queen Mary* but Cunard appeared to have a later preference for the wet type and fitted these to the *Queen Elizabeth, Caronia* and other vessels. Funnel design plays an important part in ensuring that smoke clears the decks under most operational conditions. Ideally the funnel should be high enough so that exhausting gas clears the turbulent air flowing over the ship due to its hull and superstructure. Different superstructures cause different air flow patterns and so no single funnel height or top design will suit all ships. The top must be designed to fit a particular ship or class of ships and wind tunnel tests would be carried out to determine the optimum shape.[23] It is no surprise, therefore, that *Saxonia* and *Empress of Britain* had

funnels of different size and shape.

Holland America Line's 24,300 gross ton *Statendam*, introduced in 1957, had an impressively tapered funnel but it was not as effective at clearing smuts from the deck as first thought. Operational conditions sometimes exposed weaknesses in wind tunnel testing. After a short period in service a Welsh bonnet type fitment was applied to the funnel top in order to force smoke clear of the turbulent air passing over the ship. The device worked well and even improved the funnel shape. In terms of propulsion machinery *Statendam* was a typical steam powered liner of the period, her twin compound Pametrada turbines developing 20,000 shp to give a service speed of 19 knots.

Two Foster–Wheeler 'D' type controlled superheat boilers provided steam at 625 psi and 850°F. These controlled superheat boilers had two furnaces with separate burners and these furnaces could be fired independently to suit circumstances. In the case of *Statendam*'s boilers the steam generating furnaces had four burners whilst the controlled superheat furnaces had five. Although steam generating tubes surrounded the superheat furnace, steam generation rate was regulated by means of the four burners in the steam generating furnace. Control of the superheat temperature relied upon correct operation of the five superheat furnace burners. The boilers operated under both forced and induced draught.

Although *Statendam* was typical in terms of its propulsion plant its electrical system marked a departure from that usually applied. For only the second time aboard an Atlantic liner alternating current (ac) was employed. Four 700 kW turbo-alternators powered the 440 volt, 60 hertz three-phase ac system with a 250 kW diesel driven alternator being available for emergency purposes.[24]

The first ac system aboard an Atlantic liner appeared only a year earlier aboard the Norwegian American Line's *Bergensfjord*. Her electrical supply was at the same frequency and voltage as that of the Dutch liner, the 60 hertz and 440 volt system becoming standard for shipboard installation. Alternating current had many advantages not least in the procurement of equipment and safety, but there were disadvantages especially in terms of speed control for plant such as winches and capstans. *Bergensfjord* employed the then common Ward–Leonard system of control which essentially consisted of an ac motor driving a dc generator which then powered the winch or windlass motor. The arrangement was cumbersome, but the advantages of applying ac to the rest of the ship far outweighed the disadvantages of conversion to dc for winches. Secondary circuits employed for lighting and small motors were supplied at 120 volts via a transformer. Alternating current allowed the use of fluorescent lighting which was brighter, consumed less power and was cooler than tungsten lamps. Fluorescent tubes also lasted longer reducing replacement costs.

The 18,750 gross ton *Bergensfjord* was a motor liner and naturally her alternators were powered by diesel engines. Four turbo-charged Ruston diesels developing 1,500 bhp at 360 rpm directly coupled to 1,040 kW alternators constituted the largest auxiliary diesel electric installation which had to that date been installed aboard ship. Being happy with the main engines

installed aboard *Oslofjord*, the owners once again opted for Stork diesels. Similar to the engines installed in *Oslofjord*, the twin eight cylinder engines of *Bergensfjord* were also double acting with electrically driven scavenge blowers but were of slightly greater power.[25] It may seem strange that the owners did not take advantage of improvements being made by other diesel engine manufacturers but there was considerable merit in having a large pool of engine room staff familiar with one type of engine. To have fitted a completely different design could have caused manning difficulties.

Swedish America also introduced a new motor liner the year *Statendam* entered service. *Gripsholm* was similar in appearance to *Kungsholm* of 1953, having a forward dummy funnel and two masts, but was slightly larger. Her owners returned to Italy for construction, but adopted Swedish designed and built Gotaverken engines for main propulsion. Of 9,900 ihp normal rating these engines were the most powerful ever built to that two-stroke single-acting design, but they showed one improvement over other liner diesel installations, they could burn boiler grade bunker fuel. Up to that time diesel engines operated on lighter distillate diesel oil which was more expensive. By fitting heating and filtration equipment together with modified fuel pumps and injectors the engines were capable of using the cheaper boiler oil.

A 440 volt, 60 hertz three phase electrical supply came from five diesel engine driven alternators each capable of producing 700 kW. Lighting and domestic electrical supplies at 220 volts and 127 volts were provided from transformer circuits. The four-stroke Ansaldo diesel engines which powered the alternators also consumed heavy boiler grade fuel.[26] Rising fuel costs and the increasing differential between diesel oil and heavy bunker grade fuel had given the steam plant an advantage, but that was lost once the internal combustion engine could operate on the same fuel.

CHAPTER 12

End of an Age

The coming of passenger jet aircraft, and the Boeing 707 in particular, finished off the Atlantic liner as a truly commercial proposition but national prestige could not easily be satisfied by a silver bird. Subsidies could still be extracted from governments with a wish to maintain a maritime presence on the Atlantic and to bolster declining shipbuilding industries. Even if such monies did not come as direct grants they were often made available as low interest loans, but there was nothing wrong in that as construction and operation of passenger ships helped to ease unemployment. The building of large passenger liners during the late 1950s and early 1960s created an illusion of an unchanging maritime world. Such was not the case, however, and a

Rotterdam, the Dutch liner with unconventional funnel arrangement.

number of these symbols of national pride produced during that period were destined to become objects of national embarrassment. If true commercial judgement had prevailed few of the liners constructed during that period would ever have been constructed for the 'Atlantic Ferry'.

That cannot really be said of Holland America's *Rotterdam*, which commenced operations in late 1959, as the ship was constructed with an eye to the cruise market as well as Atlantic trade. The most striking feature of the ship emanated from her machinery and that was her twin boiler uptakes rather than a conventional funnel. Positioned aft and abreast of each other, these uptakes served as exhaust ducts for the four De Schelde water tube boilers. The use of twin exhaust uptakes was not completely new having been employed for the Moore McCormack

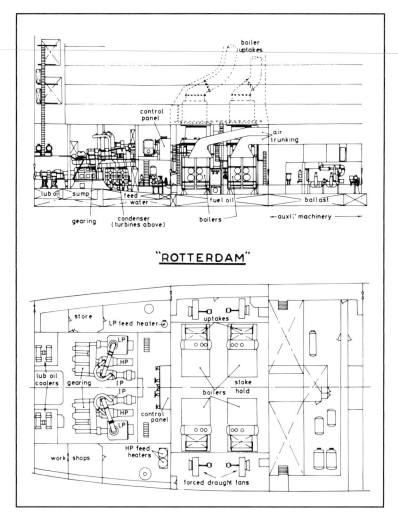

ships *Argentina* and *Brasil* which operated between New York and South America. Those ships, however, employed a dummy funnel but *Rotterdam* did not and her appearance was enhanced because of it.

Visual attraction had not been the primary purpose of the uptakes, but it must have played some part in the decision. Other factors such as provision of an uninterrupted central area throughout the accommodation must have been influential, as it was many years earlier for vessels like *Vaterland*, *Bremen* and *Normandie*. In those ships convention ruled and uptakes combined into central funnels, but *Rotterdam*'s designers were much bolder. Not only did they introduce new concepts as far as exterior design was concerned, but interior passenger spaces

were subject to the same originality of thought. First and tourist classes still had to be kept apart but that was achieved by means of horizontal rather than vertical organization of accommodation, allowing each group the run of the ship on defined decks. 'Trick' staircases and set elevators only allowed movement of the classes between their own decks.

On the engine side *Rotterdam* was positively conventional, employing a twin screw geared steam turbine drive. Each ahead turbine set comprised three stages with the HP stage employing a single row Curtis wheel and 17 rows of reaction blading, all mounted on a rotor machined from a solid forging. IP and LP stages employed reaction blading. The double reduction gearing employed identical primary wheels and secondary pinions for all three stages, primary pinions being dimensioned in order to take account of different turbine speeds. Under normal conditions ahead power of 17,500 shp could be achieved at a propeller speed of 131.5 rpm, but a maximum continuous output of 19,250 shp was available.

Four water tube boilers occupied the boiler space forward of the turbine room, these providing steam at the turbine controls of 620 psi and 835°F. Steam conditions at the boilers were somewhat higher, 660 psi and 860°F, losses always being expected between boiler outlet and turbine inlet. High boiler efficiency was assisted by a three stage feed heater and a two stage air heater which employed steam bled from the turbines as the heating medium. Each boiler had its own uptake pipe with port and starboard pairs venting through separate flue casings.

Four steam turbine driven alternators, each with a maximum continuous rating of 1,685 kW, provided electrical power at 60 hertz, but for emergency purposes a gas turbine driven unit was available. That unit, the first employed aboard an Atlantic liner, had an output of 350 kW. The turbine speed of 15,000 rpm had to be double reduced to 1,800 rpm in order to develop the correct frequency.[1] Electrical generation systems had come a long way since *City of Berlin* 80 years earlier.

Italian interests introduced the 33,400 gross ton *Leonardo da Vinci* in 1960, an improved and enlarged version of the ill-fated *Andrea Doria* for which she was the replacement. Following that tragic loss the Italia Line took no chances and incorporated 14 watertight bulkheads, 13 of which extended to the upper deck. *Andrea Doria*, 4,300 gross tons smaller and 48 ft shorter, had only 10 such bulkheads but still complied with the regulations adopted by the 1948 International Convention for the Safety of Life at Sea. Her design was such as to allow the ship to remain afloat with any two adjacent compartments flooded, but *Stockholm* found the weakness and proved that no ship is unsinkable.[2]

Construction of *Leonardo da Vinci* and plans for future Atlantic liners illustrated a confidence in the future, jet aircraft not having then made the same impact on the Mediterranean route as they had upon north European services. Complete air conditioning applied throughout passenger spaces with Denny–Brown fin stabilizers being fitted to reduce rolling. Seven lifts for passengers and two for use by engineer and deck officers eased movement through this 11 deck ship. An all electric galley with a total load of 666 kW, deck cranes and cold store cargo added to demands upon the electrical supply. At sea electrical load was met by five 1,100 kW turbo-alternators whilst in port four diesel driven alternators, each of 600 kW capacity, could be used. Hotel services, particularly air conditioning, for the 1,326 passengers placed a considerable electrical load on the ship. By contrast *Andrea Doria*, which could carry 1,247 passengers, had obtained electrical current from five 750 kW diesel sets and two 1,000 kW turbo-alternators.

With a designed speed of 23 knots *Leonardo da Vinci* required powerful machinery. Two sets of double reduction geared turbines developed a total of 70,000 shp in normal service. Four Foster–Wheeler water tube boilers produced steam at almost identical conditions to the boilers fitted in *Rotterdam*, but steam generation rate was more than four times the 50 tons per hour of the Dutch ship. Two auxiliary water tube boilers occupied a compartment between turbine and main boiler rooms. That space also housed three evaporator and distillation units which could produce a total of 600 tons of fresh water per day from sea water. Two mineralization plants made that water suitable for human consumption and avoided the ship having to take supplies whilst in port. Storage space for 450 tons of fresh water made the ship independent of shore supplies with its attendant risks and shortages.[3]

Canadian Pacific's final fling came in 1961 with the appropriately named *Empress of Canada*. Built as a replacement for the elderly *Empress of France* (formerly *Duchess of Bedford*), this new liner was based upon the pair constructed during the 1950s but with special attention being given to her role as a cruise vessel. Built by Vickers–Armstrong on the Tyne, *Empress of Canada* had an almost identical machinery installation to those earlier ships, comprising twin sets of double reduction Pametrada turbines and two Foster–Wheeler controlled superheat boilers. The normal output of 27,000 shp produced a slightly slower speed, 20 knots compared with 20.5 knots, due to her greater beam, 86 ft 6 in

compared with 85 ft. A bulbous bow was also incorporated, the aim being to reduce wave making losses and minimize pitching.

Electrical and air conditioning plant also followed the same pattern as described in the preceding chapter. In effect the only differences between the ships lay in accommodation layout and external appearance. The major visual difference was that of funnel styling. Funnels fitted to *Empress of Britain* and *Empress of England* proved to be fairly effective in keeping soot from the deck, but some nuisance had been experienced. Designers of the final 'Empress' carried out wind tunnel tests and arrived at a shape which was visually attractive and proved to be effective. Open slots at the front of the upper section were designed to produce an air flow over the exhausting flues and so carry the soot clear of all decks. Boiler room fans drew air from a vent in the after part of the funnel casing, but air for engine room ventilation came from two dummy sampson posts on the after part of the promenade deck.[4]

When it came to novel funnel designs the French Line's *France* was way in front of any contemporary vessel. Instead of smoke issuing vertically from the funnel tops, outward facing fins were provided allowing it to pass laterally

Empress of Canada, the last 'White Empress'.

and thus stay clear of the decks. The usual series of wind tunnel tests allowed perfection of the design to be ensured. In cross wind conditions a possibility existed of smoke being forced back into fin apertures facing the wind, but a clever design feature overcame that problem. Each funnel had a three way damper enabling smoke to be ejected to leeward of any crosswind or through both fins under normal conditions. Pneumatic control of the dampers from the boiler room allowed the engineers to immediately react to changing circumstances. Two stainless steel soot collectors prevented escape of the more solid particles from each boiler uptake, but only one of these was required for whichever boiler operated at reduced steaming rate whilst in port.

Two boiler rooms each contained four Penhoet water tube boilers, all capable of 90 tons of steam per hour generated at 915 psi and 930°F. A desuperheater in the main steam drum of each boiler allowed saturated steam to be produced for assorted engine room auxiliary plant and, via a reducing valve, for hotel services. Two forced draught fans supplied air to each boiler, but only one was necessary to maintain

France, her finned funnels stylish and impressive.

steaming rates up to two-thirds maximum capacity. For convenience the four forward boilers were fitted in the hull before launching, with the after set being installed whilst alongside the fitting out berth.

When she commenced service in January 1962 her owners could claim *France* to be the longest liner in the world. At 1,035 ft overall she was 4 ft longer than *Queen Elizabeth*, but her 66,300 gross tonnage was considerably lower than Cunard's giant. Without doubt *France* was a prestige ship, built to carry the flag of the country whose name she bore, but prestige did not come cheap during the 1960s. Construction cost £30 million of which French Line paid £23 million, the taxpayers of France meeting the remainder in the form of a shipbuilder's subsidy.[5]

Even with large subsidies there could never be any realistic attempt to take the Atlantic record from *United States* as machinery costs would have been totally unjustified for all but the most jingoistic of countries. Despite that *France* would be no sloth and was designed for a service speed of 31 knots and a maximum of 33 knots. Such speed required a total output of 160,000 shp from four sets of single reduction geared

Parsons type turbines. A relatively low propeller speed of 156 rpm had been chosen in order to ensure maximum propeller efficiency and avoid cavitation problems which always existed with high rotational speeds. Because single reduction gearing had been chosen in preference to the more common double reduction, a four stage turbine system had to be employed.

A double flow LP and the second stage IP turbines were positioned forward of the gear wheel, with the HP and first IP being on the propeller shaft side. Single reduction gearing meant that a very high reduction ratio of 19:1 was required for the HP pinion which rotated at 3,044 rpm, other pinions turned at 2,224 rpm. Second IP and LP turbines were positioned high up allowing the condenser to be placed below the LP turbine to give a more compact arrangement than existed aboard many other large liners.[6] Considering earlier reluctance of French marine manufacturers to adopt geared turbines, the use of single rather than double reduction gearing is not surprising.

Her main engines and boilers proved to be very reliable, but economic factors such as high fuel prices and declining Atlantic traffic conspired against the ship. Sold to Norwegian interests and renamed *Norway* the ship became viable for cruise duties, but that required a slower speed. The simple expediency of removing the forward boiler and turbine installations to make her a lower powered twin screw vessel proved the easiest option. Cruising at 16 knots, fuel consumption could be reduced dramatically whilst a smaller plant required fewer engine room staff.

France was provided with an electrical generating plant capable of supplying a small town, but that in effect is what she was. Six turbo-alternators, housed in two well separated compartments, provided the main source of supply with a 750 kW diesel alternator being available for use in port with boilers shut down. Two 200 kW diesel driven emergency alternators could supply power for 36 hours without the need for refuelling. The main alternators had a rating of 2,250 kW at 450 volts and provided three phase current at 60 hertz. Although it was never called upon, *France* had a maximum electrical capacity of some 15,400 kW and that sort of power propelled a number of smaller liners across the Atlantic.[7]

Fresh water provision for passengers and crew had always presented problems aboard large vessels, with storage capacity of several thousand tons having to be made available. The cost of water at terminal ports and supply difficulties for ships requiring short turn round times also caused concern for owners. Since the late 1800s steamers had generally evaporated sea water as a means of providing pure boiler feed water. Such a system was costly as large quantities of steam were used and it could only be justified for the production of high quality feed water. Plant also occupied considerable space. Development of low pressure evaporating plant which was more efficient, occupied less space and required very little routine attention afforded shipowners the possibility of making water aboard ship cheaper than it could be purchased. Fresh water storage capacity could also be reduced.

France had accommodation for over 2,000 passengers and with a full crew complement there would generally be some 3,000 souls on board. For all purposes each person would require at least 40 gallons (UK) of fresh water per day, and generally much more. On that basis daily consumption amounted to at least 550 tons with boiler make-up feed accounting

for even more. For a crossing over 3,000 tons of water had to be provided, the evaporating plant aboard *France* being capable of producing a maximum of 1,400 tons per day.

It is interesting to note that the evaporating equipment was supplied by Weiritam, the Paris associates of G. & J. Weir of Glasgow, manufacturers of the earliest evaporating equipment fitted in Atlantic liners. Another traditional British marine equipment manufacturer, Brown Brothers of Edinburgh, supplied the steering gear and stabilizers.

Propulsion and auxiliary plants were separated into compartments in a similar way to that of *United States*. Forward and after boiler and turbine room groupings were separated by a space containing fuel oil tanks and auxiliary equipment. Forward turbines drove the outboard screws. Aft of the aftermost turbine room was a further auxiliary engine room which also contained three of the turbo-alternators. The other three were positioned at C deck level in the forward turbine room.[8]

Without doubt *France* was the most spectacular liner to appear on the Atlantic since *United States*, but it is certain that she would never have been built but for the subsidy. With hindsight that money was not well spent in terms of jobs, both at the builders and afloat, but at the time few would have argued against it. National pride is probably stronger in France than anywhere else and maritime traditions die hard.

Italian pride in its ocean liners was also strong, especially in the wake of *Rex* and *Conte di Savoia*, but the decision to build two large Atlantic passenger liners for entry into service during 1965 seemed to be the height of folly. At over 45,000 gross tons *Michelangelo* and *Raffaello* were a symbol of rather misplaced faith in the future. It is true that the mid-Atlantic route remained fairly free from the ravages of jet airliners, but it was only a matter of time. With propulsive systems of conventional twin screw geared turbine form the ships exhibited nothing new in marine engineering terms. They did, however, exhibit very distinctive funnel designs.

If one thing characterized post-war passenger ships, it was smoke stack styling. No longer just devices for venting exhaust gases from boilers and diesel engines, they became entities in their own right and gave the ship its character. Apart from *Normandie* few pre-war liners had funnels

of real distinction. It was not just a case of producing a fine looking appendage, however, the
basic purpose still remained. Exhaust had to be
vented and no soot must be allowed to fall on
deck. These new Italian ships had twin funnels
placed towards the after part of the ship, illustrating another feature of recent marine engineering practice. Powerful machinery had become
smaller, occupying less space in the hull and as
the screws were aft it was reasonable that
machinery should migrate towards the after
part of the ship.

Michelangelo's 45 ft high funnels were capped
by large plate-like vanes through which the
exhaust pipes projected. These upswept vanes
of impressive proportions also had a functional
purpose, that being to direct exhaust gases away
from the deck. By contrast the main funnel casings
could be considered as insignificant, but the
surrounding lattice structure produced an eye
catching and distinctive form. As with all
funnels of the period, extensive wind tunnel
tests allowed the design to be perfected but only
service conditions confirmed the results.

Scandinavian owners also had plans for new
ships but they realized that Atlantic traffic alone
could not ensure an adequate return. Cruising,
with some high season Atlantic crossings,
became the order of the day and ship designs
had to suit that requirement. In 1960 the
Norwegian American Line decided upon construction of a new ship with that criterion in
mind. *Sagafjord* would carry 450 cruise passengers, but 800 on the north Atlantic. In order to
comply with rules of the Atlantic Conference
first and second class accommodation had to be
provided for Atlantic services, but the first class
of 70 berths seems to have been merely a token.

From the beginning diesel propulsion was
specified for the simple reason that few
Norwegian marine engineers had any experience with steam turbines. Similar reasoning
applied to Swedish American Line with its new
ship ordered shortly afterwards. The French
built *Sagafjord* entered service in 1965 and cost
her owners £6 million. Twin nine cylinder
Sulzer RD diesel engines, each of 12,000 bhp
rating, gave the 24,000 gross ton ship a service
speed of 20 knots. Extensive use of remote and
automatic controls for main and auxiliary engines
allowed for easy operation of the plant from a
soundproof and air conditioned compartment

in the machinery space. The engineer's lot was
becoming more bearable.

Full air conditioning of the ship placed a
heavy load on the electrical plant, which was
also diesel driven. A 440 volt 60 hertz three
phase system powered most items, but lighting
and small cabin appliances operated at 120 volts
via transformers. Diesels for driving the six
alternators were actually of Norwegian design
being recently developed Bergen LSG8 eight
cylinder engines. Alternator engines, like most
auxiliary plant, could be started from the control
room. Two Weiritam evaporators with a combined output of 240 tons per day provided the
ship's water requirements. Instead of using
steam for heating, these units received heat
from main and auxiliary diesel engine cooling
water, thus improving the plant's overall
efficiency. Apart from capital and small operating
costs the water was effectively free for that cooling water heat would have only been wasted.[9]

Swedish American's *Kungsholm* turned out to
be the final ship in that fleet although there was
much optimism when she entered service in
1966. The company returned to Britain for her
construction, awarding the contract for this
26,700 gross ton ship to John Brown & Co of
Clydebank. Twin Swedish designed and built
Gotaverken main engines were specified, experience of engineers with similar engines aboard
Stockholm and *Gripsholm* obviously playing an
important part in the choice. These two-stroke
turbo-charged engines each had nine cylinders
of 760 mm bore and 1,500 mm stroke and could
develop some 12,600 bhp at 120 rpm.[10]

Again the ship was extensively automated,
but even the crew cost savings of that feature
failed to keep *Kungsholm* an economic proposition
as an Atlantic liner. Her 750 trans-Atlantic passengers, or 400 when cruising, still required a
crew of about 450[11] and with frequent and relatively cheap air fares across the Atlantic available
by the early 1970s there was simply no contest.
Because ships, even efficient ones like *Kungsholm*, consumed more fuel for each fare paying
passenger than any jet aircraft, increased oil
prices of the 1970s sounded the death knell and
effective liner traffic ceased.

As the major Atlantic carrier, Cunard
watched carefully the inroads being made on its
traffic by jet airliners and by the early 1960s a
number of its ships were diverted away from

One of Kungsholm's *nine cylinder Gotaverken engines on test.*

scheduled services. Cruising offered better prospects, but the Atlantic liners of the older school did not make effective cruise ships. The 'Queens' were too large to enter many ports or make canal passages and they did not have full air conditioning. As late as 1959 a policy still existed to replace both 'Queens', but this was changed in 1960 following a British government decision to offer Cunard a loan of £18 million rather than a subsidy.

Queen Mary would be replaced by a single large vessel and *Queen Elizabeth* kept in service as consort, at least for the time being. To that end a certain amount of updating was required and 'Lizzie' returned to the Clyde during the winter of 1965–66 for a major refit. From an engineering viewpoint little changed apart from the fitting of full air conditioning. Despite the refit and extensive cruising *Queen Elizabeth* lost money and was removed from Atlantic service in October 1968.

As a replacement for the 'Mary' Cunard sought tenders for construction of a 75,000 gross ton ship, known widely as 'Q3'. A Tyneside consortium of Vickers Armstrong Ltd and Swan Hunter submitted the lowest tender and expectations were that the new Cunarder would come from the Tyne. Steam turbines would drive quadruple screws, eight boilers supplying steam at 850 psi and 950°F. Poor trading figures in 1961 caused Cunard to rethink the proposal and it was soon abandoned in favour of a dual purpose vessel capable of negotiating the Panama Canal.[12]

In 1964 a proposal for a smaller twin screw ship was announced by the Cunard chairman. The order for what was initially known as 'Q4' went to John Brown & Co, thus that famous Clydebank yard built the final two ships planned as Atlantic liners. Unlike the Swedish vessel, *Queen Elizabeth 2*, which 'Q4' became, was steam turbine driven in the traditional mode, although with the very latest Pametrada turbines and Foster-Wheeler ESDII boilers.

As well as a capability of negotiating the Panama Canal, design considerations included capacity for 2,000 passengers in three classes and an average Atlantic speed of 28.5 knots. Draught was not to exceed 31 ft and the ship had to have a fuel capacity sufficient for a complete Atlantic round trip. Extensive cruising meant a large fresh water storage capacity or, as was then usual, capability for production of fresh water by evaporation of sea water. Careful design and planning of pipe ducts and cable runs allowed a reduction in 'tween deck heights of some 6–9 in making provision for an extra deck. Strength calculations showed that the best position for main machinery was slightly aft of amidships and that coincided with plans for subdivision. The single rather thin funnel, designed following the almost obligatory wind tunnel tests, looked strange aboard a Cunard ship but was all that was necessary for venting the three boilers. Wind deflectors added the effect of bulk.[13]

Main engines, manufactured by John Brown & Co, consisted of a pair of double reduction, cross compound turbine sets each capable of producing 55,000 shp. The desired service speed only needed a total of between 85,000 shp and 95,000 shp, but the owner considered it better to have the maximum power which could

Above Queen Elizabeth 2, *the last Atlantic liner.*   **Below** QE2 *starboard turbine set.* (M. Harrison.)
(G. Johnson.)

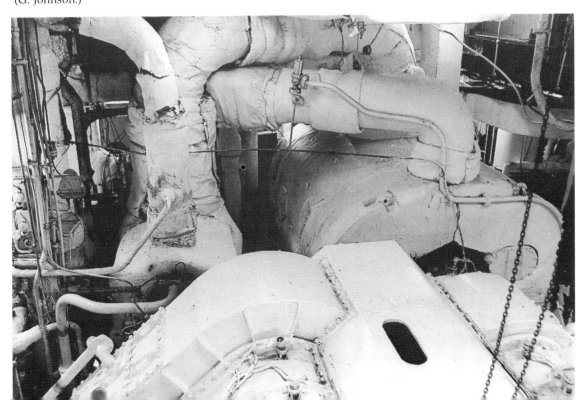

Above *Helical gearing as fitted in* QE2. (M. Harrison.)

Left *One of* QE2*'s double flow LP turbines.* (M. Harrison.)

be prudently absorbed by twin propellers.[14] The HP turbines, comprising one Curtis wheel followed by 11 impulse stages, had a maximum speed of 5,207 rpm, whilst the double flow impulse/reaction LP turbines rotated at 3,192 rpm. For astern running Cunard insisted upon a complicated arrangement of two turbines connected in series, one on the HP pinion and the other on the LP. A single HP astern Curtis wheel was placed at the forward end of the HP shaft whilst in the LP casing were placed two rows of astern blades. Full astern power could have been obtained from a single Curtis wheel and a single row of blades.[15]

Turbines and boilers occupied separate rooms, the boilers being forward of the turbines. Each boiler was provided with a bled steam air heater and a waste heat economizer. Automatic steam temperature control over the whole range of operation could be obtained by means of dampers

Above *Furnace front of one of the Foster–Wheeler boilers.* (M. Harrison.)

Right *The business end of the steamship* QE2. (M. Harrison.)

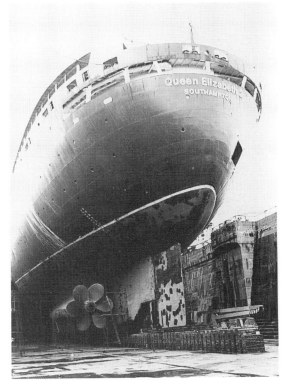

which directed combustion products over the superheater tubes. Three 400 kW electrically driven fans, one for each boiler, supplied combustion air at a maximum rate of 81,000 cu ft/ min. The boilers had seven side firing burners with automatic control of firing rate to suit port use or full power conditions. The turn down ratio of 14 to 1 allowed for wide control. Single boilers had a normal steam generating rate of 231,000 lb/hr but that could be raised to a maximum of 310,000 lb/hr. Although maximum steam temperature had been set at 950°F, choice of construction metals allowed for an increase to 1,000°F should the situation have demanded.

Three Weir's flash evaporators allowed 1,200 tons of fresh water to be produced each day allowing *QE2*, as the ship became known, to be self sufficient in boiler feed and domestic water. For domestic purposes the water produced had to be chlorinated in order to destroy all possible bacteria and then dechlorinated to make it palatable. The comprehensive sewage system complied with all regulations, allowing the vessel to discharge treated sewage safely. Two sets of fin stabilizers allowed for effective anti-roll control.[16]

From the start, in an engineering sense, QE2 became something of a problem ship. During trials several rows of blades failed on the HP port turbine due to resonant vibration. Such was the prestige impact of the ship that a Parliamentary Commission was called to investigate the incident. Stiffening of blades by the use of shrouding and stiffening wire solved the problem, but not before considerable embarrassment had been experienced by owner and builder.

Regular Atlantic service from May 1969 proved that the ship was both fast and comfortable but her schedules were intensive, leaving little time for regular maintenance. As with all ships QE2 only earned money whilst at sea and so time spent in port had to be kept to a minimum. Naturally the machinery suffered due to its intensive use. In 1973 jelly fish choked the condensers and heat exchangers, resulting in complete loss of power until they could be hosed off. Collision with an uncharted reef at Nassau in 1975 necessitated drydocking at Norfolk, Virginia, after unsuccessful attempts to stop the leak in the bulbous bow. Failure of both main feed pumps in 1982 required an unscheduled stop at Falmouth before an Atlantic crossing could be resumed.

A major incident in 1974 concerned her boilers. A combination of circumstances resulted in oil entering the feed water system and subsequently the boilers. Failed boiler tubes was the result and the ship was left without motive and electrical power. Perhaps the worst incident of all occurred two years later just south of the Scilly Isles when outward bound for New York. Fatigue failure of the claw type coupling which connected the starboard HP turbine shaft to its pinion resulted in a serious fire. Prompt action by the engineers brought the fire under control and minimized what could have been very serious damage to the turbine.[17]

The above incidents are not related in order to malign the ship, but are included to indicate that even with the best designed and operated

vessels things can go wrong and Queen Elizabeth 2 is certainly one of the best designed and operated vessels ever to cross the Atlantic. All of her predecessors on that route suffered failures of some sort. In a few cases, such as City of Paris, the incidents have been almost catastrophic, but in most the engineering staff has been able to coax the machinery into some form of response enabling their vessel to limp into port. No machinery has ever been perfect or immune from failure, but through skill and dedication generations of marine engineers have kept Atlantic liner passengers safe aboard their favourite ships.

Over the years modifications were made to QE2 in order to increase her passenger accommodation and make her more comfortable during prolonged tropical journeys. In the years to 1984 electrical load increased due to higher demand from air conditioning plant and hotel services. Electrical supply was maintained by steam driven turbo-alternators, thus the increased demand resulted in a need for more feed water capacity and higher steam generating rate. Fuel consumption increased from 0.73 tons/mile in 1969 to 0.82 tons/mile 17 years later. Some of that increase was due to the higher demand and some to a reduction in plant operating efficiency.

Cunard carried out feasibility studies in order to determine the most economical method of prolonging the ship's life and after detailed analysis decided to re-engine QE2 with diesel electric drive. It was not simply a case of considering the most economic form of propulsion, overall engine room performance was the main criterion. Steam turbine drive required 25 engineer officers and eight electrical officers, whilst the use of diesels allowed for a reduction in that number. In addition it was possible to reclassify the ship for unmanned machinery space (UMS) operations.[18]

In order to limit the time QE2 was out of service, careful planning of events was required with engines and other items of plant being designed and manufactured well in advance. Cunard's contract with the Lloyd-Werft yard at Bremerhaven contained severe penalty clauses for late delivery. Nine MAN–B&W 9L58/64 four-stroke, trunk piston diesel engines were specified to drive the alternators. Each engine, normal power range 8,400 bhp to 16,200 bhp, is

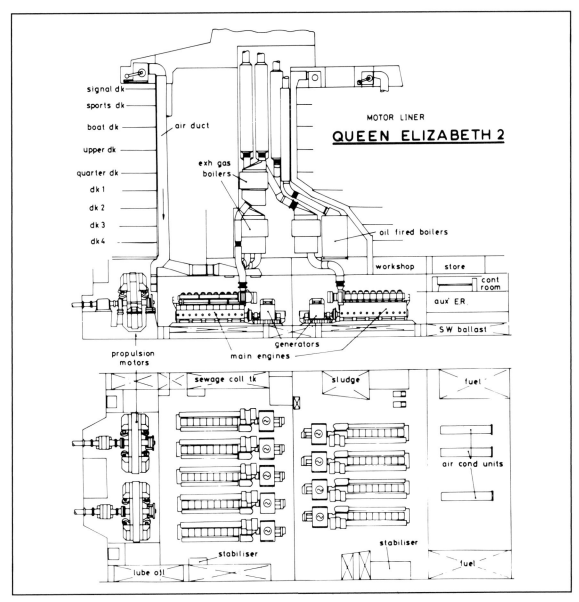

Engine room layout of the motorship QE2.

connected to an alternator rated 10.5 MW at 400 rpm whilst producing current at 10,000 volts and 60 hertz. By suitable switching the alternators provide power for hotel services, auxiliary plant and two 44 MW propulsion motors.

Power from the synchronous drive motors is transmitted to two five bladed controllable pitch (cp) propellers turning at 144 rpm. In order to improve cp propeller efficiency even further seven bladed Grim vane wheels were fitted downstream of each propeller. The theory behind these wheels has it that the inner part of the wheel acts as a turbine, being driven by water flow from the propeller whilst the outer part acts as a propeller, and there is evidence to suggest that improvements in efficiency are possible. QE2 never showed such as some vanes were lost during trials without anybody being aware of the fact and the remainder were

removed from both wheels to prevent further problems.

By means of a common busbar, any group of diesel alternators can operate in order to supply propulsion and domestic power, transformers being used for connection to the 3,300 volt domestic busbar. In order to allow the ship to operate at high efficiency even at slow speeds, the normal propeller speed can be reduced to 72 rpm by means of GEC synchrodrive converters. These thyristor units also allow for easier starting of the synchronous propulsion motors.

Although now a motorship *Queen Elizabeth 2* does make use of steam for heating purposes, accommodation, water and fuel, but that steam is usually generated by exhaust gas from the diesels. A Sunrod exhaust gas boiler is fitted in each of the nine engine uptakes with two oil fired boilers being provided to meet demand when insufficient engines are running. A further energy saving arrangement is provided by four Serk fresh water generators with a combined output of 1,000 tons per day. Under normal circumstances heat for these units is provided by the diesel engine cooling water, but with a reduced number of engines operating steam heating can be utilized. In addition a reverse osmosis fresh water generating unit of 450 tons per day capacity is also fitted.[19]

Because extensive use is made of diesel waste heat energy and electricity is used for propulsion, auxiliaries and domestic purposes the entire plant is very efficient. As a steamship overall fuel consumption at 28.5 knots amounted to 550 tons per day, but as a diesel electric vessel that has fallen to 370 tons per day, despite a slightly higher domestic load.[20]

Re-engining of *QE2* was a brave step, but one Cunard felt was justified. The investment of £100 million in a ship almost 20 years old took courage, but to build a similar vessel would have cost much more. No amount of money would, however, produce a ship like *QE2*. She is unique. She is the last Atlantic liner with a history which includes a period as a war transport,

Left *One of the nine MAN–B&W diesel engines ready for installation.* (M. Harrison.)

Right *A massive propulsion motor moved into position in QE2.* (M. Harrison.)

Below *New controllable pitch propellers and Grim wheels of QE2.* (M. Harrison.)

having carried troops of the British Task Force during the Falklands conflict in 1982. Hopefully no ship in the future will be called upon to perform such a role. She remains the only passenger ship in the world with a capacity for fast trans-Atlantic scheduled services and steady world-wide cruising. Her prestige is beyond price, but on purely commercial grounds the re-engining should guarantee a further 20 years of life.

The 150 years which have elapsed since powered ships first set out to cross the Atlantic have seen many fine vessels come and go. Though they may have offered grand accommodation, it was the machinery which gave them speed and set them apart from the sailing packets. Quest for the 'Blue Riband' did not centre around a ship's grand saloon or luxurious cabins but deep in her heart, the engine room. Hard work by those who designed, built and operated that machinery achieved the desired results, but with very little praise. *United States* may have ended that quest, but the spirit lives on in those responsible for the design, construction and operation of *QE2*'s machinery both as a steamship and a motorship.

Appendices

1
Balancing: The Yarrow–Schlick–Tweedy System

Reciprocating engines caused vibration in the early steamers and the situation was most severe in triple expansion engines where three pistons of different weights set up large unbalanced forces and couples. Balancing of the masses would avoid or minimize these forces and couples, but that proved to be difficult with three cranks. A four crank arrangement, whether triple or quadruple expansion, allowed use of the Yarrow–Schlick–Tweedy system of balancing which eliminated all primary and secondary forces as well as the primary couples. It is not necessary to understand the detail of dynamic balancing to be able to appreciate its importance, the mathematics being rather involved.

Crank arrangements for the Yarrow–Schlick–Tweedy system.

The Yarrow–Schlick–Tweedy system required a symmetrical arrangement of four cranks, but it was possible to divide the low pressure stage of a triple expansion engine between two equal smaller cylinders, thus giving four cranks. From aft the connections would be aft LP, IP, HP and forward LP. With a quadruple expansion engine the sequence from aft would be first IP, second IP, LP and HP. Essentially the low masses were connected to the outer cranks with the higher masses in the middle. For engines having tandem LP and HP stages these were connected on the middle cranks and the IP stages to the outer. In such cases these tandem pairings had identical masses.

Crank positionings were symmetrical about engine mid-length, whilst the crank angles were symmetrical about a vertical centre line. Masses,

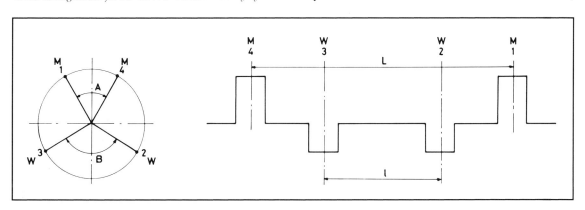

angles and lengths had to satisfy the three equations shown below. Primary forces were balanced by equation (i), secondary forces by equation (ii) and primary couples by equation (iii).

$$\text{(i)} \quad \cos\frac{A}{2} \times \cos\frac{B}{2} = \frac{1}{2}$$

$$\text{(ii)} \quad \frac{W}{M} = \cos\frac{A}{2} \Big/ \cos\frac{B}{2}$$

$$\text{(iii)} \quad \frac{L}{l} = \tan\frac{B}{2} \Big/ \tan\frac{A}{2}$$

2
Turbines

Steam turbines may be divided into two basically different types, impulse and reaction.

Impulse
This operates in a manner similar to a water wheel, where a fluid impinges on blades to cause rotation. Turbine blading has to be substantial in section so that it will withstand the impact of high velocity steam. In the nozzle or guide vanes pressure energy is transformed into velocity energy, the high velocity steam acting against moving blades fitted to the turbine disc, theoretical blade velocity being half the steam velocity. In order to reduce the high rotational speed produced by such a turbine a number of moving blade rows may be employed, steam velocity being reduced in each successive row of blades. Fixed blades are required in order to change the steam flow direction onto each following row of moving blades.

With this type of turbine there is no pressure drop across the moving blades, only velocity change. An example of the impulse turbine is found in the Curtis wheel commonly used with high powered turbines. In such units it would be used for absorbing the initial high pressure and would then be followed by a number of reaction stages in series.

Reaction
The Parsons type of turbine adopted the reaction principle, with steam causing rotation as it expanded through sets of moving blades which were shaped to form nozzles. The effect is similar to that of a rotary garden sprinkler, where water escaping through nozzles causes the head of the sprinkler to rotate. Guide blades of similar shape to the moving blades redirect flow onto successive rows of blades. There is some impulse effect as steam hits the moving blades, but pairs of blades then act like nozzles producing the reaction effect. Because of the relatively light impact loading blades may be of relatively thin section. Although classed as a reaction turbine it is strictly speaking an impulse-reaction.

The pressure drop which occurs across the moving blades causes an end thrust in the HP to LP direction. That thrust is balanced by the fitting of a dummy piston at the HP end. A face on that dummy piston is subject to HP steam in the opposite direction to the turbine thrust and the back face of the dummy is subjected to exhaust steam pressure by means of the balance pipe. Because there is no pressure drop across moving blades of an impulse turbine no dummy piston is needed.

Due to the high rotational speeds involved a special form of sealing is needed to prevent leaks. Labyrinth glands consist of a number of steel or brass strips projecting from the casing and almost touching the rotor. Expansion of steam, or air, takes place during passage

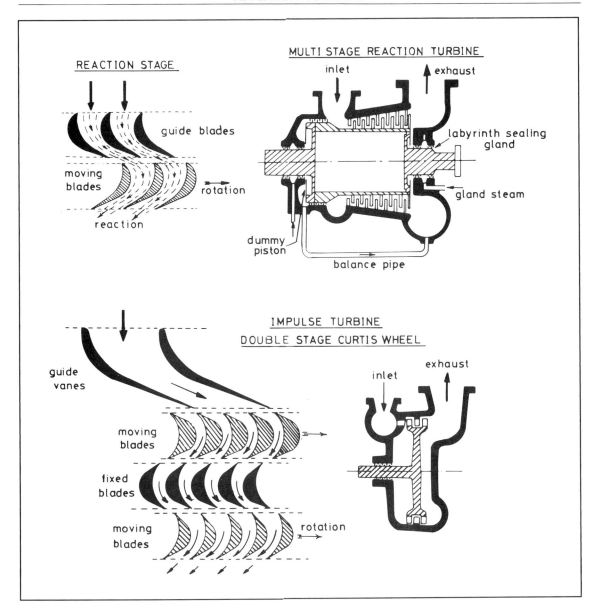

REACTION STAGE

guide blades

moving blades

rotation

reaction

MULTI STAGE REACTION TURBINE

inlet   exhaust

labyrinth sealing gland

gland steam

dummy piston

balance pipe

IMPULSE TURBINE
DOUBLE STAGE CURTIS WHEEL

guide vanes

moving blades

fixed blades

moving blades

rotation

inlet   exhaust

Impulse and reaction turbine blading.

through the gland. In order to ensure that steam does not leak out, or air does not leak in at the LP, low pressure gland steam is provided.

Gearing of the helical type provides lower propeller shaft speeds, whilst at the same time allows high turbine speeds for maximum efficiency and reduced diameter rotors. Double helices, formed in opposite directions, are required in order to prevent end thrust resulting from the action of the helix teeth. Single reduction gearing is much simpler and lighter than double reduction, but it produces a lower velocity ratio than double reduction. The latter can, however, provide low propeller speeds from small diameter high speed turbines. With early double reduction gearing, noise and alignment presented problems.

3
The Diesel Engine

The diesel engine is an internal combustion engine, which means that the fuel is actually burnt within the working cylinder. Fuel is sprayed into the cylinder which contains compressed air, the temperature produced by compression being high enough to ignite the fuel. The early true diesel concept engines had fuel blasted into the cylinder by means of high pressure air, but that required powerful compressors which consumed energy. Subsequently solid fuel injection was introduced. High pressure pumps raise fuel pressure to above 2,000 psi and when the fuel passes through very fine holes in an injector it is broken up into very fine droplets which ignite easily. The operating cycle is, however, the same.

Original engines operated on the four-stroke cycle in which there is one power piston stroke every four engine strokes or two revolutions of the crankshaft. Air inlet valves allow fresh com-

bustion air to be drawn into the cylinder whilst exhaust valves allow for removal of the exhaust gas on a separate stroke.

In order to increase engine power output for a given size, the two-stroke cycle was introduced. Here, as the name implies, there is one power stroke for every two piston strokes or every one revolution of the crankshaft. As there are no individual piston strokes to draw air into the cylinder or force air out a special arrangement, known as scavenging, had to be devised. Combustion or scavenge air has to be compressed before delivery to the engine cylinder. Exhaust gas can escape from the cylinder through valves in the cylinder cover or through ports cut in the liner. When the valve opens or the piston uncovers the ports some, but not all, of the exhaust will escape. Scavenge ports are cut in the lower portion of the cylinder and when the piston has moved far enough down its stroke these ports are uncovered. Scavenge air at a pressure higher than that of the remaining

Four-stroke cycle.

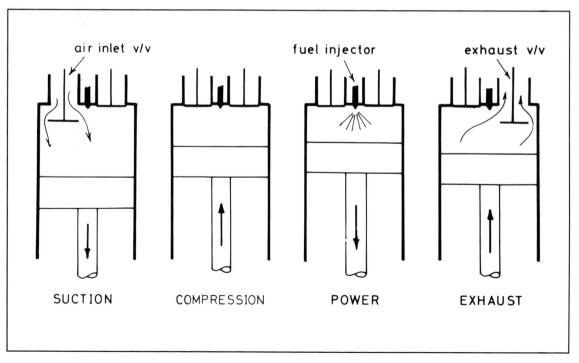

SUCTION   COMPRESSION   POWER   EXHAUST

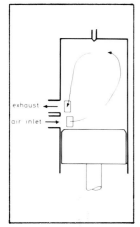

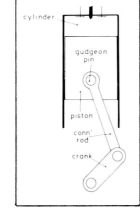

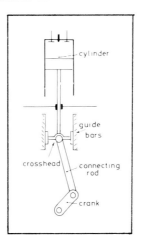

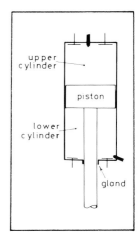

Cylinder arrangement for   *Trunk piston engine.*   *Crosshead engine.*   *Double-acting arrangement.*
two-stroke cycle.

exhaust gas can then enter the cylinder and remove that exhaust. A fresh air charge remains for compression and combustion next cycle. Higher pressure air, known as supercharging, allows more fuel to be burnt and hence more power can be obtained from the cylinder.

Two different forms of engine construction are also available, the trunk piston and the crosshead. Trunk piston engines usually operate at higher speed to drive dynamos or connect to the propeller by means of reduction gearing. Crosshead engines operate at slow speed and connect directly to the propeller. A crosshead engine has a guide which takes the side thrust reaction of the connecting rod and so avoids the piston being forced against the cylinder wall, thereby increasing cylinder wear. The cylinder can also be kept separate from the crankcase and so fuel or carbon from the cylinder does not enter the crankcase. A crosshead engine

requires more headroom.

As a means of obtaining more power from a specific size of engine, the double-acting concept was introduced but, for obvious reasons, was effectively limited to crosshead engines. In effect there could be power strokes every piston stroke because the lower working cylinder forced the piston upward, whilst air in the space above the piston was compressed. On the downward power stroke for the upper cylinder, air in the space below the piston would be compressed. Although the arrangement could increase the specific output of an engine it added to the constructional complexity and presented maintenance problems. A major problem related to the gland through which the piston rod had to pass as that gland was subjected to high pressure combustion gas. Two-stroke and four-stroke engines could be double-acting.

References

Chapter 1

General reference used in this chapter, *Glances at Atlantic Steam Navigation* by Joshua Field. Field Papers, Science Museum, London.

1. D. Griffiths, *Brunel's Great Western* (Patrick Stephens, Wellingborough, 1985), 86.
2. *Engineering* (8 February 1895), 175–77.
3. Griffiths, *Brunel's Great Western*, 82–3, 151.
4. B. H. Bartol, *Treatise on the Marine Boilers of the United States* (Philadelphia, 1851), 52–4.
5. Bartol, *Marine Boilers*, 42–8.
   also *Marine Engineer & Motorship Builder* (May 1929), 192.
6. *The Engineer* (24 March 1899), 122; (20 Oct 1899), 294–5.
   also *Marine Engineer & Motorship Builder* (June 1927), 221.
7. *The Engineer* (27 April 1860), 267; (20 Oct 1899), 394.
8. *The Engineer* (24 Oct 1856), 574.
9. *The Engineer* (26 Dec 1856), 691.
10. Griffiths, *Brunel's Great Western*, 64.
11. *The Engineer* (3 March 1893), 181–2.
    also T.W.F. Brown, 'Marine Engineering Review', *Transactions Royal Institute of Naval Architects* (22 March 1960), Table 4.

Chapter 2

1. D. Griffiths, *Brunel's Great Western* (Patrick Stephens, Wellingborough, 1985), 94.
2. T. Guppy, 'Steamship Great Britain', *Proceedings Institute of Civil Engineers*, No 4 (1845), 151–85.
   also E. Corlett, *The Iron Ship* (Moonraker Press, Wiltshire, 1974), 66, 68–70.
3. Griffiths, *Brunel's Great Western*, 82.
4. A. J. Maginnis, *The Atlantic Ferry* (Whittaker, London, 1893), 46–9.
   also C.R.V. Gibbs, *Passenger Liners of the Western Ocean* (Staples Press, London, 1952), 95.
5. Maginnis, *Atlantic Ferry*, 175.
   also Gibbs, *Liners*, 51.
6. *Cunard Line Magazine* (no date), 'Steamers of the past', No 14.
7. Maginnis, *Atlantic Ferry*, 178.
8. J. F. Spencer, 'On Surface Condensation', *Institute of Engineers & Shipbuilders, Scotland* (1861–62, vol 5), 70–83.
9. *Marine Engineer & Motorship Builder* (March 1928), 105.
10. *Marine Engineer & Motorship Builder* (Sept 1926), 352.
11. *Engineering* (29 April 1870), 298.

Chapter 3

1. A. J. Maginnis, *The Atlantic Ferry* (Whittaker, London, 1893), 72.
2. *Marine Engineer & Motorship Builder* (May 1927), 178.
3. 'Watertube boilers of the steamer Montana', *Nautical Magazine* (Nov 1873), 922–31.

4. M. Moss & J. R. Hume, *Shipbuilders to the World* (The Black Staff Press, Belfast, 1986), 30.

5. C. C. Pounder, 'Some Notable Belfast Built Engines', *Belfast Association of Engineers Transactions* (3 March 1948), 8.
    also *The Engineer*, vol 109 (Supplement 24 June 1910), i.

6. C. H. Milsom, *The Coal Was There For Burning* (Marine Media Management, London, 1975), 70.

7. Pounder, 'Belfast Engines', 9.

8. Milsom, *The Coal Was There For Burning*, various pages.

9. *The Engineer* (11 Oct 1872), 248.

10. Maginnis, *Atlantic Ferry*, 92.

11. *The Engineer*, vol 109 (Supplement 24 June 1910), ii.

12. Pounder, 'Belfast Engines', 9.

13. *Engineering* (20 Nov 1874), 406–7.

14. D. J. Lyon, *The Denny List* (National Maritime Museum, London, 1975), 117.

15. Lyon, *Denny List*, 126.

16. Maginnis, *Atlantic Ferry*, 54.
    also *Marine Engineer & Motorship Builder* (Dec 1927), 454.

17. *Engineering* (5 Aug 1881), 144.

18. *The Engineer* (3 Feb 1888), 95.

19. *Engineering* (3 Sept 1880), 196–7.

20. *Marine Engineer & Motorship Builder* (March 1929), 112.
    also *Engineering* (3 Sept 1880), 197.

21. *Engineering* (19 Sept 1879), 220–22.

22. *Engineering* (4 Sept 1874), 188–9.

23. J. F. Clarke & F. Storr, *Introduction of Mild Steel to Shipbuilding & Marine Engine Industries,* Newcastle-upon-Tyne Polytechnic Occasional Paper No 2, 1983.

24. *Engineering* (29 July 1881), 122.
    also *The Engineer* (7 April 1882), 349–52.

25. *The Marine Engineer* (1 Sept 1880), 127–31.
    also *The Engineer* (7 Oct 1881), 263–4.

26. *Marine Engineer & Motorship Builder* (Oct 1929), 421.

Chapter 4

1. *Engineering* (29 June 1883), 602.

2. *Marine Engineer & Motorship Builder* (May 1930), 191.

3. A. J. Maginnis, *The Atlantic Ferry* (Whittaker, London, 1893), 74.

4. *Engineering* (12 Oct 1883), 332.

5. *The Marine Engineer* (1 May 1885), 36.

6. *Engineering* (13 Aug 1886), 164.

7. *The Marine Engineer* (1 Nov 1884), 215.

8. *Engineering* (19 June 1885), 674.

9. *The Marine Engineer* (1 Nov 1884), 215.
    also *Engineering* (8 April 1887), 322.

10. *Engineering* (6 Jan 1896), 9.

11. *Engineering* (20 June 1893), 80; (17 March 1893), 325.

12. *The Shipping World*, (9 April 1902), 390–91.
    also *The Engineer* (6 June 1902), 558–9.

13. *Marine Engineer & Motorship Builder* (June 1931), 223–4.

14. *Engineering* (18 Jan 1884), 65; (1 Feb 1884), 103–4.

15. *Engineering* (15 May 1891), 593.

16. *Marine Engineer & Motorship Builder* (Feb 1925), 61.

17. *Marine Engineer & Motorship Builder* (Feb 1928), 72.

18. *The Engineer* (3 Feb 1888), 95.

19. *Engineering* (9 March 1888), 249.

20. *The Engineer* (27 July 1888), 77–8.
    also *Engineering* (3 Aug 1888), 123–4; (24 Aug 1888), 179.

21. *The Marine Engineer* (1 July 1890), 140.

22. *The Engineer* (18 April 1890), 314–16.
    also *The Marine Engineer* (1 July 1890), 140–48.

23. *Engineering* (8 May 1891), 559–6.

Chapter 5

1. *The Engineer* (19 Dec 1890), 490.

2. *Engineering* (19 Dec 1890), 723.

3. C. C. Pounder, 'Some Notable Belfast Built Engines', *Belfast Association of Engineers Transactions* (3 March 1948), 17.

4. *The Engineer* (19 Dec 1890), 489–503.
    also *Engineering* (19 Dec 1890), 722–3.

5. *Engineering* (8 July 1892), 58.

6. *Engineering* (24 April 1891), 487–90.

7. A. Kludas, *Deutsche Ozean–Passagierschiffe, 1850 bis 1895* (Steiger, 1983), 96–7.

8. *Engineering* (10 July 1891), 33.

9. *Engineering* (29 Aug 1890), 247–52; (12 Sept 1890), 321; (1 April 1892), 407; (22

April 1892), 497.
10. *Engineering* (29 Aug 1890), 247.
11. *The Engineer* (19 Dec 1890), 498.
12. *Engineering* (21 April 1893), 463–501.
    also *The Engineer* (13 Oct 1893), 345–58.
13. *Engineering* (21 June 1895), 800–801.
    also *The Marine Engineer* (1 March 1896), 479–80.
14. *Engineering* (4 March 1898), 267–9; (11 March 1898), 300–301.
15. *Engineering* (10 June 1898), 721–3.
16. *Engineering* (25 March 1898), 364; (8 April 1898), 429–31; (27 May 1898), 649–50.
17. *Engineering* (13 May 1898), 590–91.
18. *Engineering* (11 March 1898), 300; (10 June 1898), 721–2.
19. *Engineering* (28 Dec 1900), 823–5.
20. *Engineering* (7 Dec 1900), 724.
21. *Engineering* (13 Sept 1901), 370–71.
22. *Engineering* (12 Sept 1902), 339–40; (10 July 1903), 37–40.

(1 Dec 1905), 341–3.
also *Engineering* (1 Dec 1905), 715–26.
13. L. Peskett, 'Design of Steamships from an Owners Point of View', *Transactions Institute of Naval Architects* (3 April 1914), 177.
14. Peskett, 'Design of Steamships', 178.
15. *Lusitania*, ed M. Warren, Patrick Stephens 1986.
    Mauretania, ed M. Warren, Patrick Stephens 1987.
16. Peskett, 'Design of Steamships', Table 1.
17. Peskett, 'Design of Steamships', 177–8.
18. 'Aquitania', *Engineering* (Special Edition, 1914), reprinted by Patrick Stephens Limited, 1988.
19. *The Shipbuilder*, vol 10, 189–99; vol 11, 126–38.
20. *The Shipbuilder*, vol 11, 128–30.
21. Peskett, 'Design of Steamships', 182.
22. *The Engineer* (25 April 1930), 450.

Chapter 6

1. M. Moss & J. R. Hume, *Shipbuilders to the World* (The Blackstaff Press, Belfast 1986), 89.
2. C. C. Pounder, 'Some Notable Belfast Built Engines', *Belfast Association of Engineers Transactions* (3 March 1948), 19–21.
3. *Engineering* (1 Sept 1899), 274.
4. Pounder, 'Belfast Engines', 19–21.
    also *Engineering* (1 Sept 1899), 274; (6 Oct 1899), 346–7.
5. *The Engineer* (24 June 1910), xvi.
6. *Engineering* (1 Sept 1899), 274.
7. *Engineering* (12 April 1901), 472.
    also *The Engineer* (24 June 1910), vi.
8. *The Engineer* (13 Sept 1907), 270; (24 June 1910), vi.
9. J. F. Clarke, *Charles Parsons—An Almost Unknown Great Man* (Newcastle-upon-Tyne Polytechnic, 1984), 60.
10. Ingvar Jung, *The Marine Turbine—part 1* (National Maritime Museum, 1982), 25.
    also *The Marine Engineer* (1 Oct 1904), 252–5; (1 Jan 1905), 423; (1 May 1905), 58–9.
11. *Lusitania*, ed M. Warren, (Patrick Stephens, 1986), 13.
12. *The Marine Engineer* (1 Aug 1904), 172–8;

Chapter 7

1. L. Peskett, 'Design of Steamships from an Owners Point of View', *Transactions Institute of Naval Architects* (3 April 1914), 177.
2. M. Moss & J. R. Hume, *Shipbuilders to the World* (Black Staff Press, Belfast 1987), 133–5.
3. *The Engineer* (24 June 1910), vi.
    also C. C. Pounder, 'Some Notable Belfast Built Engines', *Belfast Association of Engineers Transactions* (3 March 1948), 21–3.
4. C.R.V. Gibbs, *Passenger Liners of the Western Ocean* (Staples Press, London 1952), 195.
5. *The Marine Engineer & Naval Architect* (June 1909), 422.
6. Moss & Hume, *Shipbuilders to the World*, 129.
7. T.W.F. Brown, 'Marine Engineering Review', *Transactions Royal Institute of Naval Architects* (22 March 1960), Tables 4 and 6.
8. *Ocean Liners of the Past—Olympic and Titanic* (Patrick Stephens 1983).
    also Pounder, 'Belfast Engines', 23–7.
9. *The Shipbuilder* (Dec 1927), 597–8.
10. *The Marine Engineer & Naval Architect* (June 1923), 205–13.
11. *The Shipbuilder*, vol 7 (Summer 1912), 11–16.
12. H. G. Prager, *Blohm & Voss* (Brassey, London 1977), 98.

13. *The Engineer* (20 June 1913), 649–50.
    also *The Shipbuilder*, vol 9, 87–98; vol 11, 125.
14. Ingvar Jung, *The Marine Turbine*—vol 3 (National Maritime Museum, Greenwich 1987), 130–33.
15. *The Engineer* (22 May 1914), 572.
    also *The Shipbuilder*, vol 9, 91.
16. *The Engineer* (12 May 1922), 522–3.
    also *The Shipbuilder* (Jan 1923), 29–36.
17. J. L. Wilson, 'Leviathan—Damage Repairs and Strength Analysis', *The Shipbuilder* (April 1931), 311–16.
18. *The Shipbuilder* (Dec 1914), 263–73; (Jan 1915), 30–35.
19. Peskett, 'Design of Steamships', Table 1.

Chapter 8

1. N. S. Swindells, 'Oil Fuel and Ships' Propulsion' *(Mari-Tech Conference, Vancouver)*, (5 June 1986), 2–3.
2. C. H. Milsom, *The Coal Was There For Burning* (Marine Media Management, London, 1975), 24.
3. Prof G. Bauer, 'Machinery Installation of the Liner *Bremen*', *Journal ASNE* 1930, vol 42, 684.
4. *Marine Engineer & Naval Architect* (July 1920), 344–5.
5. *Marine Engineer & Naval Architect* (July 1920), 348–50.
6. T.W.F. Brown, 'A Marine Engineering Review', *Transactions Royal Institute of Naval Architects* (22 March 1960), 400.
7. *Marine Engineer & Naval Architect* (Aug 1923), 285–93.
8. *Marine Engineer & Naval Architect* (Oct 1925), 377–9.
9. *Marine Engineer & Naval Architect* (March 1923), 93–100; (June 1925), 218.
10. *Marine Engineer & Naval Architect* (Aug 1923), 306.
11. *The Engineer* (25 April 1930), 450–52.
12. *Marine Engineer & Motorship Builder* (April 1930), 132–3.
13. *The Shipbuilder* (Sept 1922), 117–27.
14. *Marine Engineer & Naval Architect* (April 1922), 156–7.
15. *The Shipbuilder* (Jan 1926), 67–79.

16. J. Johnson, 'Propulsion of Ships by Modern Steam Machinery', *Transactions Institute of Naval Architects* 1929, vol 71, 62–6.
17. *The Engineer* (June 1928), 594–5.
    also *Marine Engineer & Motorship Builder* (July 1928), 259–64.
18. Johnson, 'Propulsion of Ships', 43.
19. Johnson, 'Propulsion of Ships', 40, 47, 48.
20. *The Engineer* (15 Aug 1930), 166–7; (22 Aug 1930), 206–10.
21. C. C. Pounder, 'Some Notable Belfast Built Engines', *Belfast Association of Engineers Transactions* (3 March 1948), 29–31.
22. *Marine Engineer & Motorship Builder* (July 1929), 300; (Feb 1930), 65–6.
23. *Marine Engineer & Motorship Builder* (July 1929), 301–5; (Feb 1930), 62.
24. *The Shipbuilder* (Jan 1928), 21–6
    also *Marine Engineer & Motorship Builder* (July 1928), 251–4.
25. Bauer, 'The Liner *Bremen*', 714–15.
26. *The Shipbuilder* (April 1930), 267–71; (Oct 1930), 787–97; (Dec 1930), 934–45.
    also Bauer, 'The Liner *Bremen*', 697–717.
27. Brown, 'Marine Engineering Review', Table 6.
28. *The Shipbuilder* (Dec 1930), 934.

Chapter 9

1. T.W.F. Brown, 'Marine Engineering Review', *Royal Institute of Naval Architects* (22 March 1960), Table 6.
2. *Marine Engineer & Motorship Builder* (May 1931), 165–75.
    also *Ocean Liners of the Past—Empress of Britain* (Patrick Stephens, 1972).
3. *The Shipbuilder* (June 1933), 313–17; (Aug 1933), 377–86.
4. *The Shipbuilder—Conte di Savoia* supplement (Jan 1933).
5. *The Engineer* (8 Jan 1932), 32–5; (15 Jan 1932), 62–5.
6. *The Engineer* (11 June 1937), 674.
7. J. Austin, 'Main and Auxiliary Machinery of the *Queen Mary*', *The Engineer* (15 Jan 1937), 74.
8. *The Shipbuilder—Queen Mary* supplement (June 1936).
    also *The Engineer* (15 Jan 1937), 74–5.

9. *The Engineer* (15 Jan 1937), 75.
    also Brown, *Marine Engineering Review*,
    Table 6.
10. T. A. Crowe, 'Recent Advances in Mechan-
    ical Engineering aboard Ship', *Proceedings
    Institute of Mechanical Engineers* (June 1948).
11. *The Shipbuilder* (Aug 1938), 445–9; (Sept
    1938), 506–17.
12. *The Shipbuilder* (Jan 1933), 15.
13. *Marine Engineer & Motorship Builder* (Sept
    1932), 302.
    also *The Shipbuilder* (Jan 1933), 22–4.
14. *The Shipbuilder* (Oct 1940), 331–40; (Nov
    1940), 357–61.

Chapter 10

1. T. Lehann, *A Century of Burmeister & Wain*
    (Burmeister & Wain, Copenhagen 1948),
    174.
2. H. Jefferson, *Viscount Pirrie of Belfast*
    (Mullan, Belfast 1948), 157.
3. Algot Mattsson, *The White Viking Fleet* (Tre
    Boker, Gothenburg 1987), 15.
4. *The Shipbuilder* (Jan 1926), 29.
5. *Marine Engineer & Motorship Builder* (Dec
    1925), 432.
6. *The Shipbuilder* (Jan 1926), 37.
7. *The Motorship* (May 1927), 56.
8. *Marine Engineer & Motorship Builder* (Feb
    1929), 63.
9. *The Shipbuilder* (Jan 1929), 8–9.
10. Mattson, *White Viking Fleet*, 35.
11. *The Engineer* (7 Oct 1927), 406.
    also *Marine Engineer & Motorship Builder*
    (Nov 1926), 429.
12. *Marine Engineer & Motorship Builder* (Nov
    1926), 429.
13. *The Motorship* (May 1927), 40.
14. *The Shipbuilder* (July 1929), 593.
15. *Marine Engineer & Motorship Builder* (Aug
    1929), 331.
    also *The Shipbuilder* (July 1929), 594.
16. *Marine Engineer & Motorship Builder* (Aug
    1929), 331.
17. *The Motorship* (Aug 1926), 175.
18. *Brassey's Naval & Shipping Annual* (1926),
    222.

also L. J. Le Mesurier, 'Fuel Consumption
& Maintenance Costs of Diesel Engined
Vessels', *North East Coast Institute of Engineers
& Shipbuilders Transactions* 1935.
19. *Marine Engineer & Motorship Builder* (Jan
    1928), 5.
20. *Marine Engineer & Motorship Builder* (May
    1930), 182–4.
21. M. Moss & J. R. Hume, *Shipbuilders to the
    World* (Black Staff Press, Belfast 1987), 258.
22. Moss & Hume, *Shipbuilders to the World*,
    275.
23. *Brassey's Naval & Shipping Annual* (1930),
    189.
24. D. L. Williams & R. P. De Kerbrech,
    Damned by Destiny (Teredo Books, Brighton,
    1982), 91.
25. B. Crossland, 'Harland & Wolff—B&W
    Engines', *Transactions Institute of Marine
    Engineers*, (11 March 1986), 6.
26. *Marine Engineer & Motorship Builder* (July
    1930), 265.
27. *The Motorship* (Dec 1931), 344.
28. *The Motorship* (Feb 1936), 480.
29. Conversations with former *Britannic*
    Engineer Officers, the late Albert Carmichael
    and Mr J. G. Banks.
30. *The Motorship* (Sept 1935), 194–7.
31. *The Motorship* (June 1937), 74.
32. *The Motorship* (Oct 1927), 239.
33. *The Motorship* (June 1935), 90; (Jan 1936),
    352; (March 1936), 502.
34. *The Motorship* (Jan 1937), 368.
35. Calculated values from data in Table 6,
    T.W.F. Brown, 'A Marine Engineering
    Review', *Transactions Royal Institute of Naval
    Architects* 1960.
36. *The Motorship* (June 1938), 98–103.
37. *The Motorship* (Feb 1938), 420–21.
38. Williams & De Kerbrech, *Damned by Destiny*,
    124–33.

Chapter 11

1. Ture Rinman, *The Story of an Engine*
    (Gotaverken, Gothenburg 1964), 136.
2. Algott Mattsson, *The White Viking Fleet* (Tre
    Boker, Gothenburg 1987), 35.
3. *The Motorship* (Dec 1944), 346.

4. *The Motorship* (April 1949), 6.
5. *The Motorship* (Dec 1949), 353.
6. *Engineering* (28 Jan 1949), 80.
7. *Shipbuilder & Marine Engine Builder* (April 1949), 365–6.
   also *Engineering* (28 Jan 1949), 81; (4 Feb 1949), 104.
8. *Engineering* (11 Feb 1949), 128.
9. *The Engineer* (5 Sept 1947), 227–30.
   also *Engineering* (14 Nov 1947), 464–5.
10. H. Volpich, 'Denny–Brown Ship Stabilisers' (*Institute Shipbuilding Progress*, 1955), vol 2, part 15, 530–36.
11. *Shipbuilder & Marine Engine Builder* (June 1958), 375.
12. *Shipbuilder & Marine Engine Builder* (June 1957), 395.
13. Volpich, 'Denny–Brown Stabilisers', 530–36.
    also *Shipbuilder & Marine Engine Builder* (June 1958), 375–8.
14. *Shipbuilder & Marine Engine Builder* (June 1958), 378.
15. Volpich, 'Denny–Brown Stabilisers', 536.
16. *The Naval Architect* (Jan 1987), E13.
17. *Marine Engineering Log* (Nov 1968), 69–73.
    also *The Naval Architect* (Jan 1987), E11–E15.
18. *Engineering* (June 1953), 809–11.
19. *Shipbuilder & Marine Engine Builder* (Jan 1954), 25–9.
20. *Shipbuilder & Marine Engine Builder* (Sept 1955), 550; (June 1957), 393.
21. *Shipbuilder & Marine Engine Builder* (Aug 1955), 502–505; (Sept 1955), 544–55.
22. *Shipbuilder & Marine Engine Builder* (June 1957), 384–98.
23. C. F. Morris, *Origins, Orient and Oriana* (Teredo Books, Brighton 1980), 319.
24. *The Engineer*, (7 June 1957), 886–8.
25. *Shipbuilder & Marine Engine Builder* (July 1956), 447–61.
26. *The Engineer* (21 June 1957), 963–4.

Chapter 12

1. *Shipbuilder & Marine Engine Builder* (Jan 1960), 26–30.
2. *The Engineer* (26 June 1953), 809–11.
3. *The Engineer* (19 Aug 1960), 324.
4. *Shipbuilder & Marine Engine Builder* (May 1961), 313–23.
5. *Shipping World* (7 Feb 1962), 171–5.
6. Ingvar Jung, *The Marine Turbine—part 2* (National Maritime Museum, 1986), 148–51.
7. *Shipping World* (7 Feb 1962), 176.
8. *Shipping World* (7 Feb 1962), 176–7.
9. *The Motorship* (Nov 1965), 342–53.
10. Ture Rinman, *The Story of an Engine* (Gotaverken, Gothenburg 1964), 135.
11. Algot Mattsson, *The White Viking Fleet* (Tre Boker, Gothenburg 1987), 26.
12. D. L. Williams & R. P. De Kerbrech, *Damned by Destiny* (Teredo Books, Brighton 1982), 272–4.
13. 'Queen Elizabeth 2—some design considerations', *Shipping World & Shipbuilder* (Jan 1969), 88–9.
14. *Shipping World & Shipbuilder* (Jan 1969), 108.
15. Jung, *The Marine Turbine—part 2*, 153–4.
16. *Shipping World & Shipbuilder* (Jan 1969), 112–18.
17. J. K. Tomlins, 'Farewell to the *QE2*'s Steam Turbines', *Marine Engineers Review* (Feb 1987), 18–19.
18. *Marine Engineers Review* (Feb 1987), 19.
19. 'Fit for a Queen', supplement to *The Motorship* (June 1987).
    also 'A Queen Reborn', *Marine Engineers Review* (July 1987), 20–23.
    also *Chartered Mechanical Engineer* (May 1987), 30–33.
20. Communication from Martin Harrison, Engineer Officer *QE2*.

Glossary

Busbar

A bar, usually of copper, which serves as a common connector for electrical circuits and is usually found at main electrical switchboards.

Gyroscope

A heavy flywheel rotated at high speed and supported on an axis at right angles to the plane of the flywheel. Any change in the axis of rotation results in an opposing force which can be used as a means of control or for stabilizing.

Horsepower

Nominal horsepower
This term was used with early steam engines in order to give an indication as to the capabilities of an engine. It was based upon dimensions rather than performance, and did not indicate the actual power developed by the engine in service.

Indicated horsepower
This is a measure of the actual power developed in the cylinders of a reciprocating engine, steam or diesel. It requires information regarding average cylinder pressure, engine speed and cylinder dimensions, which are used in the equation:

$$\text{Cylinder power (watts)} = P \times A \times L \times N$$
$$\text{Horsepower (hp)} = P \times A \times L \times N/550$$

where P = mean cylinder pressure (N/sq m or psi)

A = piston area (sq m or sq in)

L = Length of piston stroke (m or ft)

N = Number of piston power strokes per second (for double acting engines there is a multiplying factor of 2)

Brake horsepower
This is the actual output power obtained at the drive shaft of a reciprocating engine and is measured using some form of a brake, hence the name. Brake power is always less than indicated power because of friction in the cylinders and at bearings as well as the power used to operate the engine valves.

Shaft horsepower
This is the term used to define the shaft output power developed by a turbine or, in some cases, the power actually passed to the drive shaft of a geared installation with a number of diesel engines or electric drives. It is, in effect, the same as brake power.

Precession

Movement of the axis of a rotating body to a new position.

Precession motor
The drive motor by which the axis of rotation of a gyroscopic stabilizer may be changed.

Rudders

Spade rudder
A form of rudder which does not have its lower part supported in a bearing.

Balanced rudder
A rudder which has part of its area in front of the axis about which it turns. Water force acting on both parts when the rudder is turned is almost equal, so the steering motor does not need to exert very high forces in order to turn the rudder.

Oertz rudder
A patent design of rudder with a streamlined form which blends with the stern frame. This was intended to reduce water resistance.

Superheated steam

Steam requires heat for its production, and the temperature at which steam forms, known as the saturation temperature, depends upon the pressure. At normal atmospheric pressure that temperature is 100°C, but as pressure increases so does the temperature. Heat applied to the steam in order to raise its temperature above the saturation temperature is known as superheat. This means that the steam contains more energy and so can do more useful work per unit mass.

Valve Arrangements

Eccentric
A circular disc offset from the centre of the crankshaft which is used to operate a valve through an eccentric strap and rod.

Slide valve
The most common form of valve used with lower pressure and unsuperheated steam engines. It consists of a 'D'-shaped casting which slides over slots in the valve casing and so directs steam to and from the cylinder.

Piston valve
Serves the same purpose as a slide valve but is used for higher pressure steam and superheated steam. Two pistons connected to the same operating rod slide in a cylindrical valve chest to direct the steam.

Poppet valve
The sort of valve used on petrol and diesel engines in order to direct air and exhaust flows to and from the cylinder. They are spring loaded and operated by means of push rods and rocker levers from cams rotated by the engine itself. In some cases they were fitted to steam engines.

Expansion valve
This was a valve in the main steam pipe to the engine which could be shut off at some point before the piston had completed its travel. This allowed the steam in the cylinder to expand and so reduced steam consumption. It was used with early steam engines, but was displaced by the development of link mechanisms for operating valves.

Stephenson link motion
A valve link mechanism by means of which the travel of a valve can be regulated, so controlling the steam flow to an engine in order to vary the power it can produce. Stephenson link motion, developed by an employee of Robert Stephenson & Co, the locomotive builders, employs two eccentrics, one for forward and one for reverse running. In full gear the engine will operate at full power in the set direction, but by moving the expansion link, the ends of which are connected to the eccentric rods, a combined forward and reverse effect may be obtained for actual valve movement. Depending upon which eccentric has greatest influence, the engine will operate forward or reverse but with reduced steam compared with full gear.

Index